PROBLEM SOLVING in MATHEMATICS

Cover design by Bev and Charles Dana

This work was developed under an ESEA Title IVC grant from the Oregon Department of Education, Office of Policy and Program Development. The content, however, does not necessarily reflect the position or policy of the Oregon Department of Education and no official endorsement of these materials should be inferred.

Distribution for this work was arranged by LINC Resources, Inc.

ISBN 0-86651-181-4

Order Number DS01407

8 9 10 11 12 13 14 15 16-MA-95 94 93 92 91

PROBLEM SOLVING IN MATHEMATICS

PROJECT STAFF

DIRECTOR: OSCAR SCHAAF

WRITERS: RICHARD BRANNAN
MARYANN DEBRICK
JUDITH JOHNSON
GLENDA KIMERLING
SCOTT McFADDEN
JILL McKENNEY
OSCAR SCHAAF
MARY ANN TODD

PRODUCTION: MEREDITH SCHAAF
BARBARA STOEFFLER

PRINTING: LANE EDUCATION SERVICE DISTRICT PRODUCTION DEPARTMENT

EVALUATION HENRY DIZNEY
ARTHUR MITTMAN
JAMES ELLIOTT
LESLIE MAYES
ALISTAIR PEACOCK

PROJECT GRADUATE STUDENTS: FRANK DEBRICK
MAX GILLETT
KEN JENSEN
PATTY KINCAID
CARTER McCONNELL
TOM STONE

ACKNOWLEDGMENTS:

TITLE IV-C LIAISON: Ray Talbert
Charles Nelson

Monitoring Team

Charles Barker
Ron Clawson
Jeri Dickerson
Richard Olson
Ralph Parrish
Fred Rugh
Alton Smedstad

ADVISORY COMMITTEE:

Name	Institution
Mary Grace Kantowski	University of Florida
John LeBlanc	Indiana University
Richard Lesh	Northwestern University
Edwin McClintock	Florida International University
Len Pikaart	Ohio University
Kenneth Vos	The College of St. Catherine

A special thanks is due to the many teachers, schools, and districts within the state of Oregon that have participated in the development and evaluation of the project materials. A list would be lengthy and certainly someone's name would be inadvertently omitted. Those persons involved have the project's heartfelt thanks for an impossible job well done.

The following projects and/or persons are thanked for their willingness to share pupil materials, evaluation materials, and other ideas.

Don Fineran, Mathematics Consultant, Oregon Department of Education
Steve Meiring, Mathematics Consultant, Ohio Department of Education
Iowa Problem Solving Project, Earl Ockenga, Manager
Math Lab Curriculum for Junior High, Dan Dolan, Director
Mathematical Problem Solving Project, John LeBlanc, Director

CONTENTS

INTRODUCTION

Vhat is PSM?

ROBLEM SOLVING IN MATHEMATICS is a rogram of problem-solving lessons and teaching echniques for grades 4–8 and (9) algebra. Each rade-level book contains approximately 80 essons and a teacher's commentary with teaching uggestions and answer key for each lesson. *Problem Solving in Mathematics* is not intended to be complete mathematics program by itself. Neither is it supplementary in the sense of being xtra credit or to be done on special days. Rather, t is designed to be integrated into the regular nathematics program. Many of the problem-olving activities fit into the usual topics of whole umbers, fractions, decimals, percents, or equa-ion solving. Each book begins with lessons that each several problem-solving skills. Drill and ractice, grade-level topics, and challenge ctivities using these problem-solving skills com-lete the book.

ROBLEM SOLVING IN MATHEMATICS is esigned for use with all pupils in grades 4–8 and 9) algebra. At-grade-level pupils will be able to do he activities as they are. More advanced pupils nay solve the problems and then extend their earning by using new data or creating new prob-ems of a similar nature. Low achievers, often dentified as such only because they haven't eached certain computational levels, should be ble to do the work in PSM with minor modifica-ions. The teacher may wish to work with these upils at a slower pace using more explanations nd presenting the material in smaller doses.

Additional problems appropriate for low achievers re contained in the *Alternative Problem Solving n Mathematics* book. Many of the activities in hat book are similar to those in the regular ooks except that the math computation and ength of time needed for completion are scaled lown. The activities are generally appropriate for upils in grades 4–6.]

Why Teach Problem Solving?

Problem solving is an ability people need throughout life. Pupils have many problems with varying degrees of complexity. Problems arise as they attempt to understand concepts, see relationships, acquire skills, and get along with their peers, parents, and teachers. Adults have problems, many of which are associated with making a living, coping with the energy crisis, living in a nation with peoples from different cultural backgrounds, and preserving the environment. Since problems are so central to living, educators need to be concerned about the growth their pupils make in tackling problems.

What Is a Problem?

MACHINE HOOK-UPS

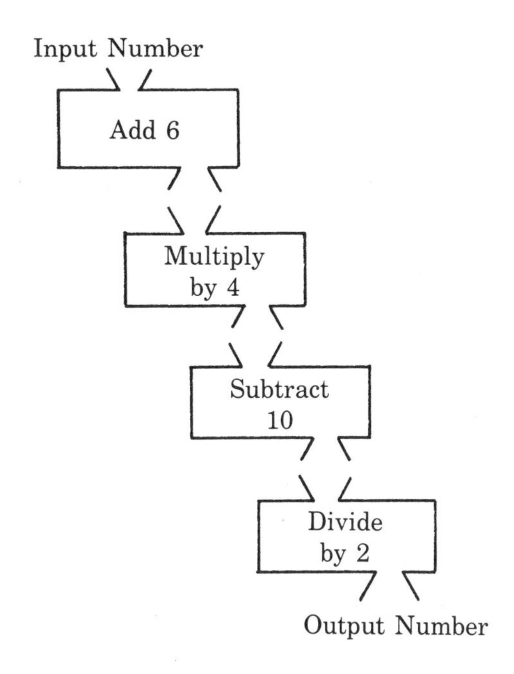

It is highly recommended that teachers intending to use *Problem Solving in Mathematics* receive training in implementing the program. The *In-Service Guide* contains much of this valuable material. In addition, in-service audio cassette tapes are available. These provide indepth guidance on using the PSM grade-level books and an overall explanation of how to implement the whole program. The tapes are available for loan upon request. Please contact Dale Seymour Publications, Box 10888, Palo Alto, CA 94303 for further information about the tapes and other possible in-service opportunities.

	Input Number	Output Number
a.	4	
b.	8	
c.	12	
d.		39
e.		47
f.		61

Suppose a 6th grader were asked to fill in the missing output blanks for *a*, *b*, and *c* in the table. Would this be a problem for him? Probably not, since all he would need to do is to follow the directions. Suppose a 2nd-year algebra student were asked to fill in the missing input blank for *d*. Would this be a problem? Probably not, since she would write the suggested equation,

$$\frac{4\ (x + 6) - 10}{2} = 39$$

and then solve it for the input. Now suppose the 6th grader were asked to fill in the input for *d*, would this be a problem for him? Probably it *would* be. He has no directions for getting the answer. However, if he has the desire, it is within his power to find the answer. What might he do? Here are some possibilities:

1. He might make *guesses*, do *checking*, and then make refinements until he gets the answer.
2. He might fill in the output numbers that correspond to the input numbers for *a*, *b*, and *c*.

	Input Number	Output Number
a.	4	
b.	8	
c.	12	
d.		39

   and then observe this pattern: For an increase of 4 for the input, the output is increased by 8. Such an observation should lead quickly to the required input of 16.

3. He might start with the output and *work backwards* through the machine hook-up using the inverse (or opposite) operations.

For this pupil, there was no "ready-made" way for him to find the answer, but most motivated 6th-grade pupils would find a way.

A *problem*, then, is a situation in which an individual or group accepts the challenge of performing a task for which there is no immediately obvious way to determine a solution. Frequently, the problem can be approached in many ways. Occasionally, the resulting investigations are nonproductive. Sometimes they are so productive as to lead to many different solutions or suggest more problems than they solve.

What Does Problem Solving Involve?

Problem solving requires the use of many *skills*. Usually these skills need to be used in certain combinations before a problem is solved. A combination of skills used in working toward the solution of a problem can be referred to as a *strategy*. A successful strategy requires the individual or group to generate the information needed for solving the problem. A considerable amount of creativity can be involved in generating this information.

What Problem-Solving Skills Are Used in PSM?

Skills are the building blocks used in solving a problem. The pupil materials in the PSM book afford many opportunities to emphasize problem-solving skills. A listing of these skills is given below.

THE PSM CLASSIFIED LIST
OF PROBLEM-SOLVING SKILLS

A. Problem Discovery, Formulation
   1. State the problem in your own words.
   2. Clarify the problem through careful reading and by asking questions.
   3. Visualize an object from its drawing or description.
   4. Follow written and/or oral directions.

B. Seeking Information
   5. Collect data needed to solve the problem.
   6. Share data and results with other persons.
   7. Listen to persons who have relevant knowledge and experiences to share.
   8. Search printed matter for needed information.
   9. Make necessary measurements for obtaining a solution.
   10. Record solution possibilities or attempts.
   11. Recall and list related information and knowledge.

C. Analyzing Information
   12. Eliminate extraneous information.
   13. Find likenesses and differences and make comparisons.
   14. Classify objects or concepts.
   15. Make and use a drawing or model.
   16. Make and/or use a systematic list or table.
   17. Make and/or use a graph.
   18. Look for patterns and/or properties.
   19. Use mathematical symbols to describe situations.
   20. Break a problem into manageable parts.

D. Solve—Putting It Together—Synthesis
   21. Make predictions, conjectures, and/or generalizations based upon data.
   22. Make decisions based upon data.
   23. Make necessary computations needed for the solution.
   24. Determine limits and/or eliminate possibilities.
   25. Make reasonable estimates.
   26. Guess, check, and refine.
   27. Solve an easier but related problem. Study solution process for clues.
   28. Change a problem into one you can solve. (Simplify the problem.)
   29. Satisfy one condition at a time.
   30. Look at problem situation from different points of view.
   31. Reason from what you already know. (Deduce.)
   32. Work backwards.
   33. Check calculated answers by making approximations.
   34. Detect and correct errors.
   35. Make necessary measurements for checking a solution.
   36. Identify problem situation in which a solution is not possible.
   37. Revise the conditions of a problem so a solution is possible.

E. Looking Back—Consolidating Gains
   38. Explain how you solved a problem.
   39. Make explanations based upon data.
   40. Solve a problem using a different method.
   41. Find another answer when more than one is possible.
   42. Double check solutions by using some formal reasoning method (mathematical proof).
   43. Study the solution process.
   44. Find or invent other problems which can be solved by certain solution procedures.
   45. Generalize a problem solution so as to include other solutions.

F. Looking Ahead—Formulating New Problems
   46. Create new problems by varying a given one.

What Are Some Examples of Problem-Solving Strategies?

Since strategies are a combination of skills, a listing (if it were possible) would be even more cumbersome than the list of skills. Examples of some strategies that might be used in the "Machine Hook-Ups" problem follow:

Strategy 1. *Guess* the input; *check* by computing the output number for your guess; if guess does not give the desired output, note the direction of error; *refine* the guess; compute; continue making refinements until the correct output results.

Strategy 2. *Observe* the *patterns* suggested by the input and output numbers for the *a*, *b*, *c* entries in the table; *predict* additional output and input numbers by extending both patterns; *check* the predicted input for the *d* entry by computing.

Strategy 3. *Study* the operations suggested in the machine hook-up; *work backwards* through the machine *using previous knowledge* about inverse operations.

An awareness of the strategies being used to solve a problem is probably the most important step in the development of a pupil's problem-solving abilities.

What is the Instructional Approach Used in PSM?

The content objectives of the lessons are similar to those of most textbooks. The difference is in the approach used. First, a wider variety of problem-solving skills is emphasized in the materials than in most texts. Second, different styles of teaching such as direct instruction, guided discovery, laboratory work, small-group discussions, nondirective instruction, and individual work all have a role to play in problem-solving instruction.

Most texts employ direct instruction almost exclusively, whereas similar lessons in PSM are patterned after a guided discovery approach. Also, an attempt is made in the materials to use intuitive approaches extensively before teaching formal algorithms. Each of the following is an integral part of the instructional approach to problem solving.

A. TEACH PROBLEM-SOLVING SKILLS DIRECTLY

Problem-solving skills such as "follow directions," "listen," and "correct errors" are skills teachers expect pupils to master. Yet, such skills as "guess and check," "make a systematic list," "look for a pattern," or "change a problem into one you can solve" are seldom made the object of direct instruction. These skills, as well as many more, need emphasis. Detailed examples for teaching these skills early in the school year are given in the commentaries to the *Getting Started* activities.

B. INCORPORATE A PROBLEM-SOLVING APPROACH WHEN TEACHING TOPICS IN THE COURSE OF STUDY

Drill and practice activities. Each PSM book includes many pages of drill and practice at the problem-solving level. These pages, along with the *Getting Started* section, are easy for pupils and teachers to get into and should be started early in the school year.

Laboratory activities and investigations involving mathematical applications and readiness activities. Readiness activities from such mathematical strands as geometry, number theory, and probability are included in each book. For example, area explorations are used in grade 4 as the initial stage in the teaching of the multiplication and division algorithms and fraction concepts.

Teaching mathematical concepts, generalizations, and processes. Each book includes two or more sections on grade-level content topics. For the most part, these topics are developmental in nature and usually need to be supplemented with practice pages selected from a textbook.

C. PROVIDE MANY OPPORTUNITIES FOR PUPILS TO USE THEIR OWN PROBLEM-SOLVING STRATEGIES

One section of each book includes a collection of challenge activities which provide opportunities for emphasizing problem-solving strategies. Generally, instruction should be nondirective, but at times suggestions may need to be given. If possible, these suggestions should be made in the form of alternatives to be explored rather than hints to be followed.

D. CREATE A CLASSROOM ATMOSPHERE IN WHICH OPENNESS AND CREATIVITY CAN OCCUR

Such a classroom climate should develop if the considerations mentioned in A, B, and C are followed. Some specific suggestions to keep in mind as the materials are used are:

- Set an example by solving problems and by sharing these experiences with the pupils.
- Reduce anxiety by encouraging communication and cooperation. On frequent occasions problems might be investigated using a cooperative mode of instruction along with brainstorming sessions.
- Encourage pupils in their efforts to solve a problem by indicating that their strategies are worth trying and by providing them with sufficient time to investigate the problem; stress the value of the procedures pupils use.
- Use pupils' ideas (including their mistakes) in solving problems and developing lessons.
- Ask probing questions which make use of words and phrases such as
  I wonder if . . . .
  Do you suppose that . . . .
  What happens if . . . .
  How could we find out . . . .
  Is it possible that . . . .
- Reinforce the asking of probing questions by pupils as they search for increased understanding. Pupils seldom are skilled at seeking probing questions but they can be taught to do so. If instruction is successful, questions of the type, "What should I do now?," will be addressed to themselves rather than to the teacher.

What Are the Parts of Each PSM Book?

PROBLEM SOLVING IN MATHEMATICS

Grade 4	Grade 5	Grade 6	Grade 7	Grade 8	Grade 9
Getting Started	Getting Started	Getting Started	Getting Started	Getting Started	Getting Started
Place Value Drill and Practice	Whole Number Drill and Practice	Drill and Practice	Drill and Practice-Whole Numbers	Drill and Practice	Algebraic Concepts and Patterns
Whole Number Drill and Practice	Story Problems	Story Problems	Drill and Practice-Fractions	Variation	Algebraic Explanations
Multiplication and Division Concepts	Fractions	Fractions	Drill and Practice-Decimals	Integer Sense	Equation Solving
Fraction Concepts	Geometry	Geometry	Percent Sense	Equation Solving	Word Problems
Two-digit Multiplication	Decimals	Decimals	Factors, Multiples, and Primes	Protractor Experiments	Binomials
Geometry	Probability	Probability	Measurement-Volume, Area, Perimeter	Investigations in Geometry	Graphs and Equations
Rectangles and Division	Estimation with Calculators	Challenges	Probability	Calculator	Graph Investigations
Challenges	Challenges		Challenges	Percent Estimation	Systems of Linear Equations
				Probability	Challenges
				Challenges	

Notice that the above chart is only a scope of PSM—not a scope and sequence. In general, no sequence of topics is suggested with the exceptions that *Getting Started* activities must come early in the school year and *Challenge* activities are usually deferred until later in the year.

Getting Started Several problem-solving skills are presented in the *Getting Started* section of each grade level. Hopefully, by concentrating on these skills during the first few weeks of school pupils will have confidence in applying them to problems that occur later on. In presenting these skills, a direct mode of instruction is recommended. Since the emphasis needs to be on the problem-solving skill used to find the solution, about ten to twelve minutes per day are needed to present a problem.

Drill And Practice No sequence is implied by the order of activities included in these sections. They can be used throughout the year but are especially appropriate near the beginning of the year when the initial chapters in the textbook emphasize review. Most of the activities are not intended to develop any particular concept. Rather, they are drill and practice lessons with a problem-solving flavor.

Challenges Fifteen or more challenge problems are included in each book. In general, these should be used only after *Getting Started* activities have been completed and pupils have had some successful problem-solving experiences.

Many of the other sections in PSM are intended to focus on particular grade-level content. The purpose is to provide intuitive background for certain topics. A more extensive textbook treatment usually will need to follow the intuitive development.

Teacher Commentaries Each section of a PSM book has an overview teacher commentary. The overview commentary usually includes some philosophy and some suggestions as to how the activities within the section should be used. Also, every pupil page in PSM has a teacher commentary on the back of the lesson. Included here are mathematics teaching objectives, problem-solving skills pupils might use, materials needed, comments and suggestions, and answers.

How Often Should Instruction Be Focused on Problem Solving?

Some class time should be given to problem solving nearly every day. On some days an entire class period might be spent on problem-solving activities; on others, only 8 to 10 minutes. Not all the activities need to be selected from PSM. Your textbook may contain ideas. Certainly you can create some of your own. Many companies now have published excellent materials which can be used as sources for problem-solving ideas. Frequently, short periods of time should be used for identifying and comparing problem-solving skills and strategies used in solving problems.

How Can I Use These Materials When I Can't Even Finish What's in the Regular Textbook?

This is a common concern. But PSM is not intended to be an "add-on" program. Instead, much of PSM can replace material in the textbook. Correlation charts can be made suggesting how PSM can be integrated into the course of study or with the adopted text. Also, certain textbook companies have correlated their tests with the PSM materials.

Can the Materials Be Duplicated?

The pupil lessons may be copied for students. Each pupil lesson may be used as an overhead projector transparency master or as a blackline duplicator master. Sometimes the teacher may want to project one problem at a time for pupils to focus their attentions on. Other times, the teacher might want to duplicate a lesson for individual or small group work. Permission to duplicate pupil lesson pages for classroom use is given by the publisher.

How Can a Teacher Tell Whether Pupils Are Developing and Extending Their Problem-Solving Abilities?

Presently, reliable paper and pencil tests for measuring problem-solving abilities are not available. Teachers, however, can detect problem-solving growth by observing such pupil behaviors as

- identifying the problem-solving skills being used.
- giving accounts of successful strategies used in working on problems.
- insisting on understanding the topics being studied.
- persisting while solving difficult problems.
- working with others to solve problems.
- bringing in problems for class members and teachers to solve.
- inventing new problems by changing problems previously solved.

What Evidence Is There of the Effectiveness of PSM?

Although no carefully controlled longitudinal study has been made, evaluation studies do indicate that pupils, teachers, and parents like the materials. Scores on standardized mathematics achievement tests show that pupils are registering greater gains than expected on all parts of the test, including computation. Significant gains were made on special problem-solving skills tests which were given at the beginning and end of a school year.

Also, when selected materials were used exclusively over a period of several weeks with 6th-grade classes, significant gains were made on the word-problem portion of the standardized test. In general, the greater gains occurred in those classrooms where the materials were used as specified in the teacher commentaries and in-service materials.

Teachers have indicated that problem-solving skills such as *look for a pattern, eliminate possibilities*, and *guess and check* do carry over to other subjects such as Social Studies, Language Arts, and Science. Also, the materials seem to be working with many pupils who have not been especially successful in mathematics. And finally, many teachers report that PSM has caused them to make changes in their teaching style.

Why Is It Best to Have Whole-Staff Commitment?

Improving pupils' abilities to solve problems is not a short-range goal. In general, efforts must be made over a long period of time if permanent changes are to result. Ideally, then, the teaching staff for at least three successive grade levels should commit themselves to using PSM with their pupils. Also, if others are involved, this will allow for opportunities to plan together and to share experiences.

How Much In-Service Is Needed?

A teacher who understands the meaning of problem solving and is comfortable with the different styles of teaching it requires could get by with self in-service by carefully studying the section and page commentaries in a grade-level book. The different styles of teaching required include direct instruction, guided discovery, laboratory work, small group instruction, individual work, and nondirective instructions. The teacher would find the audio tapes for each book and the *In-Service Guide* a valuable resource and even a time saver.

If a school staff decides to emphasize problem solving in all grade levels where PSM books are available, in-service sessions should be led by someone who has used the materials in the intended way. For more information on this in-service see the *In-Service Guide*.

What Materials Are Needed?

REQUIRED MATERIALS	Grade 4	5	6	7	8	9
blank cards	X	X	X	X	X	X
bottle caps or markers	X			X		
calendar						X
calculators (optional for some activities)	X	X	X	X	X	X
cm squared paper, strips and singles						X
coins				X	X	
colored construction paper (circle fractions)	X	X				
cubes		X	X	X		X
cubes with red, yellow and green faces					X	
Cuisenaire rods (orange and white) or strips of paper		X				
dice (blank wooden or foam, for special dice)	X					
dice, regular (average 2 per student)	X	X	X	X	X	
geoboards, rubber bands, and record paper	X		X			
graph paper or cm squared paper				X		X
grid paper (1")			X			
metric rulers					X	X
phone books, newspapers, magazines		X		X		
protractors and compasses					X	
scissors	X	X	X	X		
spinners (2 teacher-made)			X			
tangrams	X					
tape measures				X		
thumbtacks (10 per pair of students)		X				
tile	X		X			
tongue depressors	X					
uncooked spaghetti or paper strips			X			

RECOMMENDED MATERIALS	Grade 4	5	6	7	8	9
adding machine tape				X		
centimetre rulers			X	X		
colored pens, pencils, or crayons		X				
coins, toy or real	X					
coins (two and one-half)						X
cubes					X	
demonstration ruler for overhead		X				
dominoes					X	
geoboard, transparent (for overhead)	X		X			
money - 20 $1.00 bills per student			X			
moveable markers		X	X		X	
octahedral die for extension activity				X		
overhead projector	X	X	X	X	X	X
place value frame and markers			X			
straws, uncooked spaghetti, or toothpicks		X				
transparent circle fractions for overhead	X	X				

Where Can I Find Other Problem Solving Materials?

RESOURCE BIBLIOGRAPHY

The number in parentheses refers to the list of publishers on the next page.

For students and teachers:

AFTER MATH, BOOKS I—IV by Dale Seymour, et al.
Puzzles to solve -- some of them non-mathematical. (1)

AHA, INSIGHT by Martin Gardner
Puzzles to solve -- many of them non-mathematical. (3)

THE BOOK OF THINK by Marilyn Burns
Situations leading to a problem-solving investigation. (1)

CALCULATOR ACTIVITIES FOR THE CLASSROOM, BOOKS 1 & 2 by George Immerzeel and Earl Ockenga
Calculator activities using problem solving. (1)

GEOMETRY AND VISUALIZATION by Mathematics Resource Project
Resource materials for geometry. (1)

GOOD TIMES MATH EVENT BOOK by Marilyn Burns
Situations leading to a problem-solving investigation. (1)

FAVORITE PROBLEMS by Dale Seymour
Problem solving challenges for grades 5-7. (3)

FUNTASTIC CALCULATOR MATH by Edward Beardslee
Calculator activities using problem solving. (4)

I HATE MATHEMATICS! BOOK by Marilyn Burns
Situations leading to a problem solving investigation. (3)

MATHEMATICS IN SCIENCE AND SOCIETY by Mathematics Resource Project
Resource activities in the fields of astronomy, biology, environment, music, physics, and sports. (1)

MIND BENDERS by Anita Harnadek
Logic problems to develop deductive thinking skills. Books A-1, A-2, A-3, and A-4 are easy. Books B-1, B-2, B-3, and B-4 are of medium difficulty. Books C-1, C-2, and C-3 are difficult. (6)

NUMBER NUTZ (Books A, B, C, D) by Arthur Wiebe
Drill and practice activities at the problem solving level. (2)

NUMBER SENSE AND ARITHMETIC SKILLS by Mathematics Resource Project
Resource materials for place value, whole numbers, fractions, and decimals. (

The Oregon Mathematics Teacher (magazine)
Situations leading to a problem solving investigation. (8)

PROBLEM OF THE WEEK by Lyle Fisher and William Medigovich
Problem solving challenges for grades 7-12. (3)

RATIO, PROPORTION AND SCALING by Mathematics Resource Project
Resource materials for ratio, proportion, percent, and scale drawings. (1)

STATISTICS AND INFORMATION ORGANIZATION by Mathematics Resource Project
Resource materials for statistics and probability. (1)

SUPER PROBLEMS by Lyle Fisher
Problem solving challenges for grades 7-9. (3)

For teachers only:

DIDACTICS AND MATHEMATICS by Mathematics Resource Project (1)

HOW TO SOLVE IT by George Polya (3)

MATH IN OREGON SCHOOLS by the Oregon Department of Education (9)

PROBLEM SOLVING: A BASIC MATHEMATICS GOAL by the Ohio Department of Education (3)

PROBLEM SOLVING: A HANDBOOK FOR TEACHERS by Stephen Krulik and Jesse Rudnik (1)

PROBLEM SOLVING IN SCHOOL MATHEMATICS by NCTM (7)

Publisher's List

1. Creative Publications, 3977 E Bayshore Rd, PO Box 10328, Palo Alto, CA 94303
2. Creative Teaching Associates, PO Box 7714, Fresno, CA 93727
3. Dale Seymour Publications, PO Box 10888, Palo Alto, CA 94303
4. Enrich, Inc., 760 Kifer Rd, Sunnyvale, CA 94086
5. W. H. Freeman and Co., 660 Market St, San Francisco, CA 94104
6. Midwest Publications, PO Box 448, Pacific Grove, CA 93950
7. National Council of Teachers of Mathematics, 1906 Association Dr, Reston, VA 22091
8. Oregon Council of Teachers of Mathematics, Clackamas High School, 13801 SE Webster St, Milwaukie, OR 97222
9. Oregon Department of Education, 700 Pringle Parkway SE, Salem, OR 97310

Grade 4

I. GETTING STARTED

TEACHER COMMENTARY - GRADE 4

I. GETTING STARTED

Teachers usually are successful at teaching skills in mathematics. Besides computation skills, they emphasize skills in following directions, listening, detecting errors, explaining, recording, comparing, measuring, sharing, ... They (You!) can also teach problem-solving skills. This section is designed to help teachers teach and students learn specific problem-solving skills.

<u>Some Problem-Solving Skills</u>

Five common but powerful problem-solving skills are introduced in this section. They are:

. guess and check
. look for a pattern
. make a systematic list
. make and use a drawing or model
. make a reasonable estimate

Students <u>might</u> use other skills to solve the problems. They can be praised for their insight but it is usually a good idea to limit the list of skills taught during the first few lessons. More problem-solving skills will occur in the other sections.

<u>An Important DON'T</u>

When you read the episodes that follow in this <u>Getting Started</u> section notice how the lessons are <u>very teacher directed</u>. The main purpose is to teach the problem-solving skills. Teachers should stress the skills verbally and write them on the board. <u>Don't</u> just ditto these activities and hand them out to be worked. Teacher direction through questions, summaries, praise, etc. is <u>most</u> important for teaching the problem-solving skills in this section. We want students to focus on specific skills which will be used often in all the sections Later, in the <u>Challenge Problems</u> section, students will be working more independently.

Using The Activities

If you heed the important Don't on the previous page, you are on your way to success! The problems here should fit right in with your required course of study as they use whole number skills, elementary geometry and money concepts. In most cases, students will have the prerequisites for the problems in this section although you might want to check over each problem to be sure.

No special materials are required although markers, coins and boxes are helpful for some of the problems. The large type used for the problems makes them easier to read if they are shown on an overhead screen. In most cases students can easily copy the problem from the overhead. At other times you might copy the problem onto the chalkboard.

When And How Many

The Getting Started section should be used at the beginning of the year as it builds background in problem-solving skills for the other sections. As the format indicates only one problem per day should be used. Each should take less than twelve minutes of classtime if the direct mode of instruction is used. The remainder of the period is used for a lesson from the textbook or perhaps an activity from Place Value Drill and Practic or the Whole Number Drill and Practice sections of these materials. Some suggestions as to which pages might be appropriate will be refered to from time to time in the commentaries for each of the Getting Started activities

REMEMBER: One Problem Per Day when you are using this Getting Started section.

Guess And Check

The episode that follows shows how one teacher teaches the skill of guess and check. Notice that she very closely directs the instruction and constantly uses the terminology.

It is near the beginning of the year and Ms. Saxton is about to start a math lesson. After getting the attention of the class, she begins.

Ms. S: I'm trying to find two numbers. The sum of the numbers is 20 and the difference of the two numbers is 8. I wonder if the numbers are 10 and 10. Are they? (Waits for hands.) Pete?

Pete: I forgot what difference means.

Ms. S: It means how much bigger one number is than another. It's the answer after you subtract.

Pete: Well, 10 and 10 aren't right then.

Ms. S: How do you know?

Pete: 'Cause there isn't any difference between 10 and 10!

Ms. S: By checking my guess you found out it was off. We need a difference of 8. Are the numbers 0 and 20? Anne?

Anne: (Thinking out loud.) Zero and 20 make 20, but they are 20 apart. No---too far apart.

Ms. S: Zero and 20 are too far apart? What can you say about 10 and 10?

Pete: They were too close together.

Ms. S: Guessing and checking helped you decide 10 and 10 are too close together and 0 and 20 are too far apart. Let's refine the guesses. Refine means to make better guesses. Can you make a better guess? (Some puzzled, some thinking, some hands.)

Marty: 12 and 8.

Sharla: (Computing on her paper.) No, 12 and 8 are too close together. The difference is 4.

Steve: 13 and 9. No, I mean 13 and 7.

Ms. S: Why did you pick 13 and 7?

Steve: They have to add to 20 and I made the numbers more apart. Let's see--13 and 7 are 6 apart. Oh! It's got to be 14 and (thinks) 6!

Ms. S: Steve, you made a close guess, checked it and refined it to get the right answer. Did you know that guess and check is a good way to solve problems? We're going to use it a lot this year. I'm putting it up on the wall so we'll all remember how important it is!

Let's try another problem......

GUESS AND CHECK

WEEK 1 - DAY 1

a. Find 2 numbers whose sum is 20 and whose difference is 8.

b. Find 2 numbers whose sum is 25 and whose difference is 11.

c. Find 2 numbers whose sum is 43 and whose difference is 9.

****

WEEK 1 - DAY 2

a. Make this drawing:

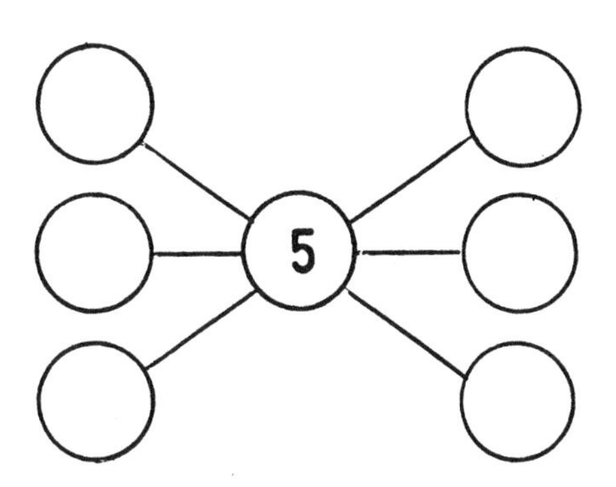

Place the numbers
2, 3, 4, 6, 7, and 8
in the circles.

Make the sum along each
line equal to 15.

b. Make this drawing:

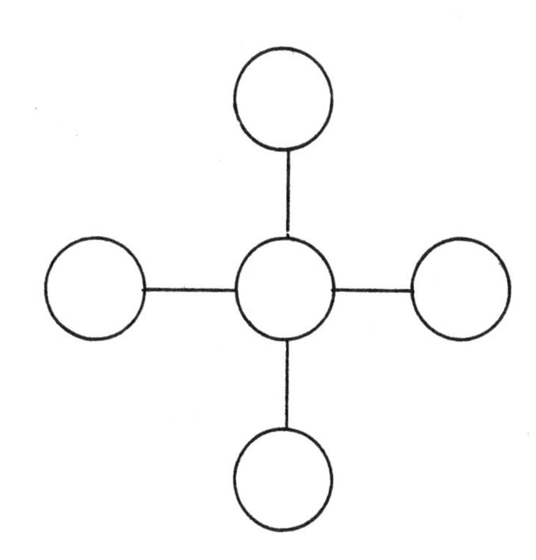

Put different numbers
in each circle.

Make the sum across and
the sum down 13.

Guess And Check

Day 1. Answers:

a. 14 + 6

b. 18 + 7

c. 17 + 26

Comments and suggestions:

. A detailed description of how to use this problem to emphasize Guess and Check is given in the introduction to this skill (page 3)

. Keep a record of the guesses and how far off they are on the chalkboard. Ask pupils how the record on the board helped them refine their guesses.

. Have pupils work parts (b) and (c) independently or in pairs. Ask them how guess and check helped them solve the problem.

Day 2. Answers: a. Any arrangement of

2 + 5 + 8
3 + 5 + 7
4 + 5 + 6

All arrangements have 5 as the "middle number."

b. Some solutions:

(1 + 5 + 7 / 2 + 5 + 6) (2 + 6 + 5 / 3 + 6 + 4) (1 + 7 + 5 / 2 + 7 + 4) (1 + 8 + 4 / 2 + 8 + 3)

Comments and suggestions:

. Work part (a) as a demonstration, having pupils guess the combinations of the 3 numbers which add up to 13.

. Some pupils may notice that the number in the middle circle (5) is also the mid-number of 2, 3, 4, 5, 6, 7, 8.

. Pupils should be able to complete part (b) independently.

. Write their different solutions on the board and encourage pupils to share their solution methods. Point out that problems often have more than one solution.

WEEK 1 - DAY 3

Each row, column, and diagonal of this magic square adds to 15.

Use the numbers 2, 3, 5, 6 8, and 9 to complete the magic square.

		4
7		
	1	

****

WEEK 1 - DAY 4

a. Lee's age is 4 times Dale's.
   Kirby's age is twice Dale's.
   The sum of all three ages is 21.
   How old is each?

b. Lynn is 3 times as old as Kim.
   In 3 years Lynn will be twice as old as Kim.
   How old are Lynn and Kim now?

****

WEEK 1 - DAY 5

Marty has 9 coins which have a total value of 48¢.
What coins does Marty have?

Day 3. Answer:

2	9	4
7	5	3
6	1	8

Comments and suggestions:

. Pupils may need help in understanding the problem and why it is called a magic square.

. Suggest they start with the column that ends in 1 and select 2 more numbers that would make 14. (14 + 1 = 15)

. Suggest they try 8 and 6. They will find that this guess does not work. Ask them for another possibility.

Day 4. Answers: a. Kirby - 6 years
Dale - 3 years
Lee - 12 years

b. Lynn - 9 years
Kim - 3 years

Comments and suggestions:

(a) Problem (a) may be difficult for the pupils. Before introducing the problem, give examples so pupils will understand the meaning of "Lee's age is 4 times Dale's," etc.

. Work the problem together as a class. To get started, suggest that they try 6 for Dale's age. Ask the class to figure out the rest of the ages, then check to see if the sum of the three ages is 21.

. Ask a class member for another guess. Make a record of the guesses used.

. Discuss together how this guessing process eventually leads to a correct solution.

(b) Ask the class whose age they should guess first. (Kim's)

. As they check a guess you may need to help pupils interpret "3 times as old as," "in 3 years" and "twice as old as." Have them record the guesses they tried.

Day 5. Answers: 3 dimes, 3 nickels, 3 pennies

Comments and suggestions:

. Pupils can be given real (or toy) coins to use and can work in small groups to find a solution. OR The use of simple drawings can be suggested or modeled while working with the whole class at the overhead projector.

1¢ 5¢ 10¢

. Make a record of their guesses so they can be easily compared.

. Give the class opportunity to discuss how guessing helped them solve the problem.

. "Too High - Too Low" on page 47 in the <u>Place Value Drill and Practice</u> section makes a good follow-up to this problem.

ook For A Pattern

By now your pupils are familiar with the skill guess and check. One eacher introduced the next problem-solving skill, look for a pattern, n this way.

r. Mills: Who remembers what method we used to solve problems last week?

arie: We guessed.

r. Mills: Is that all?

aoul: We also checked! It's up on the poster! (giggles)

r. Mills: That's right and we're going to add another problem-solving skill to the poster today. (Writes it up.) What does it say?

lass: Look for a pattern.

r. Mills: Look for a pattern--this week we are going to practice looking for patterns. Here's our problem. (Shows 1, 0, 2, 0, 3, ___, ___, ___ on overhead.) We want to fill in the next three blanks. Can you see a pattern in the numbers?

endra: There are zeros between the numbers.

at: They go up by one.

r. Mills: What goes in the blanks?

everal: 0, 4, 0

r. Mills: Let's try the next one. (Shows 21, 32, 43, 54, ___, ___, ___, ___) Who can tell me the numbers and the pattern they used?

oren: 65, 76, 87, 98. Both parts of the number go up by one.

r. Mills: Good. Kim, do you have something to say?

im: I thought they went up by 11.

r. Mills: Oh! You saw a different pattern--that's good. Would you get the same answers as Loren?

im: Yes. I'd get 65, 76, ... the same.

r. Mills: Sometimes several different patterns can be seen in the same problem. Often one pattern isn't enough to solve a problem and we have to look for another one.

Let's see what patterns we can find in these.....

LOOK FOR A PATTERN

WEEK 2 - DAY 1

Look for a pattern. Fill in the missing numbers.

a. 1, 0, 2, 0, 3, 0, ___, ___, ___

b. 21, 32, 43, 54, ___, ___, ___

c. 3, 6, 9, ___, ___, ___

d. 1, 2, 4, 8, ___, ___, ___

e. 1, 2, 4, 7, 11, ___, ___, ___

****

WEEK 2 - DAY 2

Look for a pattern. Fill in the missing letters.

a. A, B, C, ___, ___, ___

b. A, C, E, G, ___, ___, ___

c. E, H, K, ___, ___, ___

d. AA, AB, AC, ____, ____, ____

e. CR, CS, CT, ____, ____, ____

f. AB, EF, IJ, ____, ____, ____

g. AZ, BY, CX, ____, ____, ____

Look For A Pattern

Day 1. Answers:

a. 1, 0, 2, 0, 3, 0, 4, 0, 5

b. 21, 32, 43, 54, 65, 76, 87

c. 3, 6, 9, 12, 15, 18

d. 1, 2, 4, 8, 16, 32, 64

e. 1, 2, 4, 7, 11, 16, 22, 29

Comments and suggestions:

. A detailed description of how to emphasize Look For A Pattern (parts a and b) is given in the introduction to this skill on page 11. Continue in the same way with parts (c), (d), and (e)

. Pupils usually complete the sequence suggested in part (c) by skip counting or by adding 3 to get the next term Often they do not consciously recognize that multiplication is involved. In part (d) nearly all pupils get the next term by doubling. Part (e) is more difficult since the difference between terms increases from one term to the next.

. An alternative approach is to present the parts, one at a time, verbally. Pupils could then copy and complete the sequences on their paper.

. Whatever approach is used, allow time for pupils to give their answers along with their explanation.

. Certain pupils may have different answers which are just as correct as those given above.

Day 2. Answers:

a. A, B, C, D, E, F

b. A, C, E, G, I, K, M

c. E, H, K, N, Q, T

d. AA, AB, AC, AD, AE, AF

e. CR, CS, CT, CU, CV, CW

f. AB, EF, IJ, MN, QR, UV

g. AZ, BY, CX, DW, EV, FU

Comments and suggestions:

. Use either of the approaches suggested for part (a) above. Whatever approach is used, allow time for pupils to give their answers along with their justification.

. Certain pupils may have different answers which are just as correct as those given above.

WEEK 2 - DAY 3

Look for a pattern. Shade in the appropriate region.

a.

     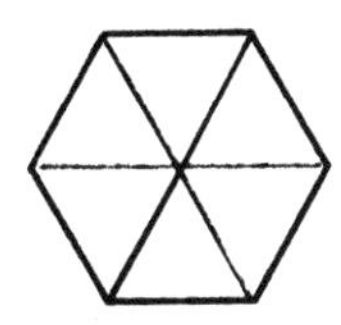

b.

   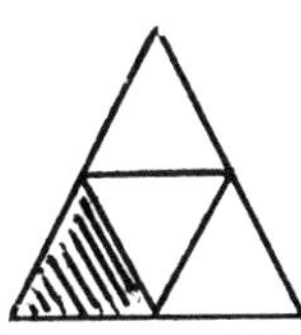   

c.

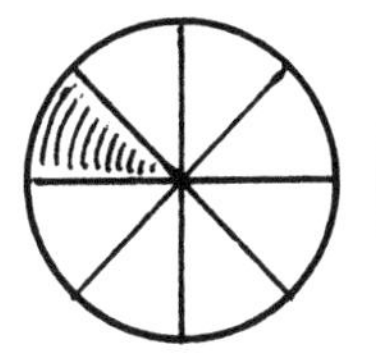 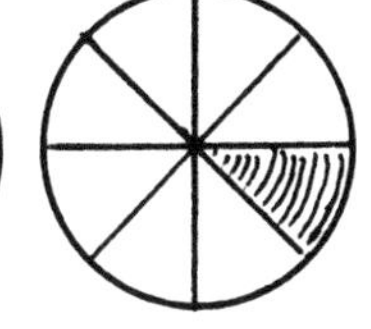   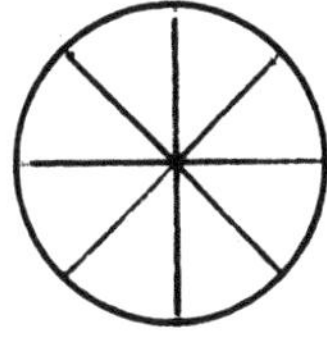 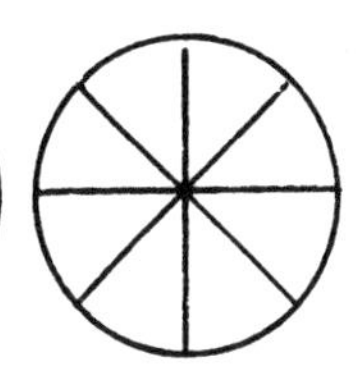 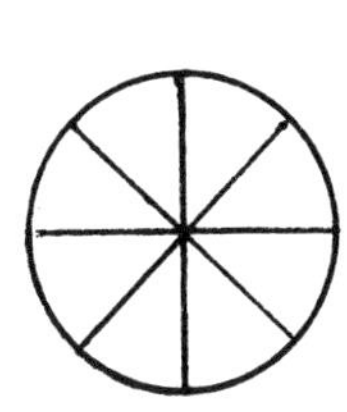

Look For A Pattern

Day 3. Answers: a.

b.

  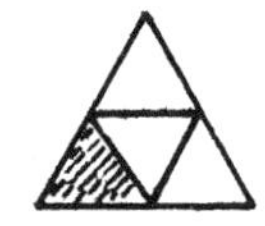

c.

Comments and suggestions:

- Duplicate the problem for pupil use. Also prepare a transparency and work part (a) with them. Let them complete parts (b) and (c) on their own.
- Have pupils explain the pattern they used. Some may see patterns other than those suggested here.
- This activity may be more difficult than those for Day 1 and Day 2. Nevertheless, pupils need this type of challenge and an opportunity to work with geometric patterns.

WEEK 2 - DAY 4

Find a rule that gives the third number from the first two numbers. Fill in the blanks.

a.	b.	c.
8, 3, 11	5, 2, 10	10, 4, 6
9, 5, 14	7, 5, 35	15, 7, 8
4, 8, ___	6, 4, ___	19, 9, ___
6, ___, 20	9, ___, 45	7, ___, 1
___, 7, 19	___, 10, 30	___, 11, 12

****

WEEK 2 - DAY 5

Find these answers.

10 + 1 =

100 + 10 + 1 =

1000 + 100 + 10 + 1 =

Predict these answers, then check by adding.

10,000 + 1000 + 100 + 10 + 1 =

200 + 20 + 2 =

5000 + 500 + 50 + 5 =

Day 4. Answers:

a.			b.			c.		
8,	3,	11	5,	2,	10	10,	4,	6
9,	5,	14	7,	5,	35	15,	7,	8
4,	8,	(12)	6,	4,	(24)	19,	9,	(10)
6,	(14),	20	9,	(5),	45	7,	(6),	1
(12),	7,	19	(3),	10,	30	(23),	11,	12

Comments and suggestions:

- This activity uses basic addition, multiplication and subtraction facts.
- Introduce the activity by working part (a). This example should provide pupils enough direction so they can proceed independently.
- Ask pupils what patterns they used and how the patterns helped them solve the problems.
- Ask pupils to invent similar activities for their neighbors to do. An important goal of problem-solving instruction is for pupils to invent problems.

Day 5. Answers:

11	11,111
111	222
1,111	5,555

Comments and suggestions:

- Prepare this activity to be shown on an overhead.
- Rewrite on the chalkboard the first three problems in vertical for and have the class as a group carry out the addition. The purpose of the activity is for pupils to recognize the pattern and then to use it for finding the other three sums mentally.
- Challenge pupils to make up similar problems whose sums can be don mentally. Some pupils might extend the pattern a bit to include examples such as $5000 + 400 + 30 + 2 =$
- Ask: "What kind of problems don't work this way?"
  (Example: $3000 + 900 + 400 + 5 =$)
- Since this activity emphasizes place value, "Ten Tosses" on page 51 and "Five To Make 2005" on page 61 make a good follow-up for this Getting Started activity.

ake A Systematic List

The first problem on the next page can be used to introduce the third roblem-solving skill, make and use a systematic list or table. Ms. Casper ntroduced the problem by showing these three transparent circles and three lanks on the overhead:

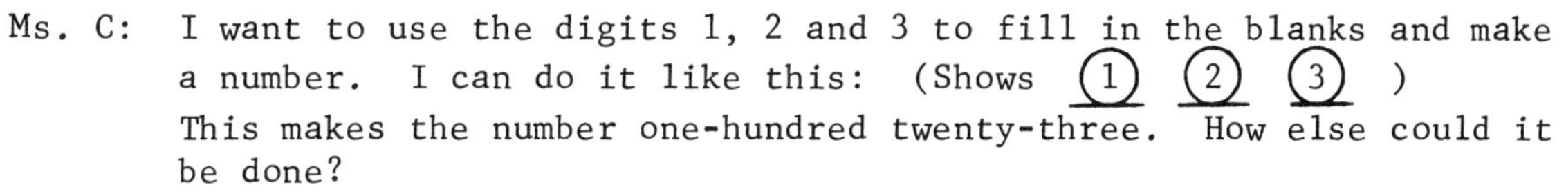

Ms. C: I want to use the digits 1, 2 and 3 to fill in the blanks and make a number. I can do it like this: (Shows 1 2 3) This makes the number one-hundred twenty-three. How else could it be done?

Jay: Put in 3 1 2

Ms. C: That's a good one. It makes three-hundred twelve. (Writes 123 and 312 on overhead). Now, I want to figure out all the different 3-digit numbers we can get by filling in the blanks with 1, 2, and 3. Can you help me?

Pam: 231

Ralph: 132

Ms. C: We already have four numbers. I wonder how many there are? How will we know when we have them all? Maybe we'd better make a systematic list. We are going to work on this new skill this week. Which number should we write first?

Dan: 123 'cause we found it first.

Ms. C: O.K. We'll put 123 first. Maybe we can put 132 next because it also starts with 1. Are there any other ways we can get a number that starts with 1? (Class shakes heads.) What shall we list next?

Mandy: 213 'cause it starts with 2.

Jodi: Put up 231 next.

Chris: 312 and 321 next.

Ms. C: Any more? No? Do you see how a systematic list can help solve a problem? Let's see if you can use a systematic list to find all the 3-digit numbers using 2, 5 and 8 ...

123
132
213
231
312
321

MAKE A SYSTEMATIC LIST

WEEK 3 - DAY 1

a. List the 3-digit numbers that can be made using each of these numbers one time only: 1, 2, 3 .

b. Now list all the 3-digit numbers that can be made using these numbers: 2, 5, 8 .

****

WEEK 3 - DAY 2

a. What scores can you get with 3 darts?
All the darts hit the target.
Use this table. Find out.

5	3	Total
✓✓✓		15
✓✓	✓	13

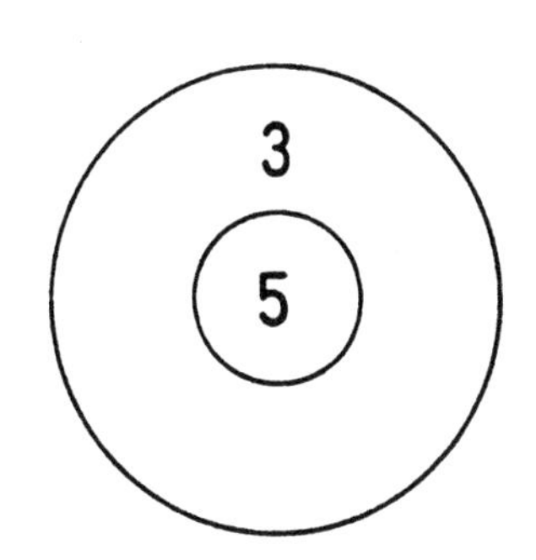

b. Here is a new dart board.
What scores can you get with 3 darts?

5	3	1	Total
✓✓✓			15
✓✓	✓		13

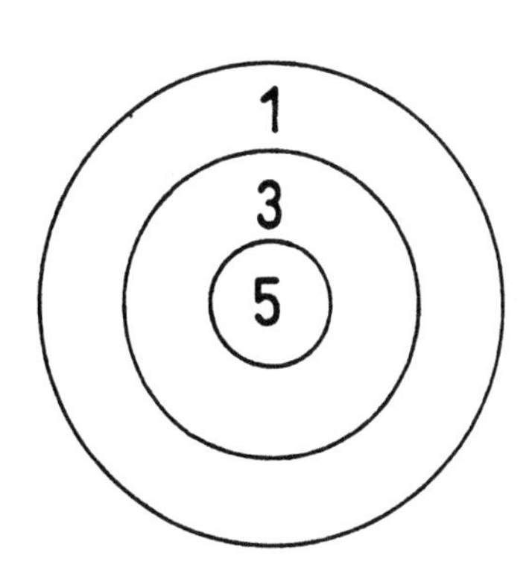

Make A Systematic List

Day 1. Answers:

a.
123
132
213
231
312
321

b.
258
285
528
582
825
852

Comments and suggestions:

. Detailed ideas on using these activities to emphasize the skill, make a systematic list, are given on the previous Teacher Commentar page 19.

. Note that in the final comment Ms. Casper introduces pupils to the listing of all three-digit numbers using 2, 5 and 8. Let pupils work this independently.

. Have pupils present their lists and verbalize any differences they have noted.

Day 2. Answers:

a.

5	3	Total
✓✓✓		15
✓✓	✓	13
✓	✓✓	11
	✓✓✓	9

b.

5	3	1	Total
✓✓✓			15
✓✓	✓		13
✓✓		✓	11
✓	✓✓		11
✓	✓	✓	9
✓		✓✓	7
	✓✓✓		9
	✓✓	✓	7
	✓	✓✓	5
		✓✓✓	3

Comments and suggestions:

. Prepare this activity for use on an overhead. Work through part (a) with the total class.

. For part (b) have them copy the table and then complete filling it out independently.

. Have each pupil compare his listing with a class member.

. Have different listings placed on the bulletin board and have pupils note the different system. used.

Make A Systematic List (cont.)

WEEK 3 - DAY 3

I had a dollar.

I spent 79¢.

I got 21¢ change.

My change could have been:

Number of dimes	Number of nickels	Number of pennies
✓✓		✓
✓	✓✓	✓

SM 81

Day 3. Answers: One possible list:

dimes	nickels	pennies
2	0	1
1	2	1
1	1	6
1	0	11
0	4	1
0	3	6
	2	11
	1	16
	0	21

Comments and suggestions:

- Prepare this activity for use on the overhead.
- Have pupils make the chart suggested for recording the number of ways. Pupils should be reminded that only a piece of the chart is shown.
- Go over the ways shown and discuss one or two "game plans" for completing the chart. Remark that a "game plan" helps us know when we have recorded all the different ways.
- Let them complete their charts on their own.
- Have them share their results an ask them to explain what system they used--there are several tha work well.

Day 4. Answers: Answers will vary.

Comments and suggestions:

- This activity introduces pupils to a different approach to making a systematic list.
- Present the activity orally and then record using a system for tallying.
- Record the numbers as they occur on several lines on the text page you select.
- Have them complete the page by working in pairs.
- Discuss the results as a class. The results should be close to each other but expect and accept some variation. It's hard to get an accurate count of so many digits!

WEEK 3 - DAY 4

Your teacher will select a page from your math textbook that has many problems in it.

Guess which digit 0, 1, 2, 3, 4, 5, 6, 7, 8, or 9 will be used most often on that page.

Turn to the page. Show how often each digit is used.

****

WEEK 3 - DAY 5

a. List the ways you can make change for a dime.

b. List the ways to make change for a quarter.
Be sure your list is organized in some manner.

Day 5. Answers: a.

n	p
2	0
1	5
0	10

Any organized listing is acceptable.

b.

d	n	p
2	1	0
2	0	5
1	3	0
1	2	5
1	1	10
1	0	15
0	5	0
0	4	5
0	3	10
0	2	15
0	1	20
0	0	25

Comments and suggestions:

. Do part (a) together.

. Start the chart for part (b) together, then have pupils complete the problem independently.

. Discuss results. Compare organization of data.

. Since this activity emphasizes place value, a good follow-up for emphasizing this listing skill is "Three Markers" on page 59.

Make and Use A Drawing or Model

Mr. Fadley introduced the problem-solving skill, make and use a drawing or model as described below.

Mr. F: Today we are going to use a new problem-solving skill: make and use a drawing or model. Here is a problem we can try it on. (Reads problem from the overhead.)

> A cricket and a flea decided to hop up a set of stairs. The flea takes 2 steps in one hop. The cricket takes 3 steps in one hop. The stairs have 12 steps. Which steps will both the cricket and flea land on?

Mr. F: What kind of a drawing could we make to help solve the problem?

Stacey: Draw a stairs.

Mr. F: How many steps should it have?

Todd: 12

Mr. F: (Draws a 12-steps stair on the chalkboard.) O.K. There is the drawing of the stairs. Now what?

Sid: Show the big hops.

Mr. F: Like this? (Draws hops on stairs with colored chalk.) Can you answer the question now?

Sheri: They both landed on the top step and (points and counts) on the sixth step.

Mr. F: That's good. Did the drawing make the problem easier to solve?

Rob: It's easy to see now.

Mr. F: I'm going to erase my drawing and have you make a drawing to solve a similar problem. The flea and cricket are going to hop up the same 12 stairs in the same way but I want you to tell me which steps neither of them land on--Do you understand the problem? (Nodding heads.)

After the students have made their own drawings and some have found the answer, 1, 5, 7 and 11, Mr. Fadley again emphasizes how the drawing helped solve the problem.

Mr. F: Here's another problem. This time the stairs has 15 steps. The flea takes 3 steps at a time and the cricket takes 5 steps at a time. Find out what steps they both land on and what steps neither of then land on ...

MAKE AND USE A DRAWING OR MODEL

WEEK 4 - DAY 1

A cricket and a flea decided to hop up a set of stairs.
The flea takes 2 steps in one hop.
The cricket takes 3 steps in one hop.
The set of stairs has 12 steps.

a. Which steps will both the cricket and the flea land on?

b. Which steps do neither of them land on?

c. This time the set of stairs has 15 steps.
The flea takes 3 steps at a time.
The cricket takes 5 steps at a time.
What steps do they both land on?

****

WEEK 4 - DAY 2

Use 12 toothpicks or straws. Make  each time.

a. Take 4 straws away. Have one square left.

b. Take 2 straws away. Have 3 squares left.

c. Take 4 straws away. Have 2 squares left.

d. Take 2 straws away. Have 2 squares left.

Make And Use A Drawing Or Model

Day 1. Answers:
a. 6th and 12th steps.
b. 1st, 5th, 7th and 11 steps
c. 15th step

Comments and suggestions:

. A detailed description of using the problem to introduce the skill, make and use a drawing or model, is given on page 27.

. Note that the final problem suggested is for working a similar problem involving 15 steps. Let pupils work on this independently

. Have pupils describe how the drawing helped them solve the problem

Day 2. Answers:

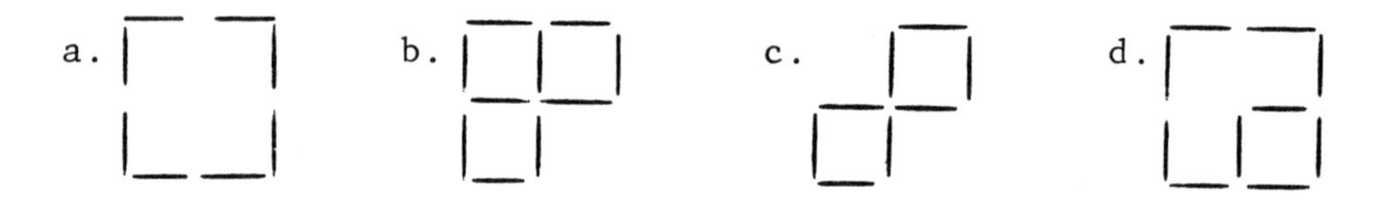

Comments and suggestions:

. This problem can be introduced as a drawing at the chalkboard or overhead.

. Have a good supply of flat toothpicks on hand. It is often hard to visulize the results of removing a line segment and it is messy to erase. Point out how using a physical model (toothpicks) will help--easy to remove, no erasing, etc.

. Pupils should record (sketch) results as they find them. This will take some insisting.

. Pupils may find part (d) difficult as it contains squares of two different sizes.

Make And Use A Drawing Or Model (cont.)

WEEK 4 - DAY 3

a. You get on an elevator on the 3rd floor of a ten-story building.
   The elevator goes
   . up to the top floor,
   . down 6 floors,
   . up 4 floors,
   . down 3 floors.
   You get off the elevator. What floor are you on?

b. You get on an elevator on the 5th floor of a twelve-story building.
   The elevator goes
   . down 2 floors
   . up to the top floor,
   . down 7 floors,
   . up 5 floors.
   You get off the elevator. What floor are you on?

****

WEEK 4 - DAY 4

a. Use 3 straight lines.
   Make the lines go completely across the pizza.
   Divide the pizza into _4_ pieces.

a.

b. Use 3 straight lines as before.
   Divide this pizza into _5_ pieces.

b. 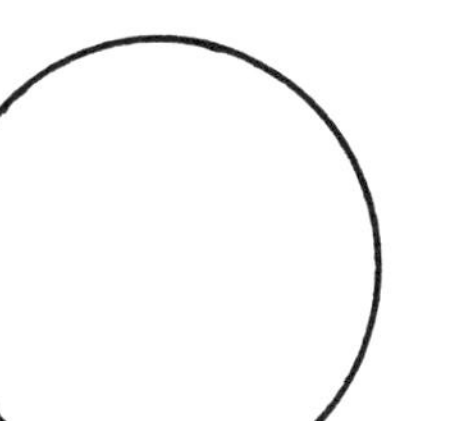

c. Use 3 straight lines.
   This time, divide the pizza into _6_ pieces.

c. 

d. Use 3 straight lines to divide this pizza into _7_ pieces.

d.

Day 3. Answers: a. You get off at the 5th floor.

b. You get off at the 10th floor.

Comments and suggestions:

. Present the first problem orally.

. Suggest pupils use a drawing to solve the problem.

. Help pupils start the drawing on lined notebook paper. Suggest they let each line represent a floor.

. Re-read the problem slowly while pupils make the appropriate drawing.

. Completed drawings <u>might</u> look something like this ⟶

. Let them work part (b) independently.

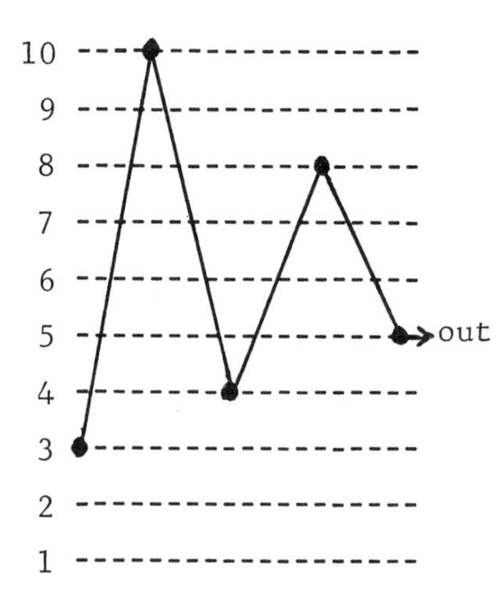

Day 4. Answers: Answers will vary somewhat.

Here are some possibilities.

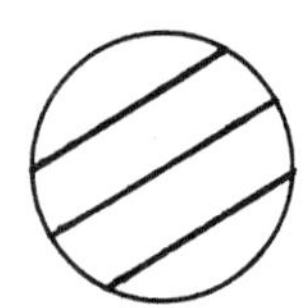
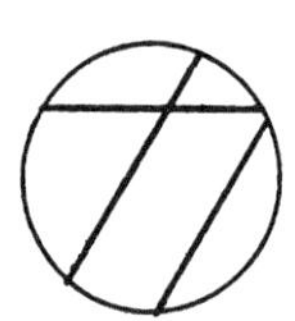

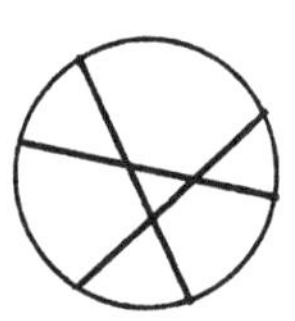

Comments and suggestions:

. Read problem (a) aloud. Draw a "pizza" on the overhead.

. Have pupils suggest possible solutions.

. Use toothpicks to show their solutions.

. Read problem (b) aloud.

. Have pupils draw a small circle (4 to 5 cm in diameter) on their paper. Provide toothpicks to those students who request them.

. Have pupils experiment to find possible solutions.

. Compare solutions. Remind pupils that a drawing or use of physical objects often helps solve problems.

. Place a solution on the overlay using toothpicks.

. Let pupils work independently on parts (c) and (d).

WEEK 4 - DAY 5

Make 3 straight lines in such a way that each animal is placed in a separate pen.

a. 

Use 3 straight lines to separate these animals.

b. 

c. 

Day 5. Answers: Answers will vary. Some possibilities are shown below.

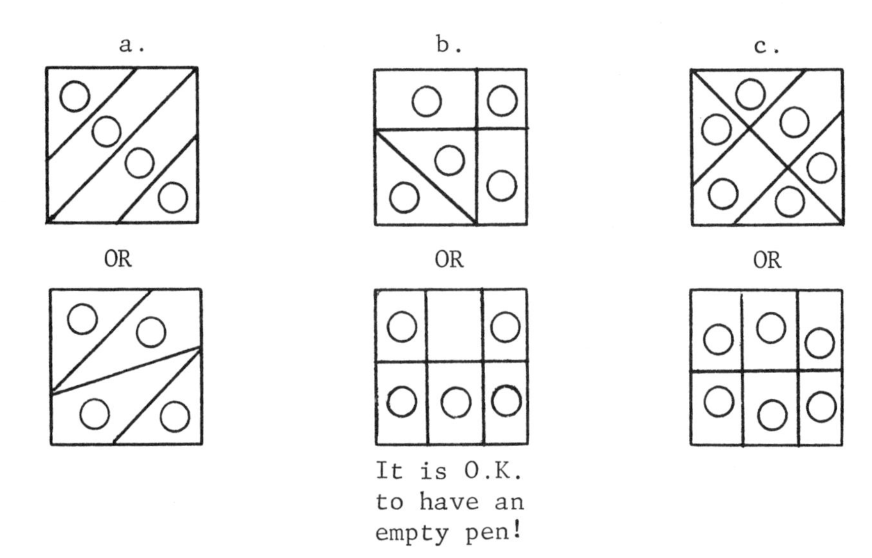

Comments and suggestions:

. Reproduce the activity for pupils to use.

. If similar "drawings" are placed on transparencies, pupils could show their solutions on the overhead.

. Toothpicks might work better than drawing in lines--especially since there are many ways to "build the pens."

. Have pupils compare this activity with the one given for Day 4. The contents are different--pens and pieces of pizza. The problems, however, are essentially the same. Possibly pupils will notice this

Comment concerning the skill, make and use a drawing or model:

This skill category is used in a more inclusive sense than the categories emphasized during the first three weeks. Situations included for this skill includes activities where drawings or physical objects (manipulatives) are used. Some activities in this classification are:

"Place Value Cut-Ups"	-	page 63	(slips of paper)
"Dots All"	-	page 95	(drawings)
Multiplication And Division Concepts, Section IV	-	pages 119 to 163	(drawings on gri paper)

Make A Reasonable Estimate

Sometimes a problem can be answered without making an exact calculation. A reasonable estimate is all that is necessary. In other situations, an answer has been calculated, but it is helpful to estimate the answer to see if the calculation is reasonable. Both types of situations occur in the problems in this section. Here is how Mr. Tubbs introduced the problem-solving skill, make a reasonable estimate.

Mr. T: Who remembers the problem-solving skills we have studied so far? Becky?

Becky: Guess and check; look for a pattern; make a systematic list; ...hm...

Mr. T: Marilyn, can you help out?

Marilyn: Make and use a drawing or model.

Mr. T: That's right. We've studied four of them. Today we are going to learn a new one, make a reasonable estimate. I will put some problems on the overhead and ask you to solve them, but first I want you to put away your pencils and paper and put on your thinking caps. We're going to estimate these in our heads.

Everyone ready? Here's the first one. (Shows problem 1-a on the overhead.) Which of these is a reasonable estimate for 3 cans of beans? $1.00, $1.50, or $2.00 ?

Kirk: It's closer to $1.50.

Mr. T: How do you know, Kirk?

Kirk: Well, each can is about 50¢ so 3 would be about $1.50.

Mr. T: Good. You used some rounding to make a reasonable estimate. What about a reasonable estimate for 2 loaves of bread and a carton of butter?

Steve: That's close to $2.00 because 2 breads come to about a dollar and butter is about a dollar.

Mr. T: O.K. Now I want you to use reasonable estimates to find two items costing close to $1.75.

Melinda: Butter and milk.

Jack: I was going to say butter and beans.

Mr. T: Do you each want to explain how you chose your answer.

Melinda: Well, butter is close to a dollar and milk is close to 75¢, so that seemed reasonable.

Jack: I saw butter was more than a dollar so I picked green beans because it was less than 75¢.

Frank: I thought it was cheese and milk because cheese is a little less than 75¢.

Mr. T: Sounds like you all have reasonable estimates; let's try another .... .

MAKE A REASONABLE ESTIMATE

WEEK 5 - DAY 1

1. Make a reasonable estimate.

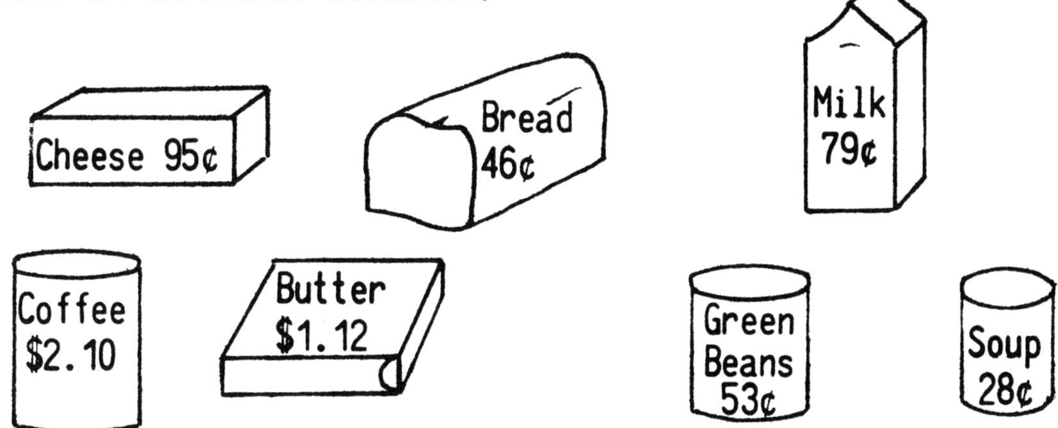

a. Will 3 cans of green beans cost closer to
   $1.00? $1.50 ? $2.50

b. Will 2 loaves of bread and a carton of butter cost closer to
   $2.00 ? $1.50 ? $2.50 ?

c. What two items will cost close to $1.75 ?

d. What two items will cost close to $3.00 ?

e. What three items will cost close to $3.00 ?

****

WEEK 5 - DAY 2

Find 4 pairs of numbers from the list below that have sums between 75 and 85.

20   61   38   10   51

40   32   18

Make A Reasonable Estimate

Day 1. Answers:

a. $1.50

b. $2.00

c. Cheese and milk; or butter and beans; or butter and milk

d. Coffee and cheese

e. Coffee, beans, and soup; or coffee, beans, and bread; or butter, cheese, and milk; or coffee, milk, and soup

Comments and suggestions:

. A detailed description for using this problem for introducing the skill, make a reasonable estimate, is given on page 35.

. In parts (d) and (e) pupils may question what it means to be close to $3.00. Class discussion may resolve the question.

. Allow flexibility in answers.

Day 2. Answers:

61 and 20
18 and 61
40 and 38
51 and 32

Comments and suggestions:

. Write the exercise on the chalkboard or on an overlay.

. Encourage pupils to round* to the nearest ten and then pick out pairs of possibilities.

. Check each estimate by computing the actual sum.

*If pupils do not know what is meant by "rounding to the nearest ten" you might proceed as follows:

. Three numerals show an exact number of tens. Which ones are these? (answer - 20, 10, and 40)

The others (61, 38, 51, 32, and 18) are almost an exact number of tens. We do not need to have an exact answer. So let us think of them as an exact number of tens. What are the best numbers to use? (answer 60, 40, 50, 30, and 20)

This "rounding," as it is called, makes adding easy. You can do it in your head.

Make A Reasonable Estimate (cont.)

WEEK 5 - DAY 3

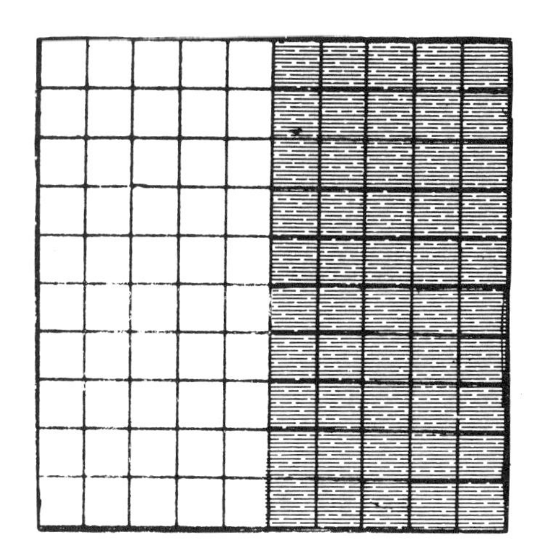

This large square contains 100 small squares.

How many small squares are shaded? Estimate first. ________

Check your estimate by counting.

Estimate the number of small shaded squares in each example below.

a. ________

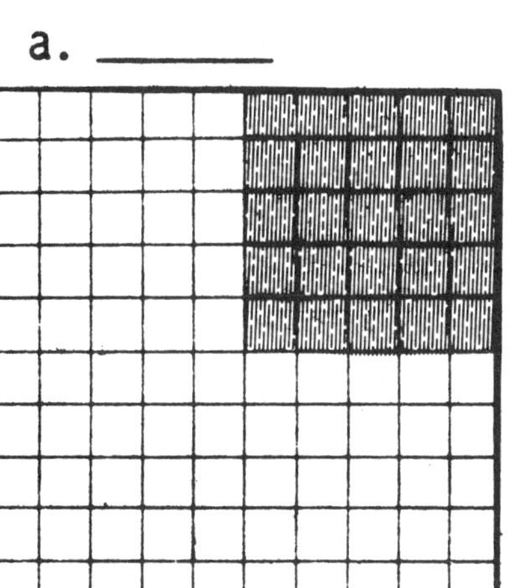

b. ________

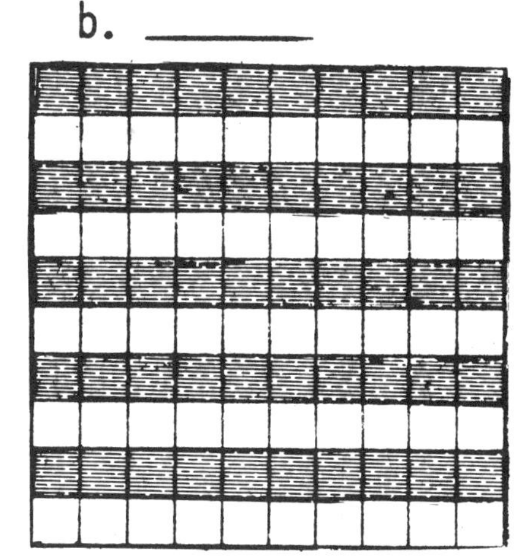

c. ________

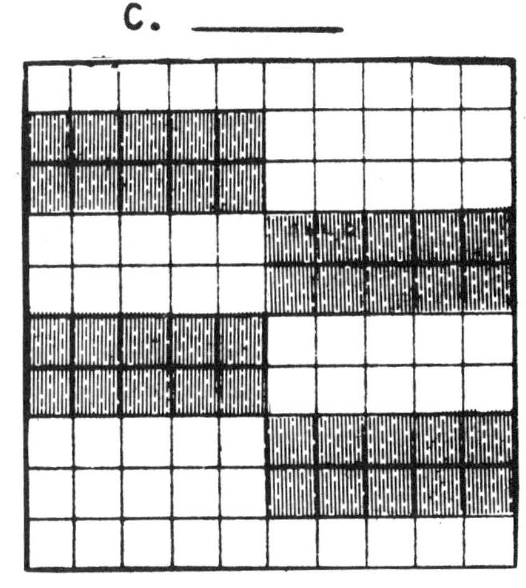

d. ________

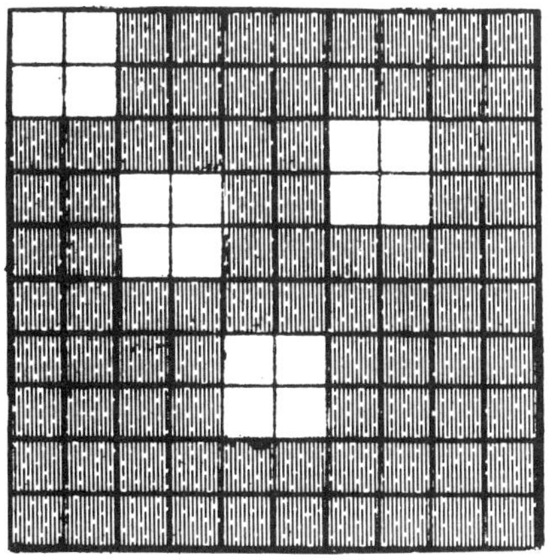

e. ________

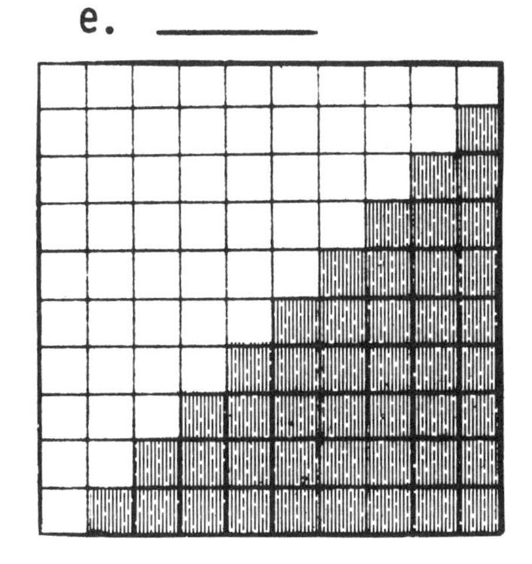

f. ________

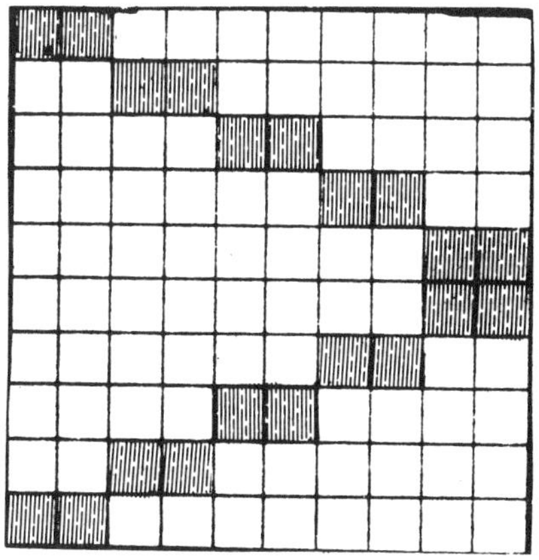

Make A Reasonable Estimate

Day 3. Answers:*

1. 50

2. a. 25 b. 50 c. 40

d. 84 e. 45** f. 20

* Exact answers are given here. However a strong focus on these exact answers defeats the purpose of this activity.

** Nearly all pupils will be surprised that the answer is 45 rather than 50.

Comments and suggestions:

. Prepare an overlay and discuss the introductory example. Prepare pupils for what they will be expected to do for parts (a)-(f).

. Flash each part for two or three seconds, allowing additional time for pupils to record their estimates.

. Repeat the showing of each part, allowing time for them to record their refined estimates.

. Have pupils discuss ways that help them make better estimates. For example, in part (d) most of the square is shaded. Five smaller squares are not and each of these have four small squares, etc.

Comments about the use of grid paper:

This type of graph paper is used extensively in this book for developing multiplication, division, and area concepts. See Sections IV and VI.

WEEK 5 - DAY 4

Calculator Cal does all his work by calculator, but sometimes he punches the wrong buttons. He worked the problems below. Which answers are wrong?

a.	397 + 101	Cal's answer:	498
b.	503 - 397	" "	382
c.	414 + 101 + 98	" "	913
d.	493 - 201	" "	292
e.	293 x 3	" "	879
f.	409 x 2	" "	818
g.	416 + 101 + 399	" "	1000

****

WEEK 5 - DAY 5

Megan is at a material shop. She has a $10 bill. Which of these purchases can she make?

a. 3 yards of material at $2.98 a yard.

b. A scissors for $8.15 plus a spool of thread at 85¢.

c. A pattern for $2.75 plus 4 yards of material at $2.10 a yard.

d. Four sets of buttons at $1.25 a set and 2 balls of yarn at $1.95 a ball.

Day 4. Answers: Exercises b, c, and g are incorrect.

Comments and suggestions:

. Reproduce the activity for the overhead. Present each part one at a time.

. Encourage pupils to round* 3-digit numbers to the nearest hundred.

. Have them identify and record each incorrect answer. Proceed rather quickly through each part.

. Have pupils indicate how they made their estimates.

* If pupils do not know what is meant by rounding to the nearest hundred, you might proceed as follows:

. There are no numbers here that are an exact number of hundreds. But for estimation, we can think of them as such numbers. For example, in part (a) 397 can be made 400 and 101 as 100.

This "rounding" changes the exercise to 400 + 100 or 500 and 498 is close. Therefore, 498 is probably the correct answer

Day 5. Answers:

a. Yes
b. Yes
c. No
d. Yes

Comments and suggestions:

. Reproduce this activity for the overhead and present the questions one at a time. Allow about 15 seconds per question. Have them record their response on paper. Check answers after all four have been given.

. Have pupils discuss the ways they used to make their estimates.

. Other estimation follow-up activities can be found in the Whole Number Drill And Practice section. e.g.

"Lunch For Sam" - page 89
"Answers Not Needed" - page 79
"Shopping At The Used Toy Store" - page 77

Grade 4

II. PLACE VALUE DRILL AND PRACTICE

II. PLACE VALUE DRILL AND PRACTICE

Jim

100	10	1

Jan

100	10	1

It took thousands of years for our system of representing numbers using place value to develop. Is it so surprising that pupils find it difficult at times? Many of the problems pupils have with whole numbers and decimals can be traced to a poor understanding of place value. Teachers know place value is very important so they continue to stress it into the seventh and eighth grades.

Nearly all the activities in this section use a game format to reinforce place value, allow for problem solving, and give informal experiences with chance (probability). Fourth graders are great game players and games can be used to motivate them to learn more about place value. Games where they are challenged to figure out winning strategies and where chance helps to keep things equal are even more motivating.

Using The Activities

The activities in this section are intended to supplement the regular class lessons on place value. They should not be used all at once but can be used with other materials over a two- or three-week period. Of course, many of the games could be repeated later in the year. The extra material needed are 2 wooden or foam cubes, 3 regular dice, and markers.

The teacher generally introduces and explains the game and then takes a non-directive role as pupils develop their own strategies for winning. Occasionally the teacher may need to ask a question or provide a clue. Pupils can share their ideas in group discussions and the teacher can summarize or make comments at that time.

In the commentary for each page, problem-solving strategies are suggested. The purpose of these comments is to give teachers a headstart on what pupils _might_ do. Teachers who have time to work each activity and reflect upon the strategies they used will probably come up with strategies different and possibly better than those we have suggested.

TOO HIGH - TOO LOW

TEACHER:

Make this chart on the chalkboard.

Too high	Too low

Divide the class into two teams.

Write a number between 1 and 1000 (or greater) on a slip of paper.

Have students from each team, in turn, guess what the number might be. As students announce their guesses, record the guesses in the appropriate column (too high/too low).

The student who "guesses" the correct number scores a point for that team and then leads next game.

Too High - Too Low

Mathematics teaching objectives:

- Develop mental arithmetic skills.
- Compare and order numbers.

Problem-solving skills pupils might use:

- Guess and check.
- Make decisions based upon data.

Materials needed:

- None

Comments and suggestions:

- Play two or three games keeping each table of guesses on the chalkboard. The "hidden" number should be placed above each table after it has been identified. Have each team take time out to discuss strategies for team members to follow. Play several more games leaving the tables of guesses on the chalkboard. The competition should end with a total-class discussion where both sides pool their ideas on strategies.
- Most pupils will begin by making random guesses. After several games are played, pupils might eventually use strategy like this:
  - The best first guess would be 500, halfway between 1 and 1000.
  - If the guess is too high, the best second guess is 250, halfway between 500 and 1. (If too low, the next guess should be 750.)
  - Keep making "halfway" guesses until the "hidden" number is found.
- Some pupils might not understand why their guesses are not possible. (For example, guessing 600 when 500 was already too high.) Pupils could do the game in pairs with pupils who understand helping those who are confused. The teacher can circulate among the games to check on progress.

Answers:

Answers will depend on guesses made by pupils.

Extension: Repeat the activity using a number between 1 and 10,000 or 1 and 100,000.

ORDER THE NUMBERS

Your teacher has one die with faces marked as follows: 7,8,8,9,9,9.

Your teacher will toss the die 9 times and announce the digit which lands face up.

After each toss, write the digit in one of the boxes below.
<u>Once a digit is written, you cannot change it.</u>

<u>Score</u>

☐☐☐ < ☐☐☐ < ☐☐☐ ____

After 9 tosses, score:

10 points if all 3 numbers are in correct order.
4 points if the first two or last 2 numbers are in correct order.

Play 4 more rounds.

<u>Score</u>

1) ☐☐☐ < ☐☐☐ < ☐☐☐ ____

2) ☐☐☐ < ☐☐☐ < ☐☐☐ ____

3) ☐☐☐ < ☐☐☐ < ☐☐☐ ____

4) ☐☐☐ < ☐☐☐ < ☐☐☐ ____

Suppose these numbers land face up: 7,7,8,8,8,9,9,9,9.
There are many different ways you could correctly fill the boxes.
List 5 (or more) correct ways.

Order the Numbers

Mathematics teaching objectives:

- Compare and order number emphasizing the importance of the left digit
- Develop some informal ideas about probability.

Problem-solving skills pupils _might_ use:

- Make decisions based upon data.
- Recognize limits and eliminate possibilities.
- Apply what you know about place value.

Materials needed:

- A wooden or foam cube marked with 7, 8, 8, 9, 9, 9.

Comments and suggestions:

- Pupils will need to know the meaning of the _less than_ symbol, $<$.
- This is a teacher-directed game which could be used with the entire class. Let pupils see what digits are on the cube. This is necessar if pupils are to develop winning strategies. After doing several rounds, have pupils suggest some good "rules" to use for getting 10 points. Play several other rounds to determine whether or not the "rules" are helpful. Here are some ideas on rules:
  - Selecting the number to be placed in the hundreds place is the key to winning.
  - A nine is easier to roll than a 7 or 8.
  - Save the hundreds place in the first frame for a 7, in the middle frame for an 8, in the last frame for a 9.

Answers:

$778 < 898 < 999$

$787 < 889 < 999$

$799 < 887 < 989$

$799 < 898 < 978$

$788 < 899 < 979$

$878 < 879 < 899$

$978 < 987 < 998$

Any arrangement with a 7, 8, 9 as first digits of the three frames is correct.

An Extension: Is it possible to have a 10-pointer if the first number is greater than 900? Between 800 and 900? If so, give examples.

TEN TOSSES

Your teacher will give you a special worksheet with workspace for four games.

Here are the directions for each game:

. Your teacher will toss an ordinary die ten times.

. After each toss, place the digit which lands face up in one of the three possible columns.

. After ten tosses, add to find your total.

. The winner is the player whose total is closest to 1,000 <u>without</u> going over.

Below are the results of a game played by Pat and Lee.

Who won the game? ________________

Pat

	100 s	10 s	1 s
Toss #1		4	—
Toss #2	3	—	—
Toss #3			6
Toss #4	5	—	—
Toss #5			5
Toss #6			2
Toss #7	1	—	—
Toss #8		2	—
Toss #9			4
Toss #10		2	—
TOTAL			

Lee

	100 s	10 s	1 s
Toss #1	4	—	—
Toss #2	3	—	—
Toss #3			6
Toss #4		5	—
Toss #5			5
Toss #6	2	—	—
Toss #7		1	—
Toss #8		2	—
Toss #9			4
Toss #10			2
TOTAL			

Ten Tosses

Mathematics teaching objectives:

. Practice addition skills.

. Develop some informal probability concepts.

. Compare and order numbers.

Problem-solving skills pupils might use:

. Recognize limits and eliminate possibilities.

. Apply what you know about addition and place value.

. Make decisions based upon data.

Materials needed:

. One ordinary die

Comments and suggestions:

. This is a teacher-directed large-group activity. Duplicate the directions and examples (page 51) on an overlay. Tell pupils the object of the game is to find winning game strategies. Play two games; discuss winning strategies. Play one more game and again discuss. Play additional games to "test" the strategies.

. Rather than duplicating the charts (page 53) you may chose to direct the pupils to prepare their own charts.

. Pupils will need the ability to add a column of numbers involving "carrying."

. As the games are played, some pupils may realize that it will help to get a total of 9 in the 100's column, but a total of 9 in the 10's column could be a disaster if carrying will be required in the 1's column.

An Extension: Make columns for the 1's, 10's, 100's and 1000's place. Toss the die ten times. Play for the closest total to 5,000 or to 10,000.

Answers:

Answers will depend on the roll of the die and the placement of the numbers by the pupils.

Pat and Lee tied with scores of 997.

Game 1

Ten Tosses

	100 s	10 s	1 s
Toss # 1			
Toss # 2			
Toss # 3			
Toss # 4			
Toss # 5			
Toss # 6			
Toss # 7			
Toss # 8			
Toss # 9			
Toss #10			
TOTAL			

Game 2

Ten Tosses

	100 s	10 s	1 s
Toss # 1			
Toss # 2			
Toss # 3			
Toss # 4			
Toss # 5			
Toss # 6			
Toss # 7			
Toss # 8			
Toss # 9			
Toss #10			
TOTAL			

Game 3

Ten Tosses

	100	10 s	1 s
Toss # 1			
Toss # 2			
Toss # 3			
Toss # 4			
Toss # 5			
Toss # 6			
Toss # 7			
Toss # 8			
Toss # 9			
Toss #10			
TOTAL			

Game 4

Ten Tosses

	100 s	10 s	1 s
Toss # 1			
Toss # 2			
Toss # 3			
Toss # 4			
Toss # 5			
Toss # 6			
Toss # 7			
Toss # 8			
Toss # 9			
Toss #10			
TOTAL			

PLACE VALUE MARK UP

Your teacher has a special die marked 0, 1, 4, 5, 8, 9.

The die will be rolled 21 times.
The digit that lands face up each time will be announced.

Each time a digit is announced, write it in a box of your choosing below.

After 21 tosses of the die, determine the number of correct answers you were able to make.

. Between 450 and 550 ☐ ☐ ☐

. Between 4,500 and 5,500 ☐ , ☐ ☐ ☐

. A 4-digit number larger than 8,000 ☐ , ☐ ☐ ☐

. An odd number between 45,000 and 55,000 ☐ ☐ , ☐ ☐ ☐

. An even number less than 50,000 ☐ ☐ , ☐ ☐ ☐

There is space for two more games on the next page.

Place Value Mark Up

Mathematics teaching objectives:

- Compare and order numbers.
- Develop informal ideas about probability.
- Use number concepts even and odd.

Problem-solving skills pupils might use:

- Recognize limits and eliminate possibilities.
- Make decisions based upon data.
- Apply what you know about place value.

Materials needed:

- A wooden or foam cube marked with 0, 1, 4, 5, 8, 9.

Comments and suggestions:

- This could be used as a teacher-directed large-group activity. Show pupils the numbers on the die. Tell them the object of the game is to find winning strategies. Play one round involving 21 tosses. Discuss winning game strategies. Play a second round, this time testing the strategies. Again, discuss winning game strategies. Continue as needed.
- Pupils could copy the game board on their papers or they could write on a transparency laid over their game board to save on paper.
- Pupils will need to know concepts of even and odd numbers.
- As the games are played, more pupils will realize that filling in the boxes at random is not a good strategy. A better strategy is to satisfy these restrictions on each number as quickly as the toss of the die allows. For example, "An even number less than 50,000" means that the first digit (because of the way the die is numbered) must be either a 1 or 4, and the last digit must be 0, 4, or 8.

An extension: Discuss whether or not the game would be easier to win if 0 were allowed to be used as the first digit in the last number

Answers:

Answers will depend on the roll of the die and the placement of the numbers by the pupils.

Place Value Mark Up (cont.)

. Between 450 and 550 ☐☐☐

. Between 4,500 and 5,500 ☐,☐☐☐

. A 4-digit number larger than 8,000 ☐,☐☐☐

. An odd number between 45,000 and 55,000 ☐☐,☐☐☐

. An even number less than 50,000 ☐☐,☐☐☐

. Between 450 and 550 ☐☐☐

. Between 4,500 and 5,500 ☐,☐☐☐

. A 4-digit number larger than 8,000 ☐,☐☐☐

. An odd number between 45,000 and 55,000 ☐☐,☐☐☐

. An even number less than 50,000 ☐☐,☐☐☐

THREE MARKERS

The example shows how to use three markers to get

5¢ + 1¢ + 1¢ = 7¢.

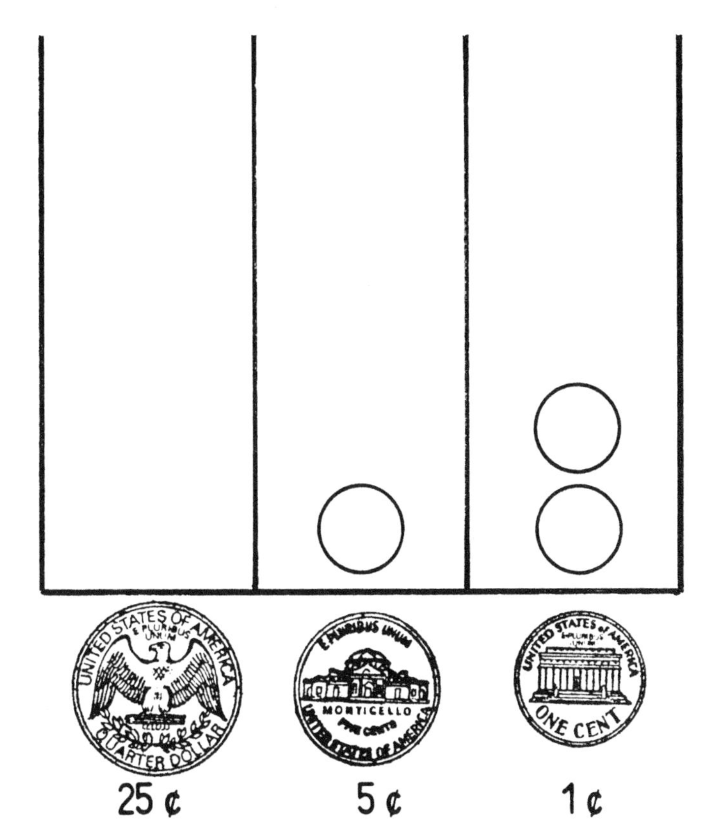

1. How can you use 3 markers to get 11¢?

    ____¢ + _____¢ + ____¢ = 11¢

2. Record all the different totals you can get. Remember, you can only use 3 markers.

Three Markers

Mathematics teaching objectives:

- Use place value concepts.
- Add using money values.

Problem-solving skills pupils might use:

- Make a systematic list.
- Look for patterns.

Materials needed:

- Each pupil will need 3 small counters to use as markers. (These can be bottlecaps, bits of torn papers, small cubes, etc.)

Comments and suggestions:

- Pass out dittoed copies of the page and 3 markers to each pupil and discuss the directions. Give pupils the answer to problem 1.
- Have pupils work problem 2 independently. Suggest they make a systematic list to help solve the problem. (If necessary, assist them in starting the list.)
- Pupils who finish quickly can be given one of the extension problems to solve.
- Finish the lesson with a comparison of pupil solutions to problem 2. Show several organized listings used by pupils on the chalkboard or overhead. Pupils will probably see certain patterns (such as - which digits appear in the 1's place in the "totals" column) in the listings.

Answers:

1. 5¢ + 5¢ + 1¢

2. 10 different totals:

25¢	5¢	1¢	Total
3			75¢
2	1		55¢
2		1	51¢
1	2		35¢
1	1	1	31¢
1		2	27¢
	3		15¢
	2	1	11¢
	1	2	7¢
		3	3¢

Extensions:

- Label "pockets" $1.00, 10¢, 1¢, as pictured below. Find all the different totals possible with 3 markers.

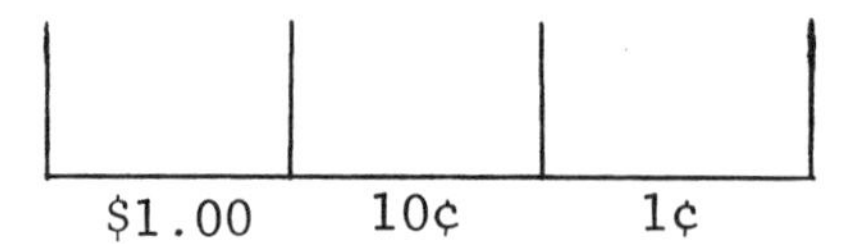

- Add another pocket as pictured at right. Still use 3 markers. Find all the different possible totals.

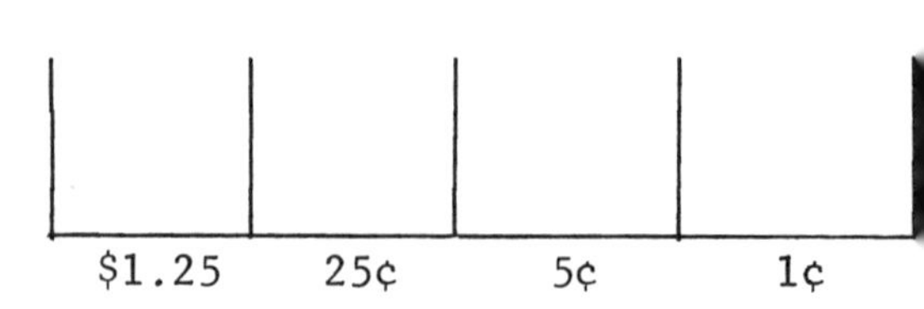

FIVE TO MAKE 2005

1. Your teacher has 3 regular dice.

   Your teacher will toss those dice 5 times.

   Each time your teacher tosses the dice

   . use the digits which land face up to make a 3-digit number.

   . record the number.

   After 5 tosses, total the five 3-digit numbers.

   Winner is the player whose total is closest to 2005 <u>without</u> <u>going</u> <u>over</u>.

Toss 1 ____________

Toss 2 ____________

Toss 3 ____________

Toss 4 ____________

Toss 5 ____________

TOTAL ____________

2. Play six more games below.

a.	b.	c.
______	______	______
______	______	______
______	______	______
______	______	______
______	______	______
TOTAL ______	TOTAL ______	TOTAL ______
d.	**e.**	**f.**
______	______	______
______	______	______
______	______	______
______	______	______
______	______	______
TOTAL ______	TOTAL ______	TOTAL ______

<u>BONUS</u>: The player with the <u>least</u> <u>difference</u> between his or her lowest and highest scores is grand winner.

Five To Make 2005

Mathematics teaching objectives:

- . Practice addition and subtraction skills.
- . Develop some informal probability concepts (when to take a chance)
- . Compare and order numbers.

Problem-solving skills pupils might use:

- . Recognize limits and eliminate possibilities.
- . Apply what you know about place value and addition.
- . Make reasonable estimates.

Materials needed:

- . 3 regular dice

Comments and suggestions:

- . This is a whole-class game.
- . Prepare an overlay of the pupil page or duplicate for pupil use.
- . Let the picture on the pupil page show the first toss. Ask "What different numbers could be recorded in the Toss 1 space?" Complete the introductory game taking suggestions from the class. The six games in part 2 are to be completed with each individual pupil making her/his own decisions.
- . Pupils should be encouraged to find a winning game strategy. For example, use care in selecting the number for the hundreds place or try to keep each number a little bit less than 400. However, let pupils figure out their own strategies.
- . If pupils have already played "Ten Tosses" (page 51), have them compare the strategies used in the two games.

Answers:

- . Answers will vary, depending on the roll of the dice.

Extensions:

- . Use 3 regular dice. Toss the dice ten times. Try to get closest to 5,005 without going over.
- . Use 4 regular dice. Make 4-digit numbers. Try to get closest to 20,005 without going over.

PLACE VALUE CUT-UPS

1. Cut out the six small boxes at the bottom of the page.
   On the back of each piece labeled 1 , write a 10 .
   On the back of each piece labeled 100 , write a 1,000 .

2. Turn these six pieces face up.

1,000	100	1,000	1	10	1

   What is the sum of the numbers? ________

3. Find six face-up pieces with a total value of

a. 2130						
b. 1221						
c. 3021						
d. 3030						

4. Turn pieces face up to show these sums. Cross out any that are not possible.

   a. 2,121 d. 3,012
   b. 2,131 e. 2,040
   c. 3,030 f. 2,301

5. Write three more sums which can be shown with the six pieces. See if you can do it without using the pieces. What rules did you use for getting the correct sums?

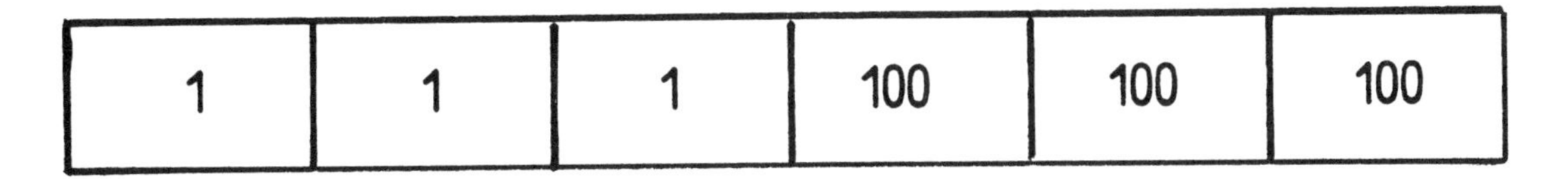

1	1	1	100	100	100

Place Value Cut-Ups

Mathematics teaching objectives:

- . Change numbers given in an expanded form to standard form.
- . Write numbers in an expanded notation form.

Problem-solving skills pupils might use:

- . Look for patterns.
- . Make explanations based upon data.

Materials needed:

- . Scissors

Comments and suggestions:

- . Duplicate the sheet for class use.
- . Work through exercises 3(a) with the total class. Let them complete the rest of the sheet individually.
- . Have pupils share their results with two or three classmates before discussing the activity with the entire class.

Answers:

2. 2112

3. a. 1000 + 1000 + 100 + 10 + 10 + 10
   b. 1000 + 100 + 100 + 10 + 10 + 1
   c. 1000 + 1000 + 1000 + 10 + 10 + 1
   d. 1000 + 1000 + 1000 + 10 + 10 + 10

4. b, e, f, not possible

5. Answers will vary. Pupils should check by using the pieces. They may find rules that work. If they do, let them try them out with each other. Do not give the rules to them or pass judgment on telling them whether they are right or wrong.

Grade 4

III. WHOLE NUMBER DRILL AND PRACTICE

III. WHOLE NUMBER DRILL AND PRACTICE

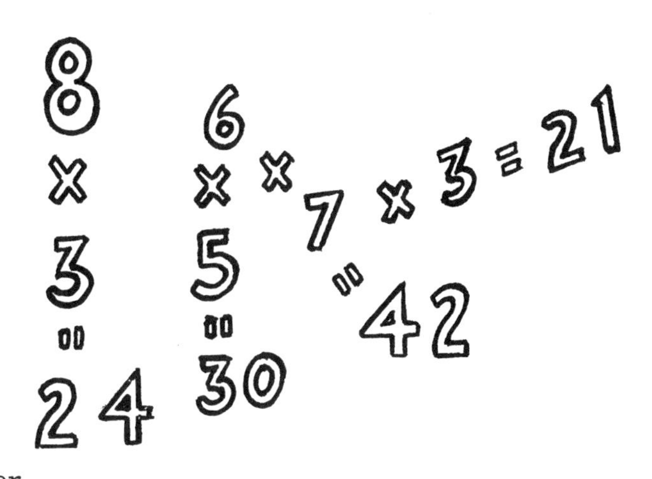

Most fourth-grade classes are a collection of pupils with varying levels of skills. What can be done to provide additional practice and learning for all pupils? One solution is to offer whole number drill and practice through problem-solving activities. While Tim is remembering that 3 x 8 is 24, not 32, Hosea might be figuring out all the possible ways to complete ____x____ = 24. Another solution is to use games. If the games are combined with problem solving, many objectives are accomplished at the same time; motivation, computation practice, and emphasizing of problem-solving skills.

One marvelous discovery in using problem-solving skills with a mixed class is that some pupils who are unskilled in computation are really good at seeing patterns or figuring out ways to solve problems. Some who hate ordinary drill problems will fill a page with computation to try to solve a problem.

Using The Activities

The problem-solving activities in this section can be incorporated with the regular teaching and review of whole number operations. They might be used instead of certain pages in the text. Realizing that pupils have different skills, many activities have suggestions for simplifying or extending the problems. Many of the activities are meant to be teacher-directed while others can be finished by pupils after a brief introduction. Masters are provided for making materials needed for the games. It is important to talk with pupils about the problem-solving skills used and to allow time for them to discuss the problem-solving strategies they are using or have tried.

The activities in this section are loosely sequenced according to difficulty but can be used in any order and at any time of the year after pupils have the prerequisites.

The material needed for this section include classroom sets of calculators and dice.

DIGIT DRAW ACTIVITIES
(Ideas for Teachers)

Ten digit cards marked 0-9 can be used for a variety of activities.

A. Have pupils draw the diagram to the right.

B. Suggest a goal, such as, getting the largest possible sum.

C. Shuffle and draw digits one at a time.

D. Pupils must write each digit as it is drawn until all spaces are filled. No changes can be made.

E. Compare and discuss results.

This activity is very adaptable. For example, in the 3-digit by 3-digit addition problem above, pupils may not get the largest sum the first time. The teacher can have the pupils use the same six digits to find the largest sum; then use the same six digits to find the smallest sum; and then use those digits to find the sum closest to, say, 700.

These activities can be used for drill and practice, concept development,and/or diagnosis. Each is highly individual, as many pupils will have a unique problem. See the next page for other suggested formats. Further variations could include:

- replacing a drawn digit so it can be used again
- restricting certain numbers, e.g., no zero is used with division problems
- allowing a special reject box giving pupils the chance to discard an unfavorable draw
- adapting whole number activities to money activities by inserting decimal points and dollar signs, e.g.,

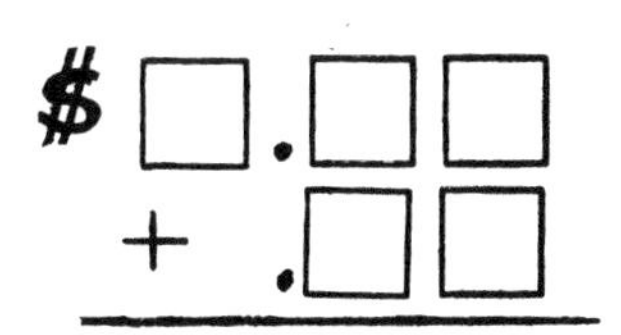

Digit Draw Activities

Mathematics teaching objectives:

. Develop place value concepts.

. Develop informal probability concepts.

. Practice computation skills.

Problem-solving skills pupils *might* use:

. Break problem into manageable parts.

. Make decisions based upon data.

. Recognize limits and/or eliminate possibilities.

Materials needed:

. Digit cards 0-9
A deck of cards with the face cards missing could be used. The ten could be the zero.

Comments and suggestions:

. This activity works well as an opener at the beginning of the class or as an ending for those last few minutes of a class when all other activities have been completed. See pages 69 and 71 for other suggestions and many variations.

. After some trials, pupils can be encouraged to share what strategies they use. "If a 9 or 8 is drawn first, put it in the 100's place. If a little digit comes first, put it in the 1's place. It's hard to decide what to do with a 5 or 6. Sometimes it's just luck!"

Answers:

. Answers will vary according to the digits drawn and the places where pupils put the digits. The largest *possible* sum is 1839 if the digits are not replaced and 9, 8, 7, 6, 5 and 4 are drawn. *Very* unlikely!

Digit Draw Activities (cont.)

OTHER FORMATS

Place Value: $\square,\square\square\square$ largest number, smallest number, or closest to 5000

Ordering: $\square\square < \square\square < \square\square$

Addition:

$$\begin{array}{r} \square\square \\ \square\square \\ +\,\square\square \\ \hline \end{array} \qquad \begin{array}{r} \square\square\square \\ +\,\square\square\square \\ \hline \end{array}$$

Subtraction:

$$\begin{array}{r} \square\square\square \\ -\,\square\square \\ \hline \end{array} \qquad \begin{array}{r} \square\square\square \\ -\,\square\square\square \\ \hline \end{array}$$

Multiplication:

$$\begin{array}{r} \square\square \\ \times\,\square \\ \hline \end{array} \qquad \begin{array}{r} \square\square\square \\ \times\,\square \\ \hline \end{array} \qquad \begin{array}{r} \square\square \\ \times\,\square\square \\ \hline \end{array} \qquad \begin{array}{r} \square\square\square \\ \times\,\square\square \\ \hline \end{array}$$

Division: $\square\overline{)\square\square}$ $\quad\square\overline{)\square\square\square}$ $\quad\square\square\overline{)\square\square\square}$

MARK OUT

Work with a partner.

Each roll 2 dice. Player with larger sum is Player A.

Play this game:

Player A - Roll the two dice.

- Add the number of dots which land face up.
- Use the row of numbers below labeled Player A.
- Mark out the sum of the dice or mark out any set of numbers that equal the sum.
- Continue to roll the dice until unable to mark out numbers equal to the sum.
- Add up the numbers not crossed out. This is your score.

Player B - Now take your turn.

- Follow the same rules, but use the row of numbers labeled Player B.

Winner is the player with the lowest score.

Player A

1	2	3	4	5	6	7	8	9	10	11	12

______ Score

Player B

1	2	3	4	5	6	7	8	9	10	11	12

______ Score

Mark Out

Mathematics teaching objectives:

. Practice mental arithmetic.

. Build readiness for probability concepts.

Problem-solving skills pupils *might* use:

. Make decisions based upon data.

. Apply what you know about dice odds.

Materials needed:

. 2 dice for each pair of pupils playing the game

Comments and suggestions:

. This activity is a game that could be played by two pupils at odd times during the day.

. After all pupils have had opportunities to play the game, you might have pupils talk about promising winning strategies.

. As the game is repeated, pupils should realize that marking out the larger numbers first is a helpful strategy.

Answers:

Answers will vary according to the numbers that come up on the dice.

Mark Out (cont.)

Continue to play more games. Record below.

Player A

1	2	3	4	5	6	7	8	9	10	11	12

________ Score

Player B

1	2	3	4	5	6	7	8	9	10	11	12

________ Score

Player A

1	2	3	4	5	6	7	8	9	10	11	12

________ Score

Player B

1	2	3	4	5	6	7	8	9	10	11	12

________ Score

Player A

1	2	3	4	5	6	7	8	9	10	11	12

________ Score

Player B

1	2	3	4	5	6	7	8	9	10	11	12

________ Score

SHOPPING AT THE USED TOY STORE

ball 12¢
comb 6¢
boat 13¢
car 2¢
vase 8¢
notebook 5¢
Pen 9¢
Truck 16¢

se the toy store. Buy gifts for friends. The gifts may be the ame or different.

. Buy 2 things.
Give clerk 10¢.
Get 3¢ change.
What did you buy?

________ , ________

. Buy 2 things.
Give clerk 15¢.
Get 2¢ change.
What did you buy?

________ , ________

. Buy 2 things.
Give clerk a dime and a nickel.
Get 3¢ change.
What did you buy?

________ , ________

. Buy 3 things.
Give clerk 1 dime and 2 nickels.
Get 2¢ change.
What did you buy?

________ , ________ , ________

or ________ , ________ , ________

5. Buy 3 things.
Give clerk a quarter.
Get 2¢ change.
What did you buy?

________ , ________ , ________

or ________ , ________ , ________

or ________ , ________ , ________

6. Buy 3 things.
Give clerk 3 dimes.
Get 3¢ change.
What did you buy?

________ , ________ , ________

or ________ , ________ , ________

or ________ , ________ , ________

or ________ , ________ , ________

or ________ , ________ , ________

or ________ , ________ , ________

or ________ , ________ , ________

Shopping At The Used Toy Store

Mathematics teaching objectives:

- Practice mental arithmetic using addition and subtraction of one- and two-digit numbers.
- Practice with naming the value of coins and making change (mentally)
- Practice using mathematics in a "real world" setting.

Problem-solving skills pupils <u>might</u> use:

- Guess and check.
- Make reasonable estimates.
- Work backwards.
- Search for and be aware of other solutions.

Materials needed:

- None

Comments and suggestions:

- Complete problem 1 together as a class. Be certain pupils understand that it is O K. to buy two of the same items.
- Pupils can complete the page on their own or work with a partner.
- Actual coins or toy money might be helpful for pupils who find the activity difficult
- Have pupils compare their solutions with others in the class.

Extensions:

- Pupils who finish the page successfully may be asked to
  - find out how many different ways they can spend 25¢ at the Used Toy Store.
  - make up their own Used Toy Store problems.

Answers:

1. Car and notebook
2. Vase and notebook
3. Comb and comb
4. Notebook, notebook and vase; vase, vase and car
5. Ball, pen and car; boat, vase and car; pen, pen and notebook
6. Accept any answer totaling 22¢

"ANSWERS" NOT NEEDED

Kirby found this page of problems in a math book. ⟶

Tell several things you notice about the problems:

____

____

____

____

The missing number in problem (1) is about how large? ________

Discuss. Find an exact answer in the "cloud" below. Fill in the blank.

Use the numbers below to complete the other problems on Kirby's page. (2 extra numbers are given.)

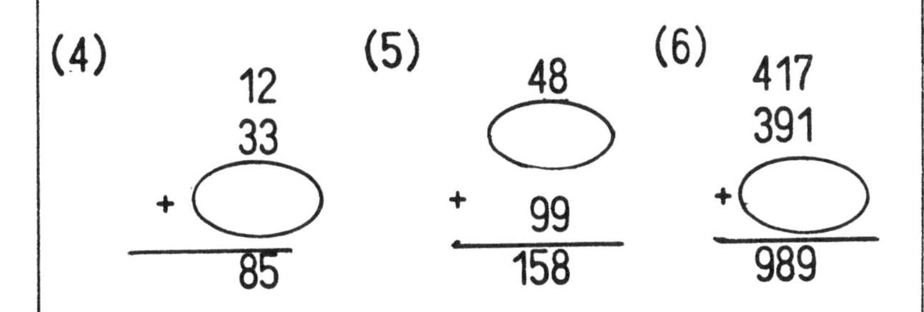

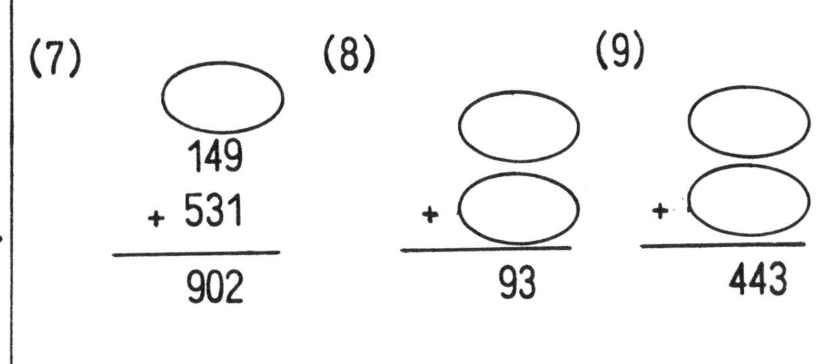

(7) 149 + 531 = 902 (with one missing addend)

(8) missing + missing = 93

(9) missing + missing = 443

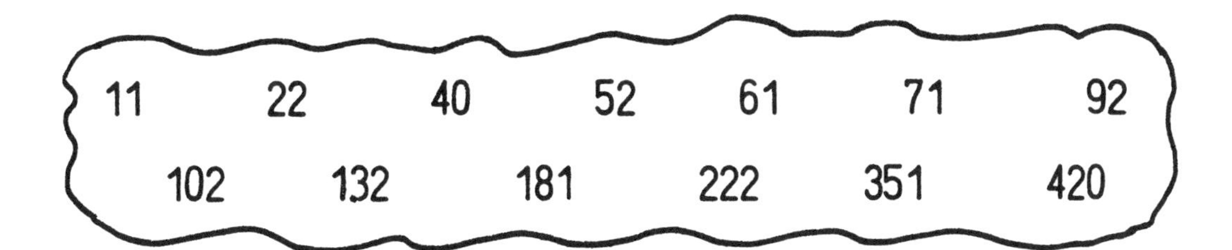

Tell some "clues" you used to complete the problems.

"Answers" Not Needed

Mathematics teaching objectives:

. Practice mental arithmetic and estimation.

Problem-solving skills pupils might use:

. Make estimates.

. Guess and check.

. Work backwards making reasonable estimates.

Materials needed:

. None

Comments and suggestions:

. This activity could be used as a "following directions" activity for individual pupils.

. If estimation is your goal, you may conduct a class discussion before letting them work on their own.

. Pupils at first may choose numbers at random from the given list of answers and then use a strategy involving guess and check. A more efficient strategy would be to make estimates before selecting numbers from the list.

. Other pupils may choose to work backwards whenever they can.

. Provide enough time before the end of the period for pupils to discuss the various strategies they used. As a way to get the discussion started, you might comment on the strategies you observed class members using.

Answers:

. Some comments pupils might mention:
  - All the exercises involve addition and the sums are given.
  - At least one addend in each exercise is missing.

1. 102	2. 420	3. 61
4. 40	5. 11	6. 181
7. 222	8. 22 + 71	9. 92 + 351

Extension:

. Pupils might make up a similar "addition" activity to be used in class.

. Possibly some pupils can make up a similar "subtraction" activity.

FOUR CIRCLED NUMBERS

1. Add the four circled numbers in each problem below and record the sum for each.

a.

1	2	(3)	4
5	(6)	7	8
9	(10)	11	12
13	14	(15)	16

Sum __________

b.

1	(2)	3	4
5	6	(7)	8
9	10	(11)	12
13	(14)	15	16

Sum __________

c.

1	2	3	4
(5)	6	7	(8)
9	(10)	(11)	12
13	14	15	16

Sum __________

d.

1	2	3	4
5	(6)	(7)	8
(9)	10	11	(12)
13	14	15	16

Sum __________

e. What do you notice about the sums?

f. What pattern do the circled numbers have?

2. Here are two other sets of four circled numbers whose sum is 34. For each, find and circle four numbers with similar patterns which total 34.

a.

1	2	3	(4)
5	6	(7)	8
9	(10)	11	12
(13)	14	15	16

1	2	3	4
5	6	7	8
9	10	11	12
13	14	15	16

b.

1	(2)	(3)	4
5	6	7	8
9	10	11	12
13	(14)	(15)	16

1	2	3	4
5	6	7	8
9	10	11	12
13	14	15	16

3. Use the number grids on the next page. Find and circle still other sets of four numbers which total 34.

Four Circled Numbers

Mathematics teaching objectives:

- Mentally add one- and two-digit numbers, four addends.

Problem-solving skills pupils might use:

- Guess and check.
- Look for patterns.

Materials needed:

- None

Comments and suggestions:

- The first two problems of the activity can be used as a class activity with the remainder of the problems being done individually.
- After completing problems 1 and 2, most pupils notice that the "four circles" form simple geometric patterns.
- Some pupils will continue to look for additional patterns.
- Other pupils will search randomly and may need help in "organizing their search."
- After some time working individually, pupils could compare their answers with a classmate and then continue their search for additional solutions.

Answers:

1. a. 34 b. 34 c. 34 d. 34 e. Sums are the same.

   f. Circled numbers are either in the middle rows or columns with two numbers from each row or column. a and b are "mirror" images - so are c and d.

2. a.

(1)	2	3	4
5	(6)	7	8
9	10	(11)	12
13	14	15	(16)

b.

1	2	3	4
(5)	6	7	(8)
(9)	10	11	(12)
13	14	15	16

Accept other answers if pupils have a reasonable explanation.

Four Circled Numbers (cont.)

1	2	3	4				1	2	3	4				1	2	3	4
5	6	7	8				5	6	7	8				5	6	7	8
9	10	11	12				9	10	11	12				9	10	11	12
13	14	15	16				13	14	15	16				13	14	15	16
1	2	3	4				1	2	3	4				1	2	3	4
5	6	7	8				5	6	7	8				5	6	7	8
9	10	11	12				9	10	11	12				9	10	11	12
13	14	15	16				13	14	15	16				13	14	15	16
1	2	3	4				1	2	3	4				1	2	3	4
5	6	7	8				5	6	7	8				5	6	7	8
9	10	11	12				9	10	11	12				9	10	11	12
13	14	15	16				13	14	15	16				13	14	15	16
1	2	3	4				1	2	3	4				1	2	3	4
5	6	7	8				5	6	7	8				5	6	7	8
9	10	11	12				9	10	11	12				9	10	11	12
13	14	15	16				13	14	15	16				13	14	15	16
1	2	3	4				1	2	3	4				1	2	3	4
5	6	7	8				5	6	7	8				5	6	7	8
9	10	11	12				9	10	11	12				9	10	11	12
13	14	15	16				13	14	15	16				13	14	15	16

4. Which solutions above have similar "circle number" patterns? Explain.

Four Circled Numbers

Answers:

3. Many solutions are possible. Here are a few of them:

(1)	2	3	(4)
5	6	7	8
9	10	11	12
(13)	14	15	(16)

1	2	3	4
5	(6)	(7)	8
9	(10)	(11)	12
13	14	15	16

(1)	2	3	4
(5)	6	7	8
9	10	11	(12)
13	14	15	(16)

1	2	(3)	(4)
5	6	7	8
9	10	11	12
(13)	(14)	15	16

4. A possible answer: For the solutions given for problem 3, the last two have similar circle number patterns --

- . First two numbers in first column, last two in last column.
- . First two numbers in last row, last two in first row.

NO PENCILS ALLOWED - ADDITION

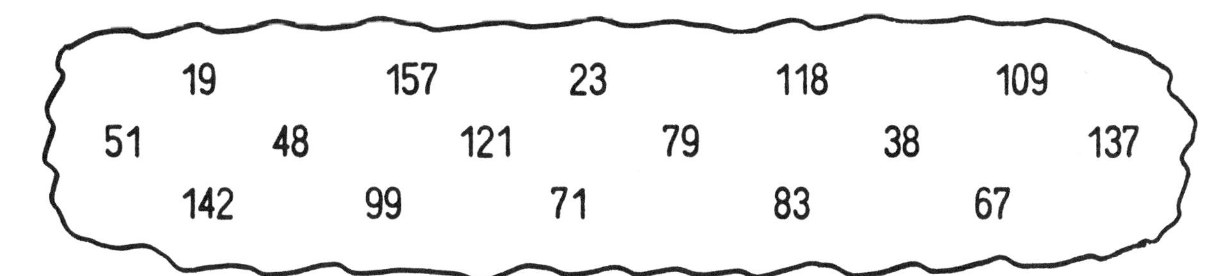

Get a calculator.

Play this game with a partner.

Player A

- . Pick two of the numbers above and mark them out.
- . Use the calculator to add the two numbers.
- . Use the Scorer's Box to find the point value of your answer.
- . Record your score below.

Sum	Point Value
0 - 60	1
61 - 120	2
121 - 180	3
181 - 240	2
241 - 300	1

Player B

- . Pick two unmarked numbers.
- . Add.
- . Record the point value of the sum.

Continue to take turns until all numbers have been marked out. Then find your total score.

SCORE SHEET

Player A	Player B

No Pencils Allowed - Addition

Mathematics teaching objective:

- Practice mental arithmetic and estimation.

Problem-solving skills pupils _might_ use:

- Make reasonable estimates.
- Guess and check.
- Make decisions based upon previously acquired knowledge.

Materials needed:

- A calculator for each pair of pupils playing the game (optional)

Comments and suggestions:

- If enough calculators are available, this activity could be used as a total class game activity with pupils grouped in pairs. This activity capitalizes on the calculator being used as a vehicle for motivating mental arithmetic and estimating.
- If calculators are not available, use a transparency of the page and play one side of the room against the other side.
- As pupils continue to play these games they should realize that an important winning strategy is to give careful attention to the point values in the chart and the ability to make reasonable estimates.

Alternate versions:

Easier:

38 47 59 68 21

41 2 79 9 62

18 32 11 52 71

Scorer's Box

Sum	Point Value
0- 30	1
31- 60	2
61- 90	3
91-120	2
121-150	1

Harder:

206 612 293 596 389

496 91 683 103 182 519

409 23 712 321 789

Scorer's Box

Sum	Point Value
0- 300	1
301- 600	2
601- 900	3
901-1200	2
1201-1500	1

Answers: Sums vary. Players check each other.

Extension: Each game could be replayed by rearranging the point value for the sums. A discussion could follow on the effect of this rearrangement

MISSING DIGITS

Complete these problems:

1. 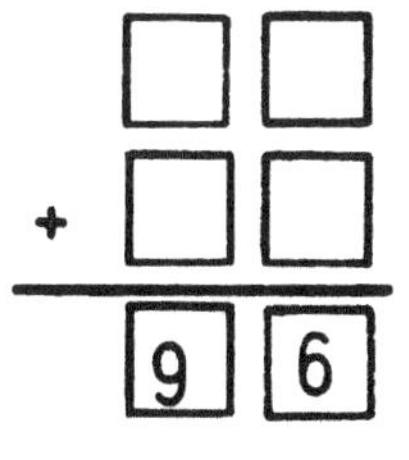

2.
```
    □ □ 8
  +   2 □
  -------
    7 4 2
```

3.
```
    □ □ 2
  + □ 5 □
  -------
    2 6 1
```

4.
```
       □ □ 1
     + □ 1 □
    ---------
    1, □ □ □
```

5.
```
      □ 8
      □ □
    + 8 □
    -----
    2 □ □
```

6.
```
    □ 0 1
  -   5 □
  -------
    □ □ 6
```

7.
```
    □ 7 □
  - □ □ 2
  -------
    3 □ □
```

8.
```
    8 6 □
  - □ 4 1
  -------
    5 1 □
```

9.
```
    □ 0 1
  - □ □ □
  -------
      6 7
```

Trade papers with a classmate.
Check and compare answers.

Circle the problems that have only one possible solution.

Make up other missing digit problems. Give them to a friend to solve.

Missing Digits

Mathematics teaching objectives:

- Practice with place value concepts (regrouping).
- Practice with addition and subtraction exercises that encourage an examination of the solution process.

Problem-solving skills pupils might use:

- Study the solution process.
- Recognize limits and/or eliminate possibilities.
- Work backwards.
- Invent a new problem by varying an old one.

Comments and suggestions:

- Each pupil needs a copy of the activity.
- The activity can be used as a diagnostic tool to determine whether pupils are lacking in computational skills and/or concepts such as regrouping.
- Encourage pupils to make at least one of the numbers involved in the addition and subtraction as large as possible.
- Some pupils could determine limits for certain problems. For example in problem 1 the two numbers must be in the range of 10 to 86.
- To get the most from this activity, you should insist that pupils check a classmate's paper and invent similar problems for others to do.

Answers:

Answers may vary, except for those shown below.

2. $\begin{array}{r} 718 \\ +\ 24 \\ \hline 742 \end{array}$

3. $\begin{array}{r} 102 \\ +\ 159 \\ \hline 261 \end{array}$

8. $\begin{array}{r} 860 \\ -\ 341 \\ \hline 519 \end{array}$

LUNCH FOR SAM

Sam has $1.58 in his pocket.

He would like to spend <u>the entire $1.58</u> for lunch.

Here is the menu.

Pick a $1.58 lunch for Sam.

Record below.

Item	Cost
Total	$ 1.58

Are there other ways this can be done?

Find out.

Use the back of this page to record your results.

Lunch For Sam

Mathematics teaching objectives:

- Use mental arithmetic and estimation.
- Practice computation with usual algorithms.
- Apply mathematics to a life-like situation.

Problem-solving skills pupils *might* use:

- Search printed material for needed information.
- Search for and be aware of other solutions.
- Make reasonable estimates as answers.
- Guess and check.
- Record solution possibilities.

Materials needed:

- Calculators (optional)

Comments and suggestions:

- After a short discussion of the activity and some casual tries, you could turn the activity over to pupils to work individually.
- If pupils quit working on the activity after making several unsuccessful attempts, you might ask certain class members to discuss some strategies they have tried, have the items listed on the chalkboard ordered according to their cost, or have one or two successful pupils give their solutions.
- You may find it worthwhile to have all successful solutions posted.
- Pupils at first may select items at random from the menu, check to see if the total is $1.58 and then make adjustments. More efficient ways should emerge such as starting with the most expensive items, first determining amount left from $1.58, and then picking the other items accordingly.

Possible answers:

hamburger	$ .65
chips	.36
milk	.18
candy bar	.14
gum	.13
apple	.12
	$1.58

hot dog	$ .55
hamburger	.65
cola	.25
gum	.13
	$1.58

hot dog	$ .55
chips	.36
cola	.25
apple	.12
i.c. cone	.30
	$1.58

hamburger	$ .65
cola	.25
chips	.36
milk	.18
candy bar	.14
	$1.58

hamburger	$ .65
pop corn	.39
pie	.40
candy bar	.14
	$1.58

2 hamburgers	$1.30
2 candy bars	.28
	$1.58

3 chips	$1.08
2 colas	.50
	$1.58

CALCULATORS AND CARDS

1. Use any two numbers on the cards.

   Complete each addition problem below.

   Check your work with a calculator.

97 204 297 405 498 607

a. ☐ + ☐ = 301

b. ☐ + ☐ = 1012

c. ☐ + ☐ = 501

d. ☐ + ☐ = 1105

e. ☐ + ☐ = 595

f. ☐ + ☐ = 795

g. ☐ + ☐ = 394

h. ☐ + ☐ = 811

i. ☐ + ☐ = 609

j. 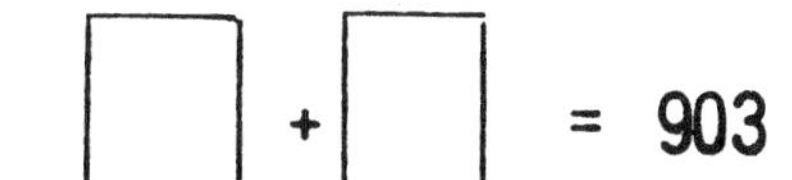 = 903

k.  = 702

or

☐ + ☐ = 702

2. Now use any three numbers on the cards. Complete these problems.

a. ☐ + ☐ + ☐ = 598

b. ☐ + ☐ + ☐ = 1202

c. ☐ + ☐ + ☐ = 1402

d. ☐ + ☐ + ☐ = 1510

e. ☐ + ☐ + ☐ = 1309

f. 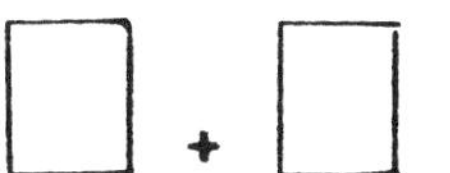  = 1107

Calculators And Cards

Mathematics teaching objectives:

. Mentally add two- and three-digit numbers.

. Use place value concepts to make reasonable estimates.

Problem-solving skills pupils might use:

. Guess and check.

. Make reasonable estimates.

Materials needed:

. One calculator for each pair of students (optional)

Comments and suggestions:

. Work a few examples as a class, then have pupils pair up to complete the page.

Answers:

1. a. 97 + 204
   b. 405 + 607
   c. 204 + 297
   d. 498 + 607
   e. 97 + 498
   f. 498 + 297
   g. 97 + 297
   h. 204 + 607
   i. 204 + 405
   j. 405 + 498
   k. 297 + 405 or 498 + 204

2. a. 97 + 204 + 297
   b. 97 + 498 + 607
   c. 498 + 297 + 607
   d. 405 + 498 + 607
   e. 498 + 204 + 607
   f. 204 + 405 + 498

TARGET TOTALS

1. Find and circle the two numbers whose sum is the number shown at the top of each puzzle.

   Check your work with a calculator.

a. 28

6	10	13
14	15	19
21	24	26

b. 33

6	10	13
14	15	19
21	24	26

c. 50

6	10	13
14	15	19
21	24	26

2. Find and circle <u>three</u> numbers whose sum is given.

a. 27

2	5	8
11	14	17
20	22	25

b. 35

2	5	8
11	14	17
20	22	25

c. 61

2	5	8
11	14	17
20	22	25

d. 42

1	8	10
15	19	22
25	30	38

e. 58

1	8	10
15	19	22
25	30	38

f. 70

1	8	10
15	19	22
25	30	38

3. Find two <u>different</u> sets of three numbers whose sum is 100.

100

40	49	76	35
32	45	30	25
55	26	33	50

Target Totals

Mathematics teaching objectives:

- . Mentally add two- and three-digit numbers.
- . Use place value concepts to make reasonable estimates.

Problem-solving skills pupils <u>might</u> use:

- . Guess and check.
- . Make reasonable estimates.

Materials needed:

- . One calculator for each pair of students (optional)

Comments and suggestions:

- . Work the problems in part 1 as a whole class activity. Use this activity after pupils have been introduced to the <u>make a reasonable estimate</u> skill.
- . Once pupils understand the task, have them complete the page, working in pairs or trios.
- . Compare solutions and strategies used as a class.

Answers:

1. a. 13 + 15   b. 14 + 19   c. 24 + 26

2. a. 2 + 5 + 20
or
2 + 8 + 17
or
2 + 11 + 14
or
5 + 8 + 14

   b. 2 + 8 + 25
2 + 11 + 22
5 + 8 + 22

   c. 14 + 22 + 25

   d. 1 + 19 + 22
8 + 15 + 19

   e. 1 + 19 + 38

   f. 10 + 22 + 38
15 + 25 + 30

3. 40 + 35 + 25
32 + 33 + 35
49 + 25 + 26

DOTS ALL

1. Count the crossing points marked by the dots (•).

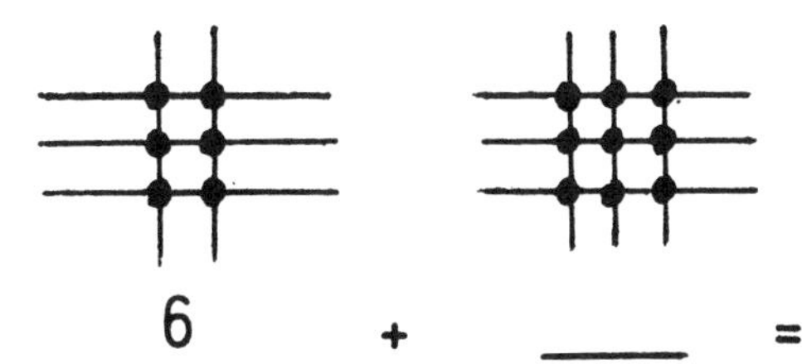

   Complete the equation. 6 + ____ = ____

2. Complete the problems below. Draw in the needed vertical lines.

a.

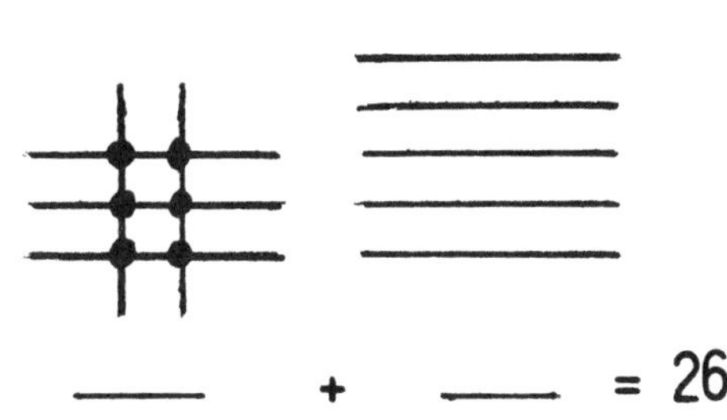

____ + ____ = 26

b.

3 + ____ = 19

c.

____ + ____ = 23

d.

____ + ____ = 26

e.

____ + ____ = 34

f.

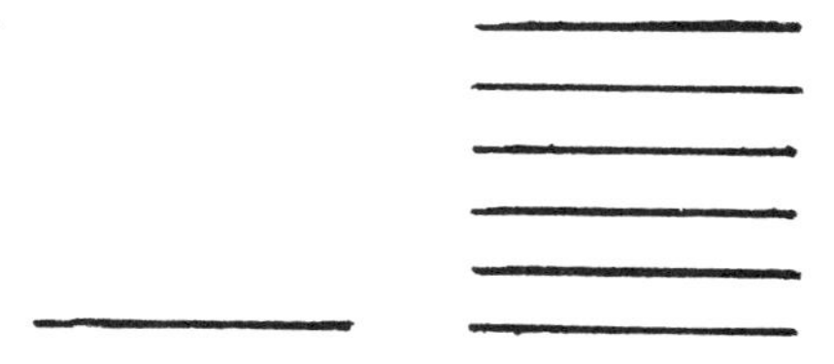

____ + ____ = 39

3. Find other solutions to problems c-f.

Mathematics teaching objectives:

. Use mental arithmetic skills.
. Work informally with equations and variables.

Problem-solving skills pupils <u>might</u> use:

. Work backwards.
. Study the solution process.
. Guess and check.
. Use a drawing.

Materials needed:

. None

Comments and suggestions:

. This could be used as an individual or group activity. We suggest it be used as a fifteen-minute class activity followed by a group discussion of results and the strategies various pupils have used.

. After this discussion, pupils should be encouraged to complete the activity, listing as many solutions as possible for each exercise and making note of the patterns they observe.

. The first few exercises involve rather simple strategies. As the amount of given data decreases, the efficient strategies probably will involve satisfying one condition at a time, guessing, making refinements, and working backwards. The strategies should become more efficient as pupils progress through the exercises.

. For pupils having difficulty while experimenting to find solutions, flat toothpicks might be provided to use in lieu of drawn-in lines.

Answers:

1. 6 + 9 = 15

2. a. 6 + 20 = 26

b. 3 + 16 = 19

c. 3 + 20 = 23

Another solution:

15 + 8 = 23

d. 6 + 20 = 26

Other solutions:

21 + 5 = 26

2 + 24 = 26

e.

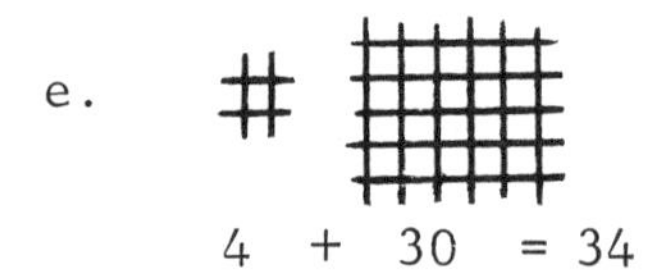

4 + 30 = 34

Possible solutions:

4 + 30 = 34
14 + 20 = 34
24 + 10 = 34

Notice the pattern--
The first addends increase by 10 as the second addends decrease by 10.

f. 4 + 35 = 39

Other solutions:

18 + 21 = 39
32 + 7 = 39

TRIPLE TIC TAC TOE

Play with a partner or play one side of the room against the other. Take turns.

Pick any 3 numbers below:

1 2 3 4 5 6

Add two of the numbers and multiply the sum by the third number.

Mark the answer on the game board with your mark (X or O).

Winner is the first player to get 3 marks in a row horizontally, vertically, or diagonally.

Game 1

48	9	35	10	27	15
20	16	42	45	22	24
12	25	33	21	54	18
7	40	28	36	14	5
8	11	44	50	32	30

Game 2

30	25	10	16	54	21
8	22	12	27	11	50
15	33	45	9	35	7
48	42	40	36	28	24
20	14	44	18	5	32

Game 3

27	9	32	10	7	15
48	8	33	14	16	30
42	40	24	35	50	25
20	22	18	28	36	12
11	44	5	45	54	21

Game 4

15	30	10	54	16	21
25	22	11	28	45	7
9	48	33	36	12	14
42	20	24	27	40	50
8	44	18	5	35	32

Triple Tic Tac Toe

Mathematics teaching objectives:

. Practice with basic addition and multiplication facts.

Problem-solving skills pupils might use:

. Guess and check.

. Recognize limits .

. Work backwards .

Materials needed:

. None

Comments and suggestions:

. Play one game with one side of the room competing against the other. (A transparency is helpful for a whole class game.)

. Then have pupils pair up and play the four games on the worksheet.

. The game can be made more difficult by requiring 4 (or 5) marks in a row to win instead of three.

. Additional game charts can be copied and played on the back of the worksheet.

Answers:

. Answers will vary according to numbers picked.

MULTIPLICATION SQUARES

Complete the multiplication tables by filling in the blanks.

X	7	3		6	4	
5		15		30	20	
4	28		4			
2		6				10
				36		
3		9			12	
					4	

X	5		7	4		3
2	10			8		
			35		40	
					24	
7		7		28		21
					48	
	20		28			

X						
		18		6		
2		12				14
				16		
4			36		16	
	3					7
				12		

X						
		40		15		
			40		72	
			15			
	8			12	36	
			45			
	14					42

Multiplication Squares

Mathematics teaching objectives:

- Practice multiplication facts by correctly filling in the missing squares of incomplete multiplication charts.
- Apply the common divisor property in filling in the numbers missing in an incomplete multiplication chart. (They do not need to know the name of the property in order to apply it.)

Problem-solving skills pupils *might* use:

- Make and/or use a table.
- Work backwards.
- Look for patterns.
- Guess and check.

Materials needed:

- None

Comments and suggestions:

- If pupils have had experience using multiplication charts, they should be able to complete the first two charts without assistance from others.
- In order to complete the last two charts, they will need to observe some chart properties.
- In the third chart, one key strategy is to recognize that the numbers in the 6, 16, 12 column must have a 2 to head the column.
- In the fourth chart, one key strategy is to recognize that the numbers in the 40, 15, 45 column must have a 5 to head the column.
- A similar key strategy needs to be applied to a row of numbers before the chart can be completed.
- At some time, either in a discovery session or a culminating sharing period, the key strategy should be discussed. Different successful strategies of pupils should be highlighted.

Answers: The complete charts are listed below:

x	7	3	1	6	4	5
5	35	15	5	30	20	25
4	28	12	4	24	16	20
2	14	6	2	12	8	10
6	42	18	6	36	24	30
3	21	9	3	18	12	15
1	7	3	1	6	4	5

x	5	1	7	4	8	3
2	10	2	14	8	16	6
5	25	5	35	20	40	15
3	15	3	21	12	24	9
7	35	7	49	28	56	21
6	30	6	42	24	48	18
4	20	4	28	16	32	12

x	3	6	9	2	4	7
3	9	18	27	6	12	21
2	6	12	18	4	8	14
8	24	48	72	16	32	56
4	12	24	36	8	16	28
1	3	6	9	2	4	7
6	18	36	54	12	24	42

x	2	8	5	3	9	6
5	10	40	25	15	45	30
8	16	64	40	24	72	48
3	6	24	15	9	27	18
4	8	32	20	12	36	24
9	18	72	45	27	81	54
7	14	56	35	21	63	42

The key strategy for completing the last two charts is to recognize, for example, that every number in a column must have a common divisor. The same idea applies to each row.

NO PENCILS ALLOWED - MULTIPLICATION

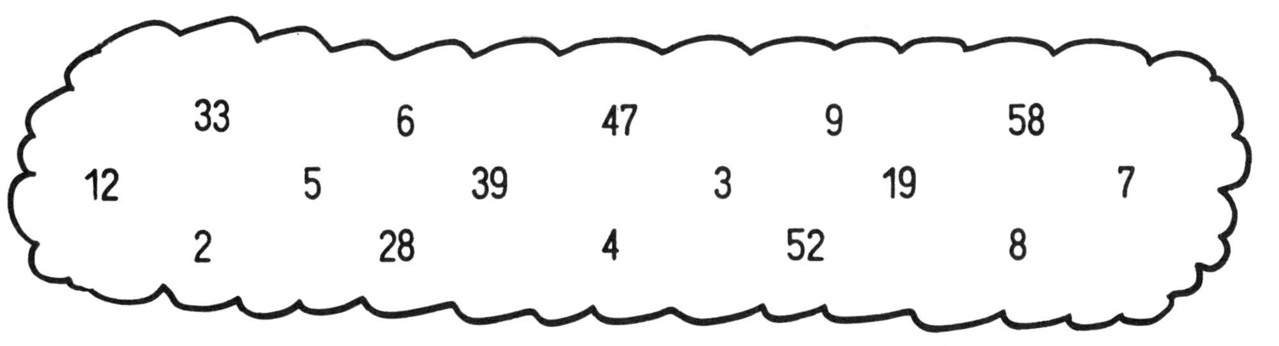

Get a calculator. Play this game with a partner.

Scorer's Box

Product	Point Value
1-100	1
101-200	2
201-300	3
301-400	2
Above 400	1

Player A
- Pick two of the numbers above and mark them out.
- Use the calculator to multiply the two numbers.
- Use the Scorer's Box to find the point value of your answer.
- Record your score below.

Player B
- Pick two unmarked numbers.
- Multiply.
- Record the point value of the product.

Continue to take turns until all numbers have been marked out, then find your total score.

SCORE SHEET

Player A	Player B

No Pencils Allowed - Multiplication

Mathematics teaching objective:

. Select two numbers whose product is within a certain range. Check your selection by using a calculator.

Problem-solving skills pupils might use:

. Make reasonable estimates.

. Guess and check.

. Make decisions based on previously acquired knowledge.

Materials needed:

. A calculator for pairs of pupils playing the game

Comments and suggestions:

. This activity capitalizes on the use of the calculator as a way of motivating mental arithmetic and estimating. It can be used as a class activity, with all pupils working with a partner if enough calculators are available.

. If calculators are not available, use a transparency of the page and play one side of the room against the other.

. After playing several games, the class as a whole might discuss effective ways of estimating.

. Later, interested pairs of pupils could play the game during free time periods.

Answers:

Products vary. Players check each other.

Extensions:

. Change the rule so the winner of the game is the person with the lowest score.

. Play this harder version.

393 297 6 226 5

205 3 415 8 116 9

7 179 4 311 2

Scorer's Box

Product	Point Value
1-1000	1
1001-2000	2
2001-3000	3
3001-4000	2
Above 4000	1

CALCULATOR BINGO

Play with a partner - or play one side of the room against the other side.

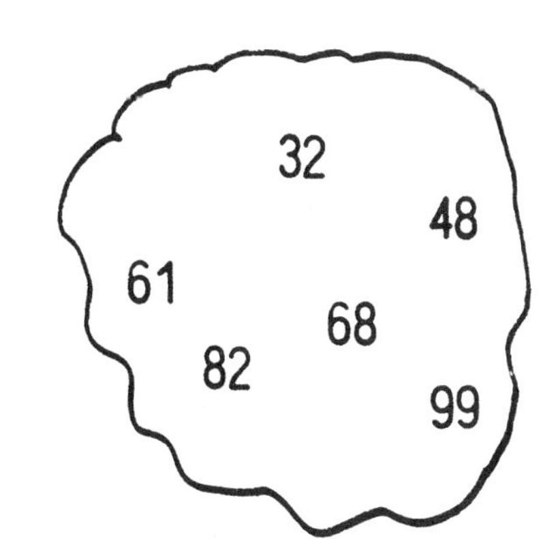

Take turns.

Pick any two numbers above, one from each side.

Use the calculator. Multiply the numbers. Place your mark (X or O) on the answer.

Three of your marks in a row, column, or diagonal wins the game.

There are gameboards for two games below. You may use the back of the page to copy and play more games.

Game 1

128	384	192	340	366	272
891	693	336	396	544	656
256	476	240	492	594	160
612	495	792	192	488	410
549	738	288	305	574	288
328	432	427	224	408	244

Game 2

272	656	160	410	574	244
366	544	594	488	305	408
340	396	492	192	288	224
288	192	336	240	792	256
384	693	476	495	738	432
128	891	427	612	549	328

Calculator Bingo

Mathematics teaching objective:

. Estimate products involving a one-digit and a two-digit number.

Problem-solving skills pupils *might* use:

. Make estimates.

. Guess and check.

. Apply previously acquired knowledge to a new situation.

Materials needed:

. Calculator(s)

Comments and suggestions:

. If enough calculators are available, pupils may work in pairs. If you have enough calculators for every 3 pupils, let pupils work in trios with one pupil acting as "official calculator person." If only one calculator is available, play one side of the room against the other.

. You may wish to play one side of the room against the other as a way of introducing the activity even if you plan to have pupils pair up later.

. The difficulty of the game can be increased by requiring four (or five) marks in a row, instead of three.

Answers:

. Answers will vary according to numbers picked.

WHAT'S MY RULE?

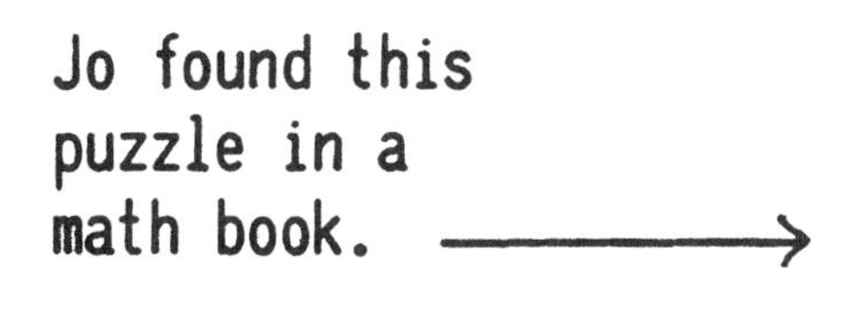

Jo found this puzzle in a math book.

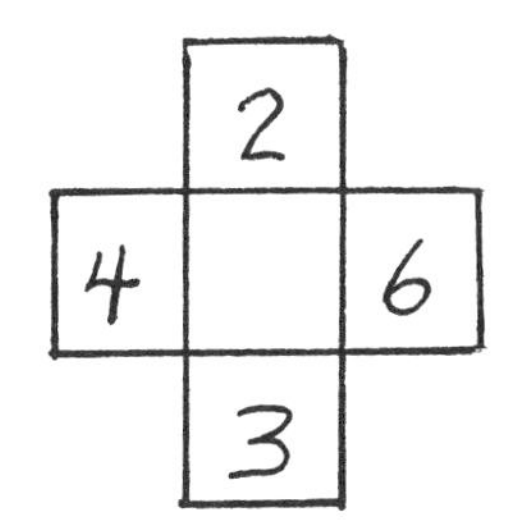

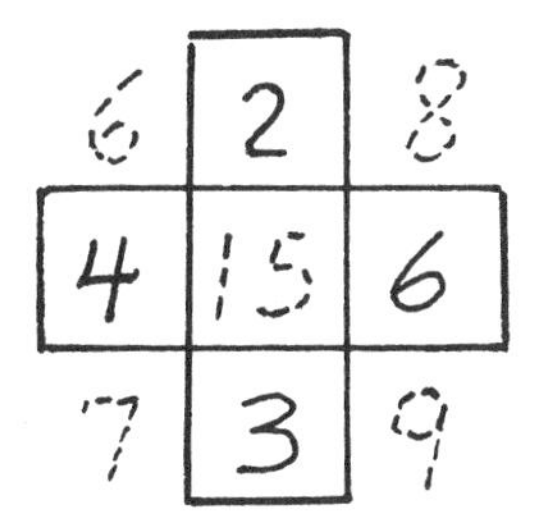

This is the way Jo completed the puzzle.

1. Complete the puzzles below.

a.

9
5 3
7

b.

5
8 2
4

c. What rule did you use? Explain. ________________

____

____

2. Now try these:

a.

9 2 7
10 8

b.

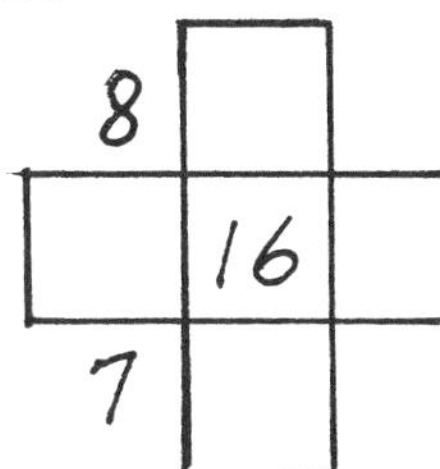

c.

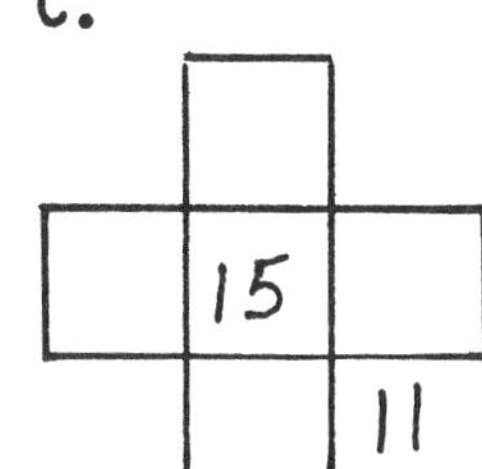

d.

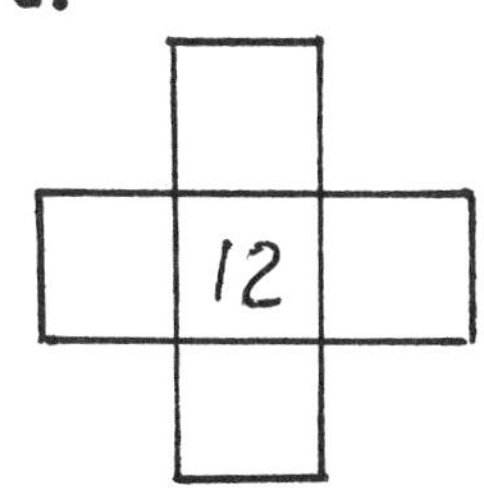

3. Compare answers. Do any of the puzzles have more than one correct solution? Explain.

What's My Rule?

Rearrangement property for additi
The sum of a "bunch" of numbers
is the same regardless of
the order used in
adding.

Mathematics teaching objectives:

. Practice basic computation skills.
. Work with the rearrangement property for addition.

Problem-solving skills pupils might use:

. Recognize number patterns or properties.
. Guess and check.
. Make explanations based upon data.
. Search for and be aware of other solutions.

Comments and suggestions:

. This activity is self-explanatory and could be used as an individual activity.

. Encourage pupils to write out the rule they used along with their explanations.

. The first puzzle along with its solution directs pupils to search for patterns. However, the patterns they see may be different. This diversity should be allowed to happen and even encouraged.

. Let pupils share their conclusions with their classmates. This sharing often stimulates interaction which results in new understandings.

. One rule (see 1-c) for finding the middle number - the sum of either of the two opposite corner numbers - is an example of the rearrangement property of addition.

Answers:

1. a.

(14)	9	(12)
5	(24)	3
(12)	7	(10)

b.

(13)	5	(7)
8	(19)	2
(12)	4	(6)

c. Pupils might have other answers they can support! Their rule should reflect their way of thinking.

A possible rule: The corner number is the sum of its two neighbors. The middle number is the sum of the four given numbers (or is one-half the sum of the corner numbers or is the sum of two diagonally opposite corner numbers).

2. a.

9	2	7
(7)	(17)	(5)
10	(3)	8

b. *

8	(6)	(9)
(2)	16	(3)
7	(5)	(8)

c. *

(4)	(1)	(9)
(3)	15	(8)
(6)	(3)	11

d. *

(4)	(3)	(7)
(1)	12	(4)
(5)	(4)	(8)

* Other solutions are possible for these problems. For example, in part (c) there are many pairs of numbers which have a sum of 15: 4, 11; 5, 10; 6, 9 etc.

3. Extension: Make a puzzle whose solution contains 9 different numbers.

Answer: The puzzle given is one. Pupils may be able to find another

13	5	7
8	19	2
12	4	6

FUNNY FUNCTION MACHINE

The Funny Function Machine accepts 2 numbers and an operation.

It then computes the answer.

Today the Funny Function Machine is going wacko. It is not printing all the information.

Figure out the missing part and fill it in.

	1st Number	Operation	2nd Number	Answer
1.	5	X	8	
2.	4	+	7	
3.	16	—	3	
4.	48	÷	6	
5.	19		7	12
6.	24		3	8
7.	9		5	45
8.	6		36	42
9.	18	+		29
10.	56	÷		8
11.	13	X		52
12.	17	—		9
13.		—	13	8
14.		X	9	63
15.		+	17	32
16.		÷	9	9

Funny Function Machine

Mathematics teaching objectives:

- Practice basic computational skills.
- Search for properties of the basic operations.

Problem-solving skills pupils might use:

- Search for and be aware of other solutions.
- Work backwards.
- Make decisions based upon data.
- Identify patterns suggested by data in lists.

Materials needed:

- None

Comments and suggestions:

- Pupils can work this page with little or no assistance from the teacher.
- Have pupils share their results in a small group or total class discussion. This sharing could lead to increased understanding.

Answers:

Page 107

1. 5 x 8 = (40)
2. 4 + 7 = (11)
3. 16 − 3 = (13)
4. 48 ÷ 6 = (8)
5. 19 (−) 7 = 12
6. 24 (÷) 3 = 8
7. 9 (x) 5 = 45
8. 6 (+) 36 = 42
9. 18 + (11) = 29
10. 56 ÷ (7) = 8
11. 13 x (4) = 52
12. 17 − (8) = 9
13. (21) − 13 = 8
14. (7) x 9 = 63
15. (15) + 17 = 32
16. (81) ÷ 9 = 9

Page 109

Many different answers for each part. A listing of different answers for a given operation and number might reveal some interesting and useful patterns. For problem 19, the following equations are correct for − and 7 :

(20) − (13) = 7
(18) − (11) = 7
(24) − (17) = 7
(15) − (8) = 7

The principle that is worth noting:

If the same number is subtracted or added to the numbers selected for the first equation, the resulting numbers suggest another correct equation.

The Funny Function Machine is really wacko now and has left out two pieces of information.

Figure out at least two possible solutions for each problem and fill them in.

	1st Number	Operation	2nd Number	Answer
17.		+		15
18.		X		18
19.		−		7
20.		÷		5
21.		+	14	
22.		X	8	
23.		−	23	
24.		÷	12	

DIGIT SHUFFLE

1. This problem uses the digits 1, 4, 7, and 9. Complete the problem.

$$\begin{array}{r} 94 \\ \times\ 17 \\ \hline \end{array}$$

2. Use the same digits. Fill in the blanks. Try to get an answer larger than 6000.

$$\begin{array}{r} \square\square \\ \times\ \square\square \\ \hline \end{array}$$

Find one other.

$$\begin{array}{r} \square\square \\ \times\ \square\square \\ \hline \end{array}$$

3. Find two problems with answers smaller than 1000.

$$\begin{array}{r} \square\square \\ \times\ \square\square \\ \hline \end{array} \qquad \begin{array}{r} \square\square \\ \times\ \square\square \\ \hline \end{array}$$

4. Find an answer close to 4000.

$$\begin{array}{r} \square\square \\ \times\ \square\square \\ \hline \end{array}$$

5. Each multiplication problem uses the digits 6, 5, 3, and 2. Circle the problem you predict would give the larger answer.

   63 x 52 or 62 x 53

   Check your prediction. Discuss your conclusions.

Digit Shuffle

Mathematics teaching objectives;

- . Estimate products involving two two-digit numbers.

Problem-solving skills pupils might use:

- . Make reasonable estimates.
- . Determine limits and/or eliminate possibilities.
- . Look for properties and patterns.
- . Search for and/or be aware of other possibilities.

Materials needed:

- . None

Comments and suggestions:

- . Begin the activity with a few minutes of teacher-directed class work.
- . Let pupils spend another 15 or 20 minutes working individually.
- . Finish the activity with a sharing session in which pupils can discuss their results along with any conclusions they are willing to make.

Answers:

1. 1598
2. 94 x 71 = 6674
91 x 74 = 6734
3. 17 x 49 = 833
19 x 47 = 893
4. 47 x 91 = 4277
41 x 97 = 3977
5. 63 x 52 = 3276
62 x 53 = 3286 ⟵ (largest product)

The larger product is associated with the numbers with the smaller difference; for example, the difference between 62 and 53 is less than between 63 and 52.

Extension for problem 5: For pupils who like to look for patterns!

A capable youngster might be asked to find a system for quickly predicting the difference between products as noted above. For your benefit, the difference can be determined by finding the difference between the digits in the units place and multiplying by the difference between the digits in the tens place and then multiplying by ten. (See example below)

60 − 20 = (40) → 40 x 2 = 80

25 x 63 = 1575 − 23 x 65 = 1495 = 80

5 − 3 = (2)

Same answer!

GRADE 4

IV. MULTIPLICATION AND DIVISION CONCEPTS AND RECTANGLES

IV. MULTIPLICATION AND DIVISION CONCEPTS AND RECTANGLES

These lessons provide an informal introduction to area, a useful measurement oncept. Also, they are designed to extend the understanding of multiplication nd division to include an interpretation involving the rectangle, its dimen- ions, and its area. This interpretation is used here for reviewing multipli- ation, introducing the division algorithm, and in a later section for eveloping a procedure for multiplying by a two-digit multiplier. Although he concept is introduced here, the word "area" is not used until a subsequent ection.

Many pupils in the fourth grade know some of their multiplication facts nd have acquired some skill in multiplying a two-digit number by a single- igit number. The approach usually used in eaching this algorithm involves the "repeated ddition" interpretation of multiplication and place alue concepts. The "repeated addition" inter- retation has many applications and should be upils' initial view of multiplication. Pupils, however, find it difficult to se this strategy when learning to multiply by a two-digit number. The "area" pproach introduced in this section is more visual and should be easier for upils to understand. In addition the area model clearly shows the relation- ship between multiplication and division and provides a visual image for the usual "box" symbolism.

$$\begin{array}{r} 18 \\ 18 \\ 18 \\ \underline{18} \\ 72 \end{array} \qquad \begin{array}{r} 18 \\ \underline{\times \ 4} \\ 72 \end{array}$$

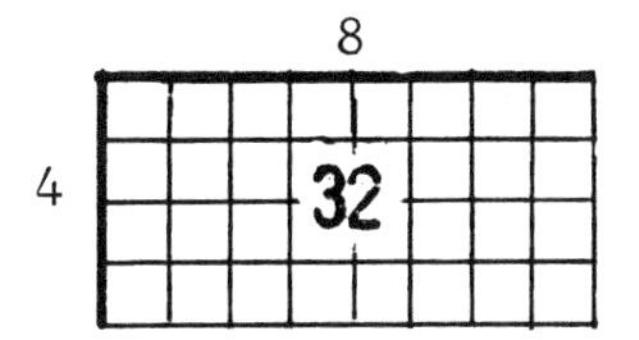

$$4 \overline{)\ 32}^{\ 8}$$

Using The Activities

sing The Activities

The pupil pages are developmental and sequential, providing a background or problem solving in multiplication and division. Work from the text or ther sources may be needed to give additional practice. The selection of he materials to be mixed with this section should be consistent with the resentation here. The teacher's role for these activities is to introduce, xplain, check as work proceeds, and summarize.

Materials needed include a classroom set of tiles (1" by 1") and a upply of grid paper from the master on page 117. If purchased, the tiles come in flats of 132 or 144 tiles and are available at ceramic tile stores. Squares cut from tagboard could serve as a substitute (see page 118). These materials are an essential part of the development built into these lessons. Special care has been taken to move instruction to and from the concrete and abstract levels, between the model and the mathematical notation. This should help pupils attach meaning to the multiplication and division symbols.

SQUARED PAPER MASTER 1

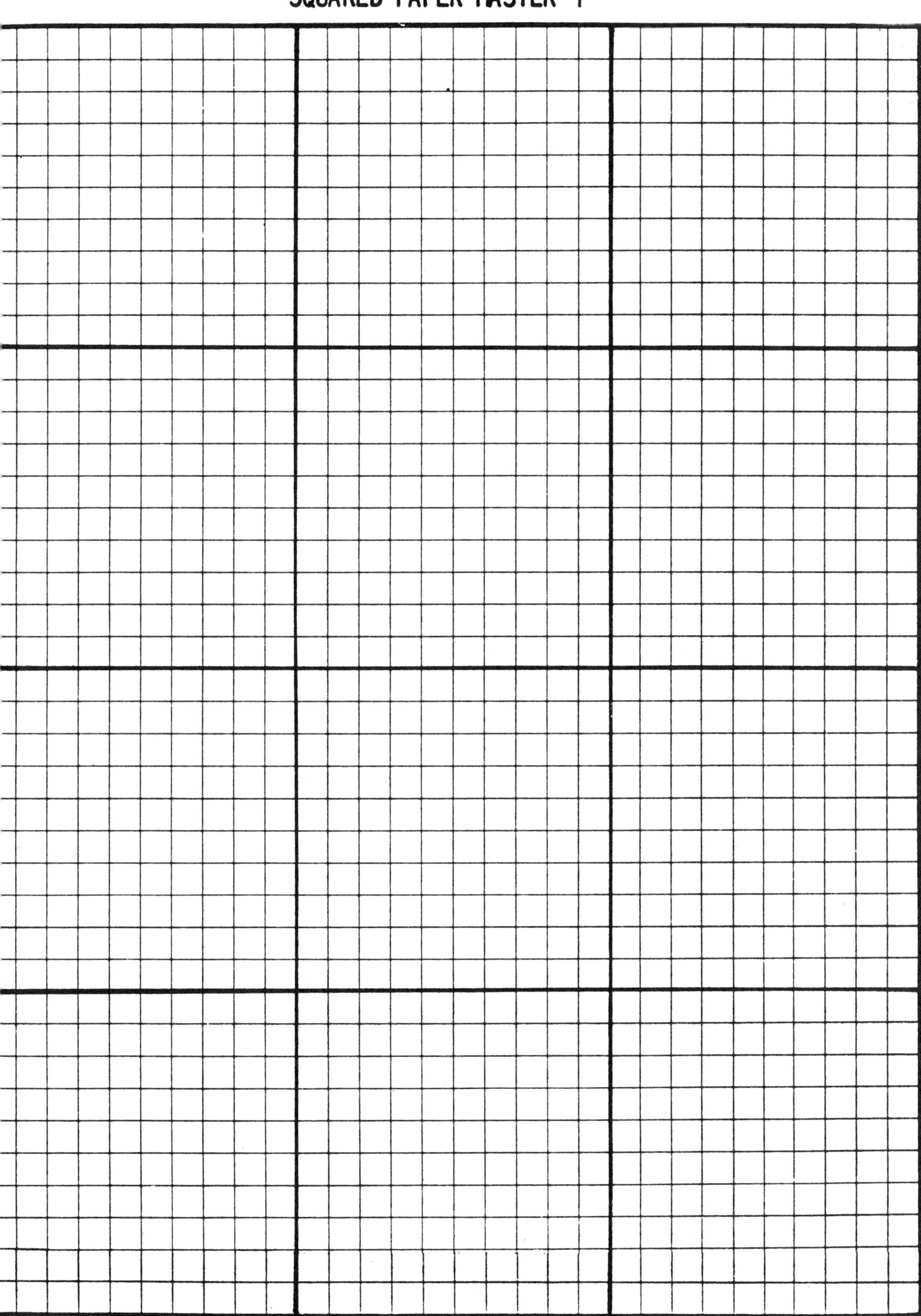

TILE PATTERN

MAKING RECTANGLES

1. Take some tiles.
   Make this 4 by 3 rectangle.

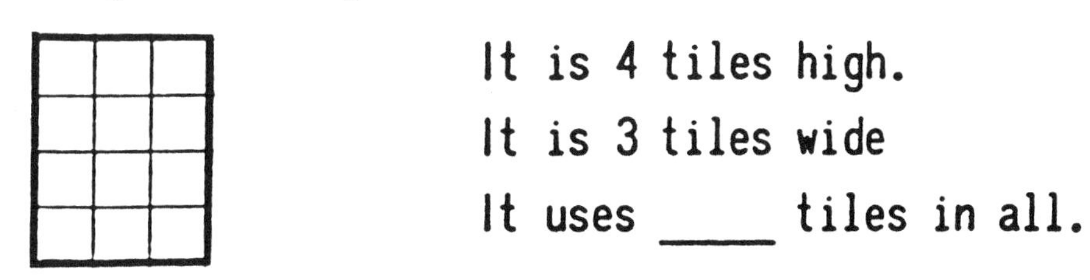

It is 4 tiles high.

It is 3 tiles wide

It uses _____ tiles in all.

2. Take 16 tiles. Make as many different rectangles as you can that each use 16 tiles.

   Use the squared paper below. Record each rectangle.
   Shade in any rectangles that are also squares.

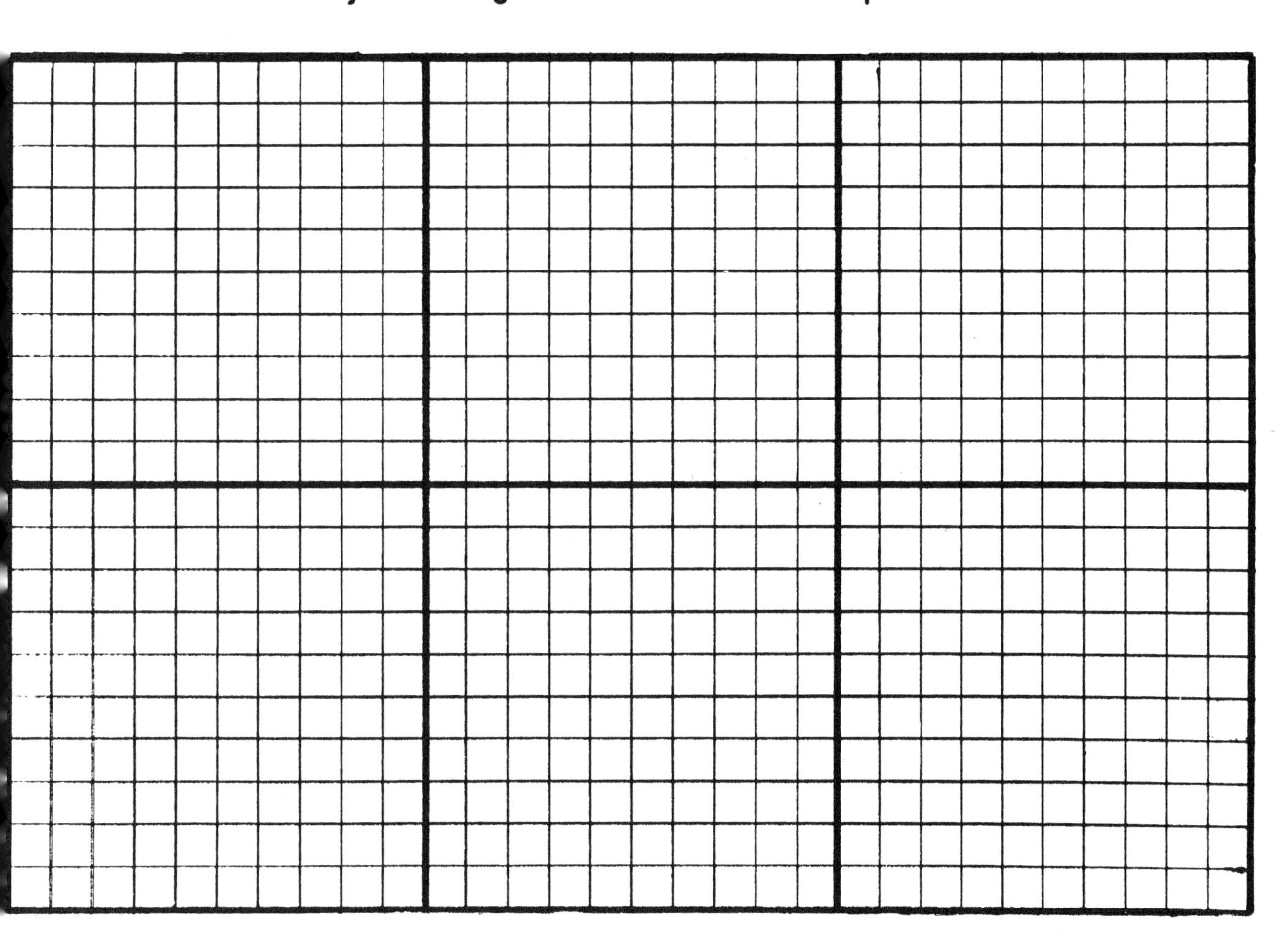

Making Rectangles

Mathematics teaching objectives:

- . Recognize that a square is one type of rectangle.
- . Form differently-shaped rectangles using a specified number of tiles or squares.
- . Develop a model for multiplication and factors.

Problem-solving skills that might be emphasized:

- . Make and use a drawing or model.
- . Search for and/or be aware of other possibilities.
- . Guess and check.

Materials needed:

- . 48 tiles for every 2 pupils Ceramic tile is best but squares made from tagboard could also be used (see page 118).

Comments and suggestions:

- . Do not mention multiplication during this lesson unless pupils continually bring it up. Then deal with it informally. A later lesson treats, in a systematic way, the connection between the rectangle and multiplication.
- . Spend two days on this lesson. Use the first four problems the first day.
- . Work problems 1-4 as a class with pairs of pupils sharing tile. Let partners struggle a bit with the "story" problems before they are given assistance.
- . Pupils may ask if a rectangle 8 tiles high and 2 tiles wide is "different" than one 2 tiles high and 8 tiles wide. This question will be dealt with in a subsequent lesson.
- . Let pupils use words like high, wide, long, in the way that best suits them individually. These terms are used loosely in everyday language.
- . Have pupils compare their rectangles with others before they record their rectangles on graph paper. Some pupils may have difficulty doing this. As an intermediate step have these pupils record their rectangles on "inch squared" graph paper.
- . For the second day work problems 5 and 6 as a class with each pupil constructing the required rectangles. The purpose of the discussion is to have pupils sense how the rectangle can be used to explain "repeated addition" type "story" problems. More of this type of story problems can be found in your text.
- . Let pupils work independently on problem 7.

Answers: 1. 12 tiles

2.

Height	1	2	4	8	16
Width	16	8	4	2	1

First show answers in random order, then systematically as above. Discuss the advantages of the latter.

It might be a good idea to place the table of answers on the chalkboard

3. Take 24 tiles. Make as many different rectangles as you can using 24 tiles.

   Use squared paper. Record the rectangles you made.

4. Use tile. Build rectangles to solve these problems. Draw the rectangles on squared paper. Write the answers inside your rectangle.

   a. Laura used large square tiles to cover her desk. The desk was 8 tiles long and 5 tiles wide. How many tiles were needed to cover the desk?

   b. Ted covered a counter with square tiles. The counter was 9 tiles long and 3 tiles wide. How many tiles did he need?

   c. Maria collected some empty pop bottles. She put them in a case. It has 4 rows with six bottles for each row. How many bottles will the case hold?

Answers: (cont.)

3.

Height	1	2	3	4	6	8	12	24
Width	24	12	8	6	4	3	2	1

4. a.

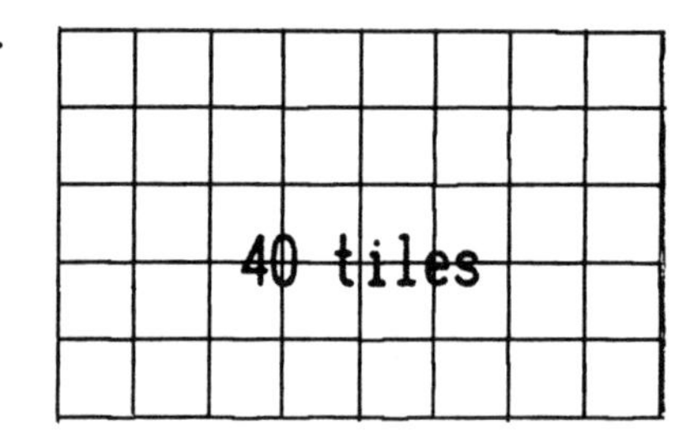

b.

27 tiles

c.

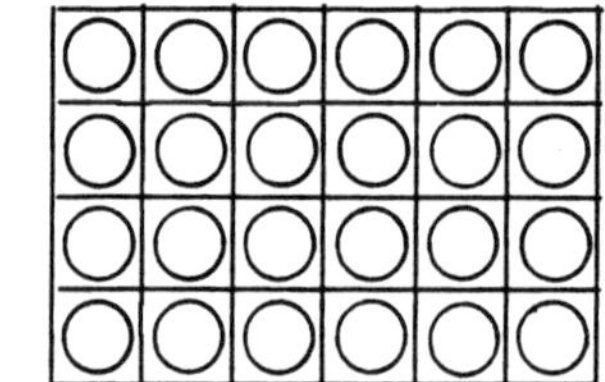

24 Bottles

5. Draw a 4 by 7 rectangle. Use squared paper. Talk about how it could be used to solve this problem:

   Three friends are visiting Matthew.
   Judy gave 7 jelly beans to each of them.
   How many jelly beans did all the children get?

6. Draw a 5 by 7 rectangle. Use squared paper. Talk about how it could be used to solve this problem:

   Carol eats one apple a day.
   How many apples does she eat in 5 weeks?

7. Imagine you have 48 tiles.
   Use squared paper.
   Draw as many different rectangles as you can.
   How wide and how long is each rectangle?

Answers: (cont.)

5. Some extraneous information is given in the problem. Pupils should have experience with such problems. The discussions might go as follows -

   A row of seven squares could represent 7 jelly beans. Each row represents one child. There are 4 rows.

   Treat the problem as a "play like" game.

6. Notice the problem assumes pupils know that there are 7 days in a week. Often story problems do not explicitly state all numbers needed to solve the problem.

   The discussion might go as follows -

   A row of seven squares shows 7 days in a week. There are 5 rows, one for each week.

7.

Height	1	2	3	4	6	8	12	16	24	48
Width	48	24	16	12	8	6	4	3	2	1

DIMENSIONS

he two rectangles below have the same dimensions.

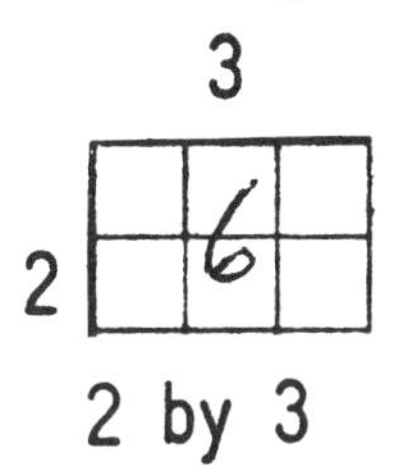

2 by 3

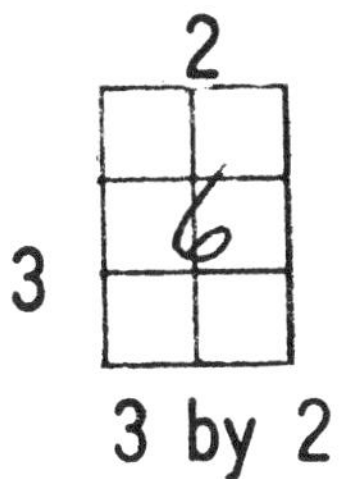

3 by 2

ach fences in 6 squares in all.

ive the dimensions of each rectangle below.
ell how many squares each fences in.

a.

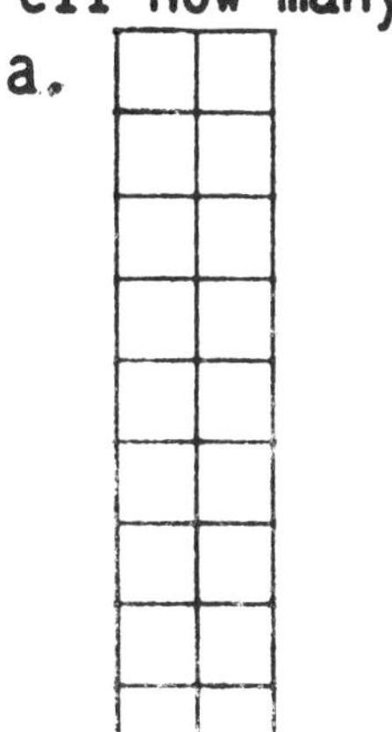

___ by ___
___ squares

b.

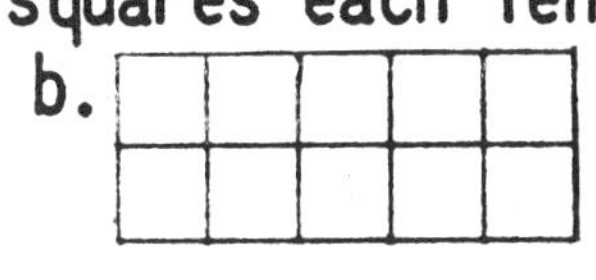

_____ by ____
_____ squares

c.

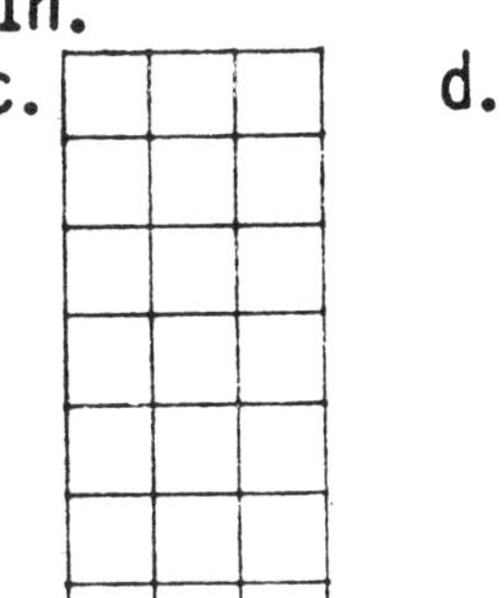

___ by ___
___ squares

d.

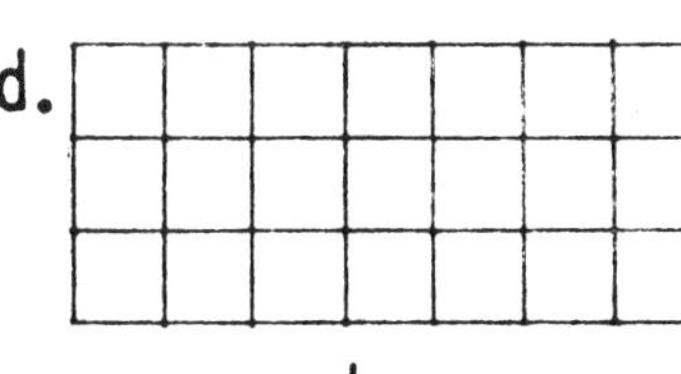

______ by ______
_____ squares

e.

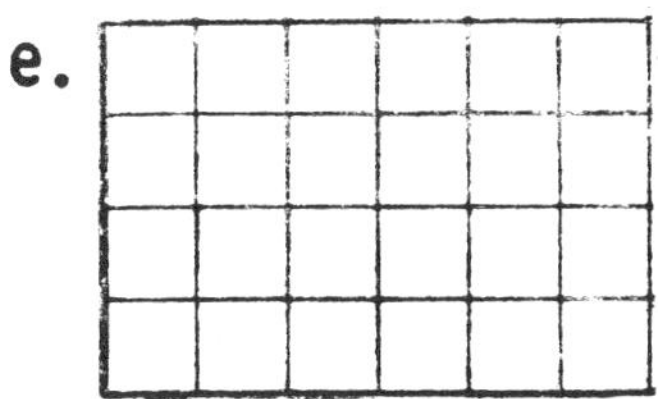

____ by ____
____ squares

f.

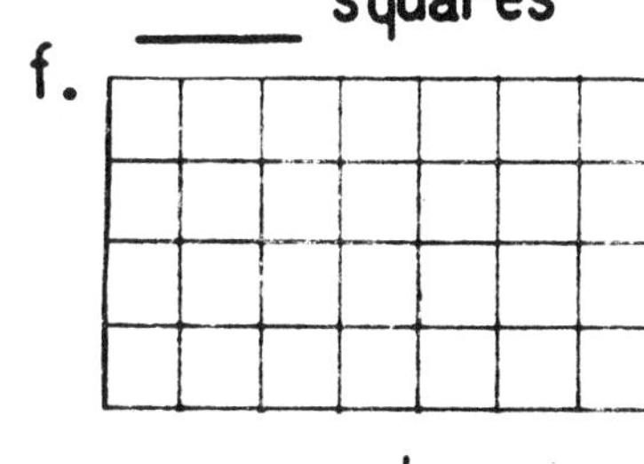

____ by ____
____ squares

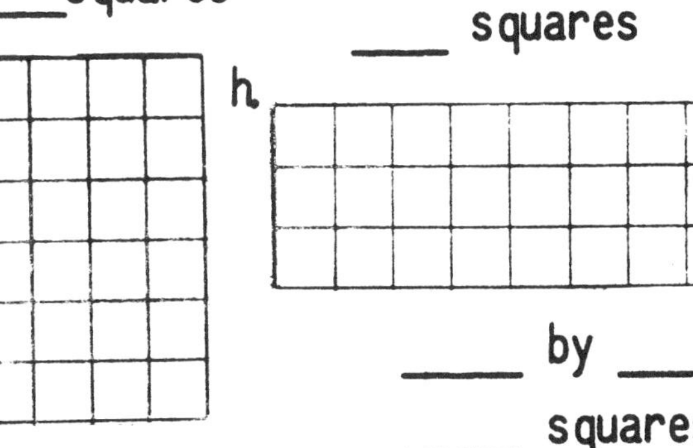

___ by ____
___ squares

h.

_____ by _____
_____ squares

i.

___ by ____
____ squares

j.

___ by ____
___ squares

k.

____ by ____
____ squares

Use crayons. Shade rectangles with the same dimensions the same color.

Discuss.

Dimensions

Mathematics teaching objectives:

- Give dimensions of various rectangles made up of unit squares.
- Discover multiplication can be used to find the number of squares in a rectangular grid of squares.
- Recognize that rectangles with the same dimensions contain the same number of unit squares and can be considered the same rectangle.

Problem-solving skills that might be emphasized:

- Make and use a drawing.
- Generalize from several examples.

Materials needed:

- Crayons

Comments and suggestions:

- Pupils can complete these two pages with little teacher direction.
- In an expression like 2 by 3, the first number (2) is associated with the height and the second number (3) is associated with the width. Pupils soon will sense that rectangles with the same dimensions in any order can be considered as the same rectangle. Therefore, it really is just a matter of choice that the first number represents the height rather than the width.

Answers:

Page 125

a. 9 by 2 -- 18 squares
b. 2 by 5 -- 10 squares
c. 8 by 3 -- 24 squares
d. 3 by 7 -- 21 squares
e. 4 by 6 -- 24 squares
f. 4 by 7 -- 28 squares
g. 6 by 4 -- 24 squares
h. 3 by 9 -- 27 squares
i. 5 by 5 -- 25 squares
j. 5 by 2 -- 10 squares
k. 1 by 8 -- 8 squares

Rectangles with same dimensions: 4 by 6, 6 by 4, 2 by 5, 5 by 2

Page 127

You will need to check pupil drawings. Pupils should notice that rectangles with the same dimensions contain the same number of unit squares and that the number of squares can be found by multiplying the dimensions.

Dimensions (cont.)

Use the squared paper.

Make rectangles with the dimensions given below.

Tell how many squares each fences in.

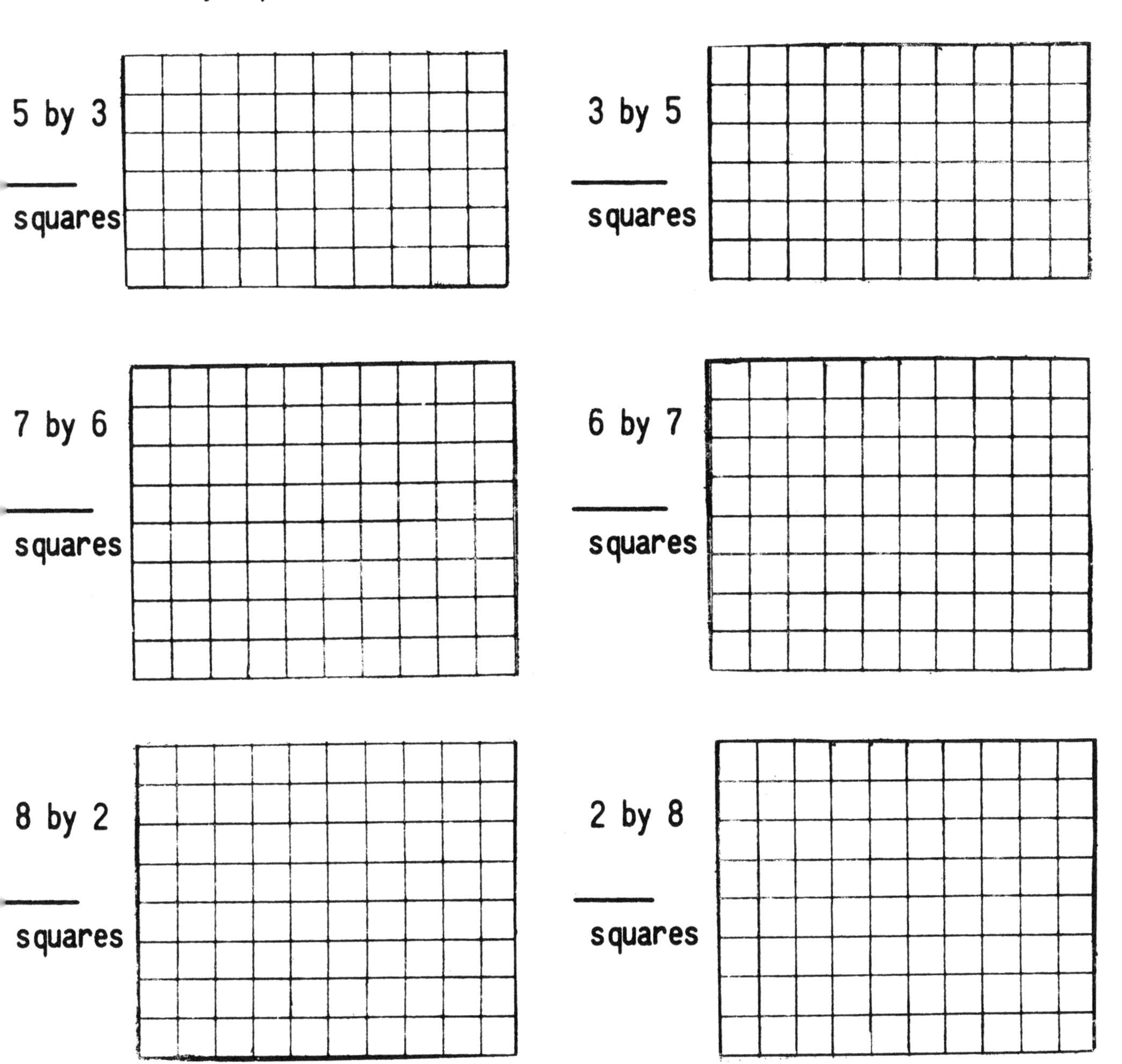

What do you notice? Discuss.

DIFFERENT RECTANGLES

Make as many rectangles as you can which fence in 12 squares. Each rectangle must have different dimensions.

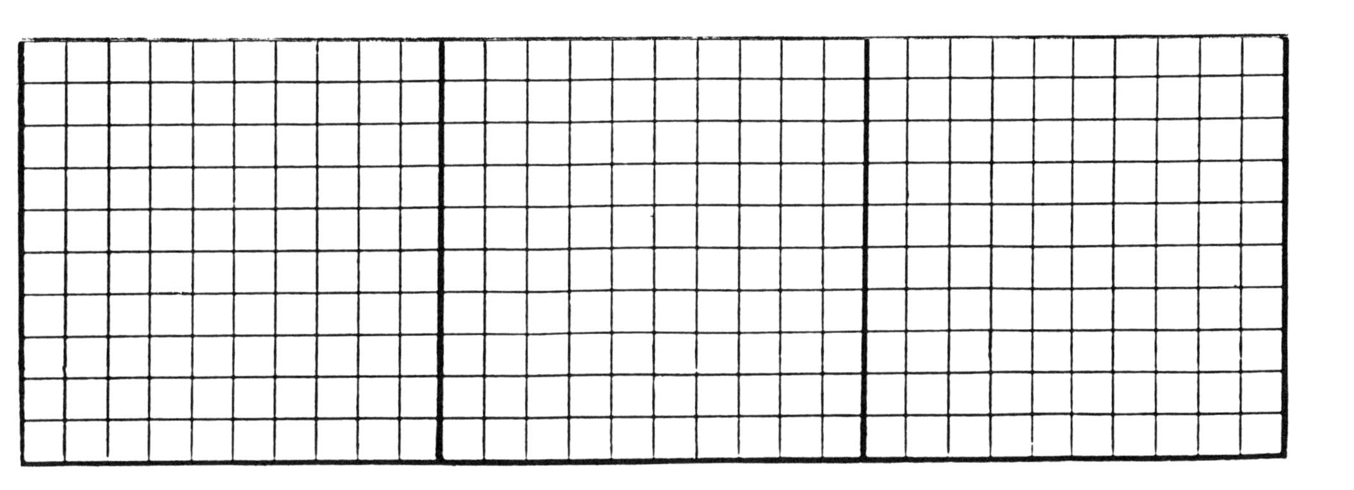

Did you find 3 different rectangles? Discuss this.

How many different rectangles can you make which fence in

- 18 squares?
- 16 squares?
- 17 squares?

Use a sheet of squared paper. Find out.

Which number of squares gave only one rectangle?

Different Rectangles

Mathematics teaching objective:

. Draw a rectangle to demonstrate a given multiplication fact.

Problem-solving skills that <u>might</u> be emphasized:

. Make and use a drawing.

Materials needed:

. A supply of dittoed grid paper showing both unit squares and 10 by 10 squares. (See pupil page 117 for a master.)

Comments and suggestions:

. In this activity, rectangles with the same dimensions--such as 3 by 6 or 6 by 3--are counted as rectangles that are the same. Also, pupils should notice different rectangles could "fence in" the same number of unit squares.

. As an extension, you might ask pupils to find other numbers which could be associated with only one rectangle. This extension could be used as an introduction to prime numbers.

. On the second page of this activity (page 131) the multiplication facts are used instead of the dimensions of a rectangle. If pupils have already been introduced to the meaning of "X" they should have little or no trouble making this transition. This rectangle model will be used later for explaining multiplication by a two-digit multiplier.

Answers:

Page 129
12 squares - 3 by 4, 2 by 6, 1 by 12 rectangles
18 squares - 1 by 18, 2 by 9, 3 by 6 rectangles
16 squares - 1 by 16, 2 by 8, 4 by 4 rectangles
17 squares - 1 by 17 rectangles

Other numbers of squares which produce exactly one rectangle - 13, 19, 23, 29 (any prime number)

Page 131
6 x 3 suggests 6 by 3 (or 3 by 6) rectangle with 18 unit squares.
5 x 4 suggests 5 by 4 (or 4 by 5) rectangle with 20 unit squares.
8 x 5 suggests 8 by 5 rectangle - 40 squares.
2 x 9 suggests 9 by 2 rectangle - 18 squares.

Extension:

Use squared paper to show 12 x 8, 7 x 19. Often squared-paper illustrations of rectangles such as these can enhance a pupil's understanding of multiplication by a single-digit multiplier.

Different Rectangles (cont.)

Use this squared paper.

Make a rectangle which shows 7 x 4.

Discuss.

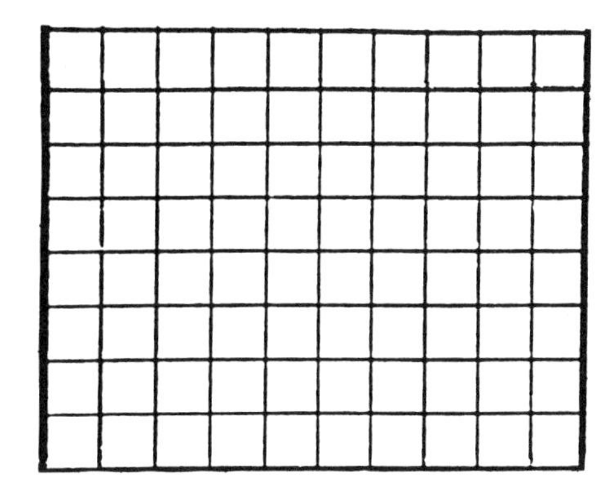

Use the squared paper below. Show:

6 x 3 5 x 4 8 x 5 2 x 9

Label each rectangle with

- its dimensions
- the total number of squares it fences in.
- the multiplication fact it shows.

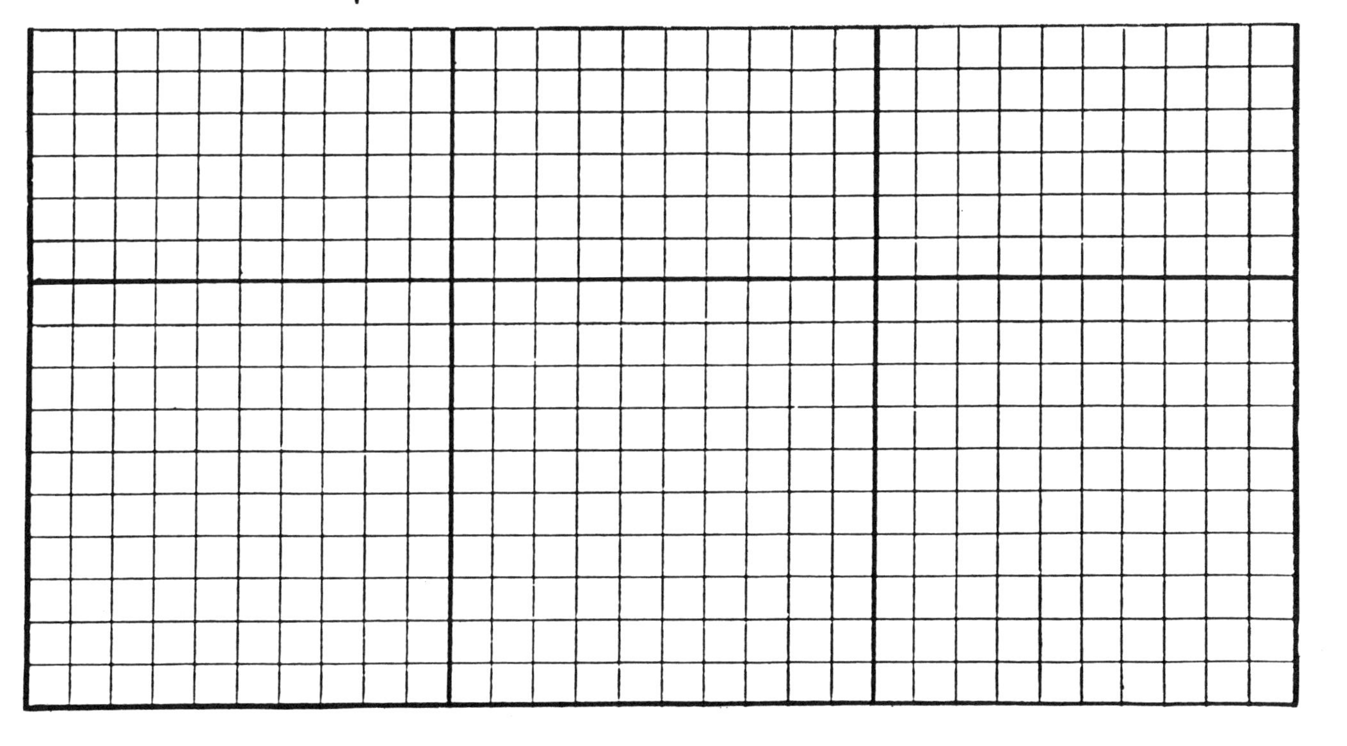

BUILDING RECTANGLES

1. Use 20 tiles. Build a rectangle that is 5 tiles high.

   How wide is the rectangle? __________

2. Use tile. Build these rectangles and give the missing dimensions.

a.	24 tiles	4 high	____ wide
b.	36 tiles	6 high	____ wide
c.	32 tiles	8 high	____ wide
d.	25 tiles	5 high	____ wide
e.	28 tiles	7 high	____ wide
f.	40 tiles	5 high	____ wide
g.	42 tiles	6 high	____ wide
h.	18 tiles	___ high	2 wide
i.	20 tiles	___ high	5 wide

Building Rectangles

Mathematics teaching objectives:

- Introduce pupils to a concrete setting (or model) which can be used in subsequent lessons to associate the rectangle with division.
- Given a number of square tiles and one dimension of a rectangle, determine the other dimension.
- Given a suggested multiplication fact with one number missing, determine the missing number by drawing an appropriate rectangle.

Problem-solving skills that might be emphasized.

- Make and use a drawing or model.
- Describe situation using mathematical expressions and vice versa.

Materials needed:

- Tiles

Comments and suggestions:

- This lesson uses rectangles to find a missing dimension as a background for division. Do not mention division during this lesson unless pupils continually bring it up. Then deal with it informally. The next lesson treats the connection between the rectangle and division in a more formal way.
- Spend two days on the lesson. Use the first three problems the first day.
- Many pupils will be able to do what is called for during the first day with little or no teacher direction.
- Have pupils compare their rectangles (problem 3) with a partner before they record their rectangle on squared paper. Some pupils may have difficulty doing this. Let them struggle a bit before giving them assistance.
- For the second day, work problem 4 (a) and (b) as a class with each pupil drawing the required rectangle. Also the required rectangle could be placed on the chalkboard or on the overhead. The purpose of the discussion is to have pupils sense that the missing dimensions of a rectangle can be used to explain two different types of story problems. More of these types of problems can be found in your text.
- Let pupils work independently on problem 5.

Answers:

1. 4 tile wide
2. a. 6   d. 5   g. 7
   b. 6   e. 4   h. 9
   c. 4   f. 8   i. 4

3. Use tile. Build a rectangle to solve these problems. Draw the rectangles. The answer is the missing dimension. Show it on the rectangle.

   a. Kelly used 28 large square tiles to cover a table top. The top was 7 tiles long. How many tiles wide was the top?

   b. Forty-nine tiles cover the closet floor. The floor is 7 tiles wide. How many tiles long is the floor?

   c. There are 27 flowers in a rectangular flower bed. A row has 9 flowers. How many rows are there in the flower bed?

4. Thirty-six squares cover a rectangle. One side is 9 squares long. Draw the rectangle on squared paper. Talk about how this rectangle can be used to solve these problems.

   a. Jose' has 36 jelly beans.
      He gives 9 beans to each friend.
      How many friends have jelly beans?

   b. Little Ashley has 36 soda crackers.
      She and her eight friends share them equally.
      How many crackers are there for each person?

Answers: (cont.)

3. a.

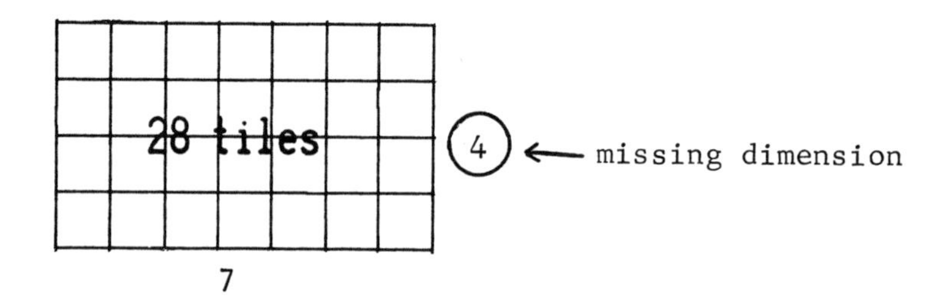

b.

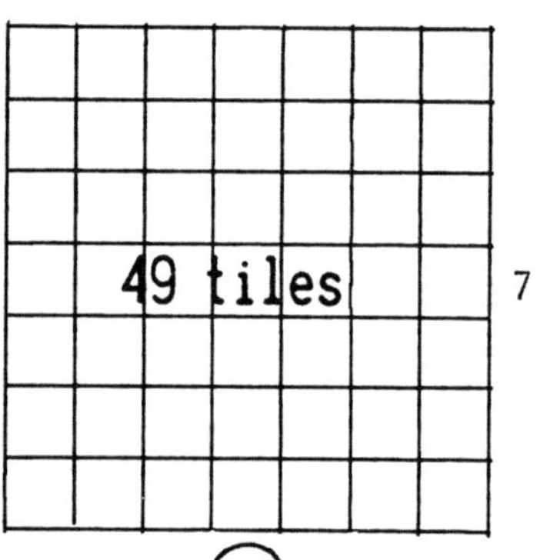

(7) ← missing dimension

Pupils may question whether a square is really a rectangle. If it does come up, emphasize that any closed four-sided figure with four square corners is called a rectangle.

c.

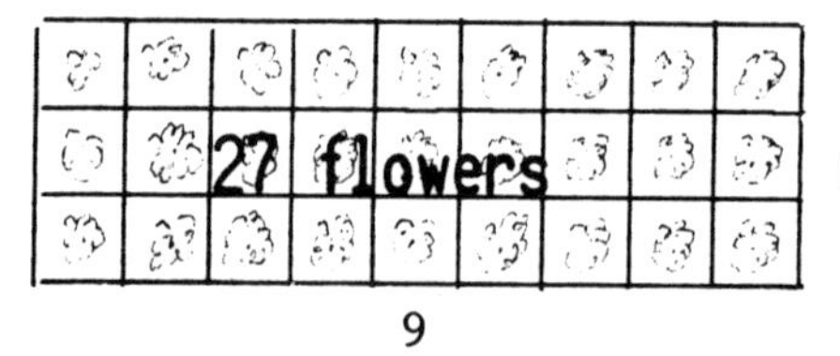

(3) ← missing dimension

4. a.

Teacher Information

Sometimes called a "repeated subtraction" type problem.

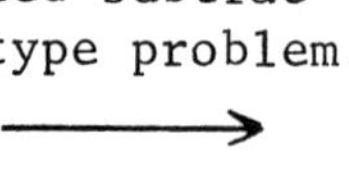

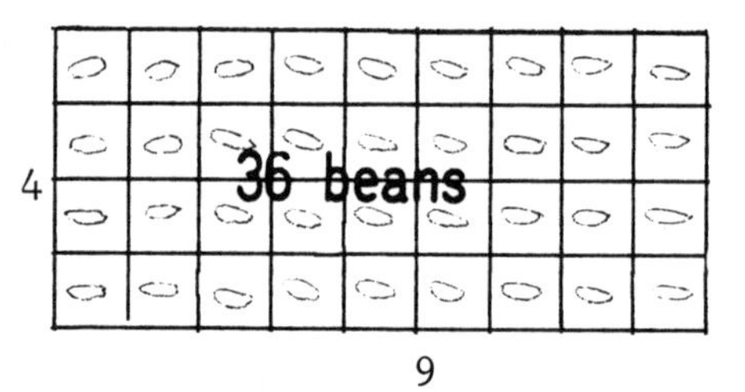

Each row takes 9 jelly beans - enough for one friend.

There are enough beans for 4 rows or 4 parts.

b.

Teacher Information

Sometimes called an "equal share" type problem. →

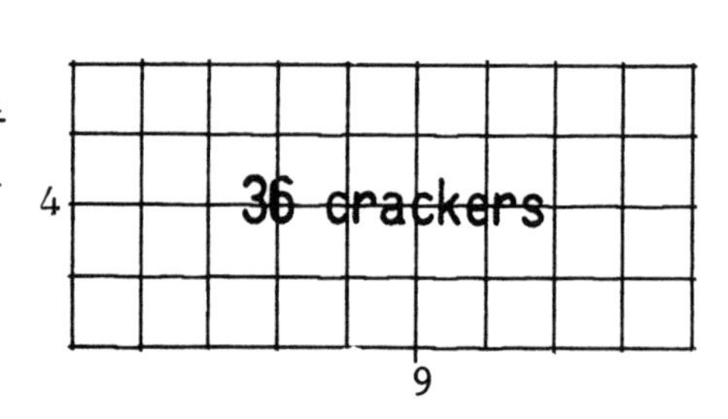

Each column is for a person's share. There are 9 persons - therefore 9 shares.

There are enough crackers so each person has 4. The size of each part is 4 crackers.

5. Make rectangles to help solve the following problems:

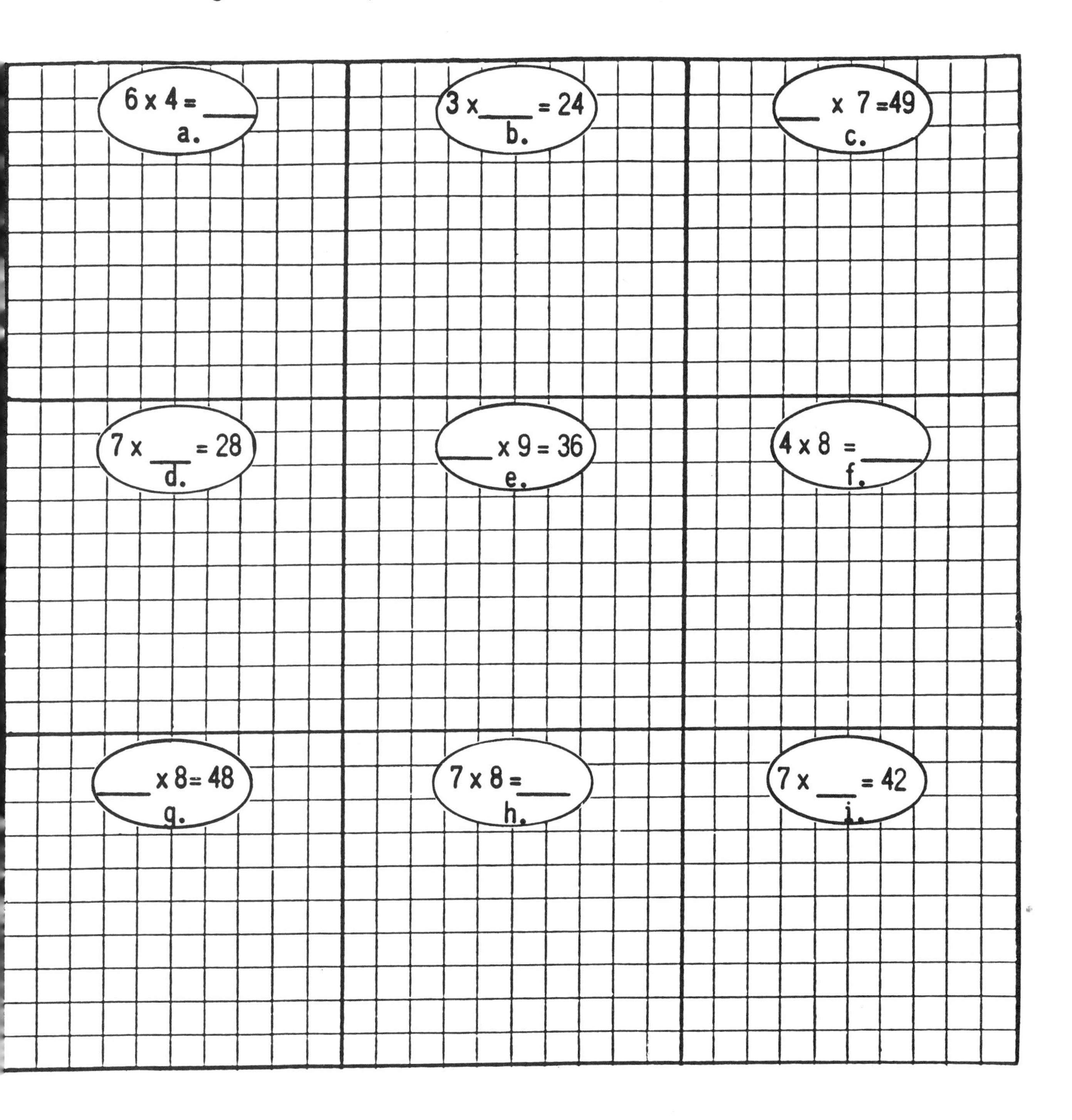

Answers: (cont.)

5.

a. 6 by 4 -- 24	b. 3 by 8 -- 24	c. 7 by 7 -- 49
d. 7 by 4 -- 28	e. 4 by 9 -- 36	f. 4 by 8 -- 32
g. 6 by 8 -- 48	h. 7 by 8 -- 56	i. 7 by 6 -- 42

DIVISION MODELS

1. This rectangle shows
   that 5 x 7 = 35.

   It also shows
   that 35 ÷ 5 = 7 .

   Use the drawing to explain this.

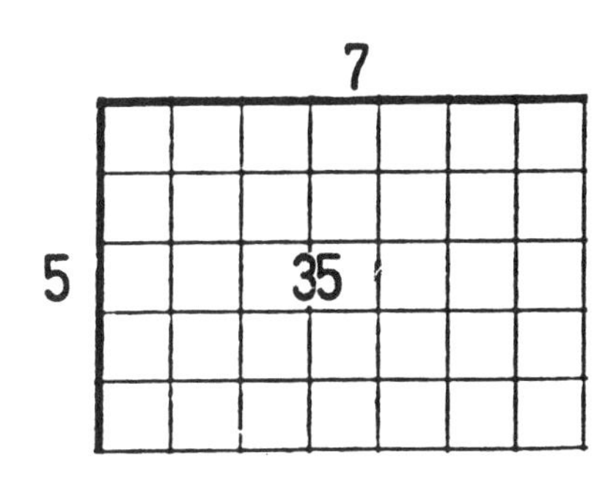

2. Write a division fact for each rectangle below. Fill in any missing dimensions.

   The first problem is done for you.

a. 4

3 12

$3\overline{)12}$ 4

b.

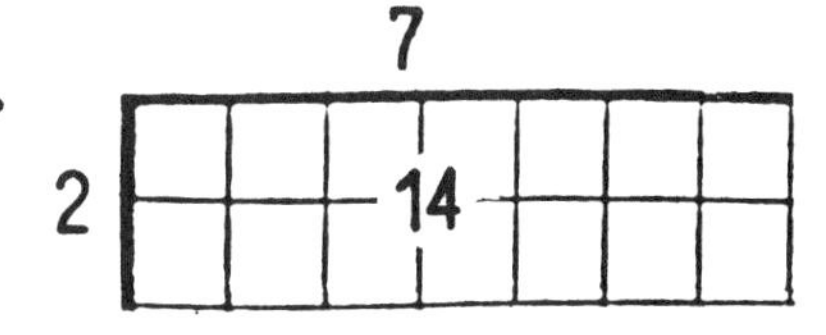

$2\overline{)14}$

c.

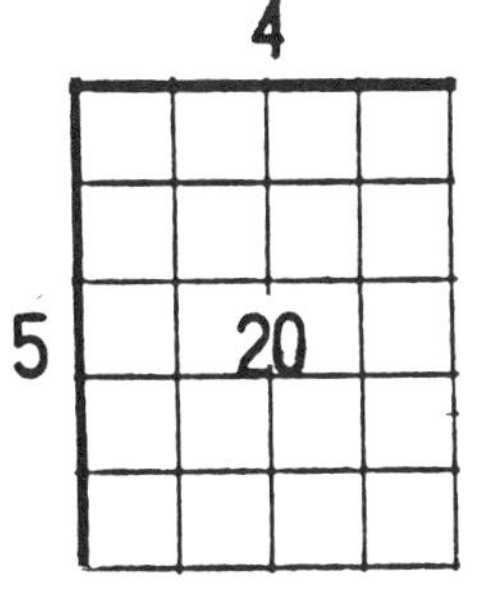

$\overline{)20}$

d.

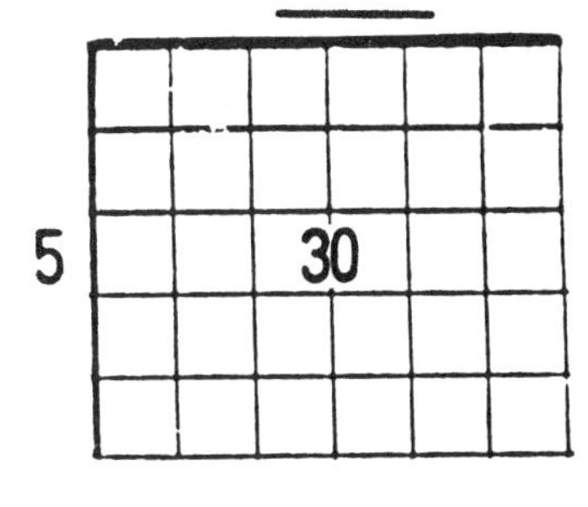

e.

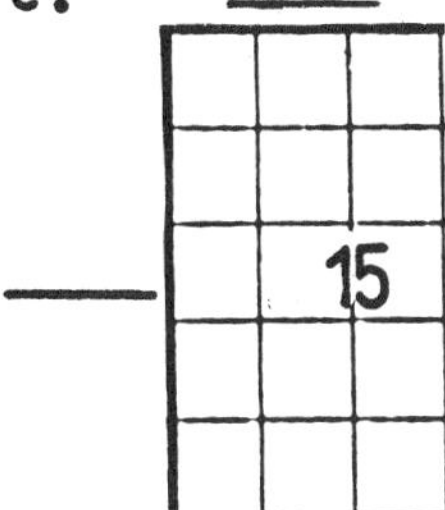

f.

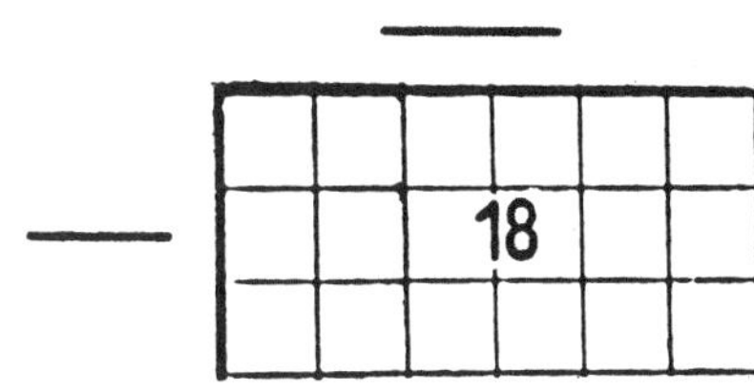

Division Models

Mathematics teaching objectives:

- Write a division expression like $3\overline{)12}^{\,4}$ to go with a given rectangle.
- Given a division expression like $3\overline{)18}$, construct with tiles and draw the rectangle suggested by the numbers.

Problem-solving skills that <u>might</u> be emphasized:

- Make and use a drawing or model.
- Describe situations using mathematical expressions and vice versa.

Materials needed:

- 42 tiles for every 2 pupils

Comments and suggestions:

- Work the first page of "Division Models" as a total class activity with each pupil filling in the blanks on his/her page. Pupils then could work the second page using tiles during a supervised work period.
- Pupils often have trouble with expressions like $15 \div 3$. These difficulties get worse when they are expected in later years to solve $3 \div 15 = ?$ (Even high school pupils will give an answer of 5 or -5 instead of $\frac{1}{5}$.) The difficulty with $15 \div 3$ seems to be in translating it to $3\overline{)15}$. Use this notation in a way that is consistent with your text.

Answers:

1. 5 rows with 7 squares in each row. Therefore 5 x 7 or 35 squares.
   35 squares with 5 in each column. Therefore $35 \div 5$ or 7 columns.

2. b. $\begin{array}{r} 7 \\ 2\overline{)14} \end{array}$ c. $\begin{array}{r} 4 \\ 5\overline{)20} \end{array}$ or $\begin{array}{r} 5 \\ 4\overline{)20} \end{array}$

   d. Missing dimension is 6. ⟶ $\begin{array}{r} 6 \\ 5\overline{)30} \end{array}$

   The drawing matches $\begin{array}{r} 5 \\ 6\overline{)30} \end{array}$ if rectangle is turned sideways.

   e. Missing dimensions are 5 and 3. $\begin{array}{r} 5 \\ 3\overline{)15} \end{array}$ or $\begin{array}{r} 3 \\ 5\overline{)15} \end{array}$

   f. Missing dimensions are 3 and 6. $\begin{array}{r} 6 \\ 3\overline{)18} \end{array}$ or $\begin{array}{r} 3 \\ 6\overline{)18} \end{array}$

3. Use tiles. Build a rectangle for each division problem below. Record on squared paper.

a. $4\overline{)28}$ b. $7\overline{)28}$ c. $7\overline{)42}$

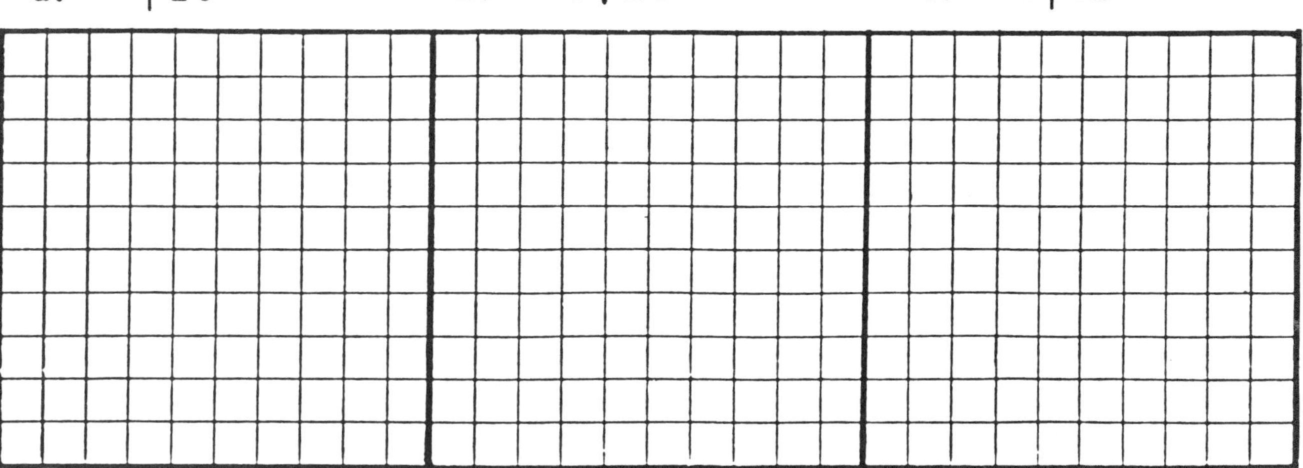

d. $6\overline{)42}$ e. $8\overline{)32}$ f. $4\overline{)32}$

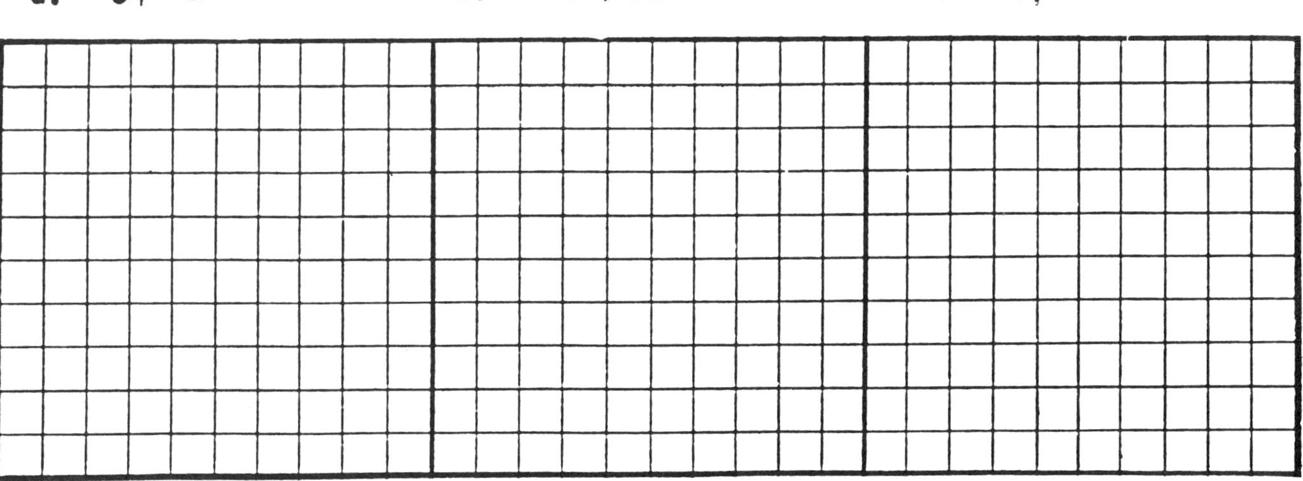

Answers: (cont.)

3. Rectangles with the following dimensions--

a. 4 by 7	b. 7 by 4	c. 7 by 6
d. 6 by 7	e. 8 by 4	f. 4 by 8

Notice there are only three different rectangles even though the given six division expressions are different--an observation worth some discussion time.

MORE DIVISION MODELS

1. Use the squared paper below.
   Make and label rectangles which show:

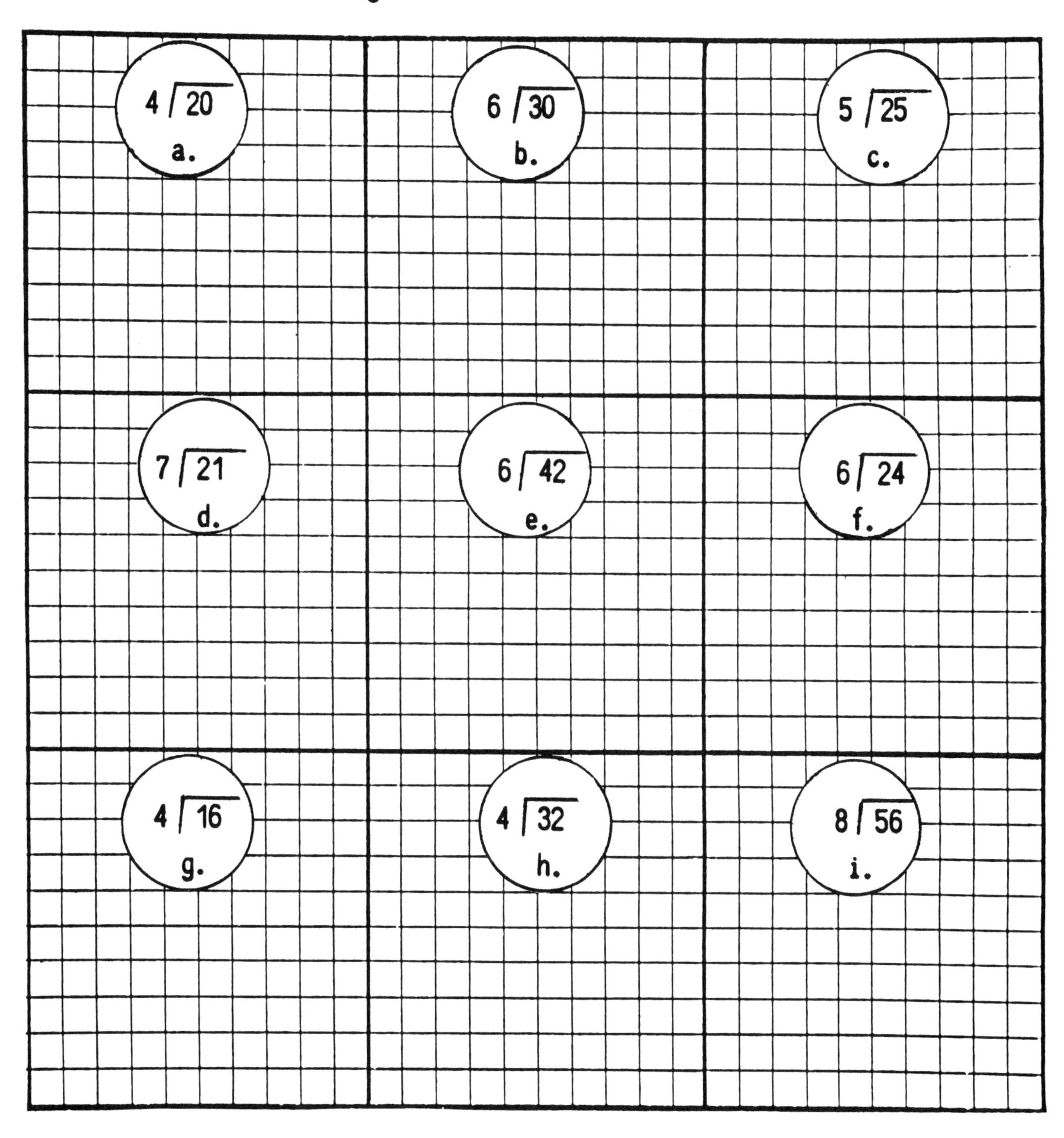

More Division Models

Mathematics teaching objectives:

- Emphasize the rectangle model for solving division problems like:

$$4\overline{)20} \qquad \begin{array}{r} 5 \\ 4\overline{)} \end{array} \qquad \begin{array}{r} 3 \\ \overline{)15} \end{array}$$

Problem-solving skills that <u>might</u> be emphasized:

- Make and/or use a drawing or diagram.
- Describe situations using mathematical expressions and vice versa.

Materials needed:

- None

Comments and suggestions:

- Have pupils work individually, followed by a short period of time for checking their drawings with a classmate.
- If your course of study requires division expressions written in the form $36 \div 4 =$ ____ , provide similar activities involving this alternative expression.

Answers:

1.

a. 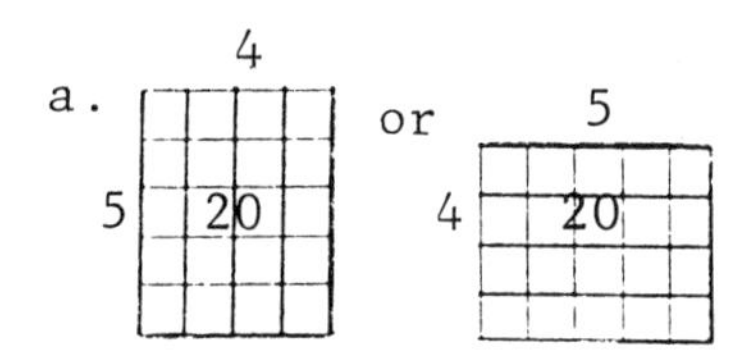

b. 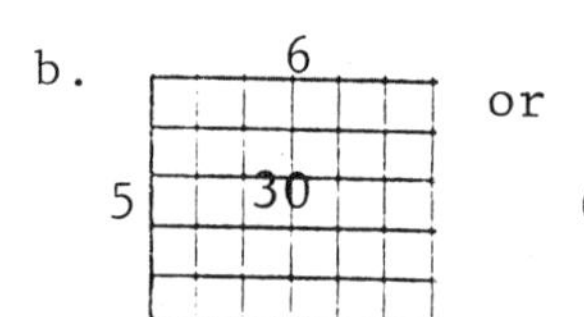

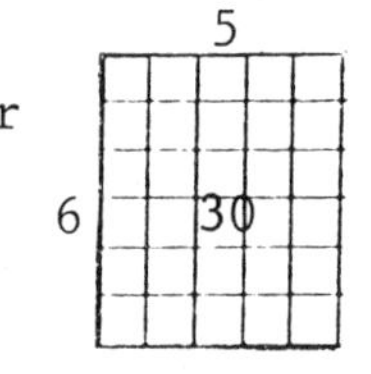

c. 5 / 5 / 25

d. 7 by 3--21 squares

e. 6 by 7--42 squares

f. 6 by 4--24 square

g. 4 by 4--16 squares

h. 4 by 8--32 squares

i 8 by 7--56 squares

2. Make rectangles to help solve the following problems:

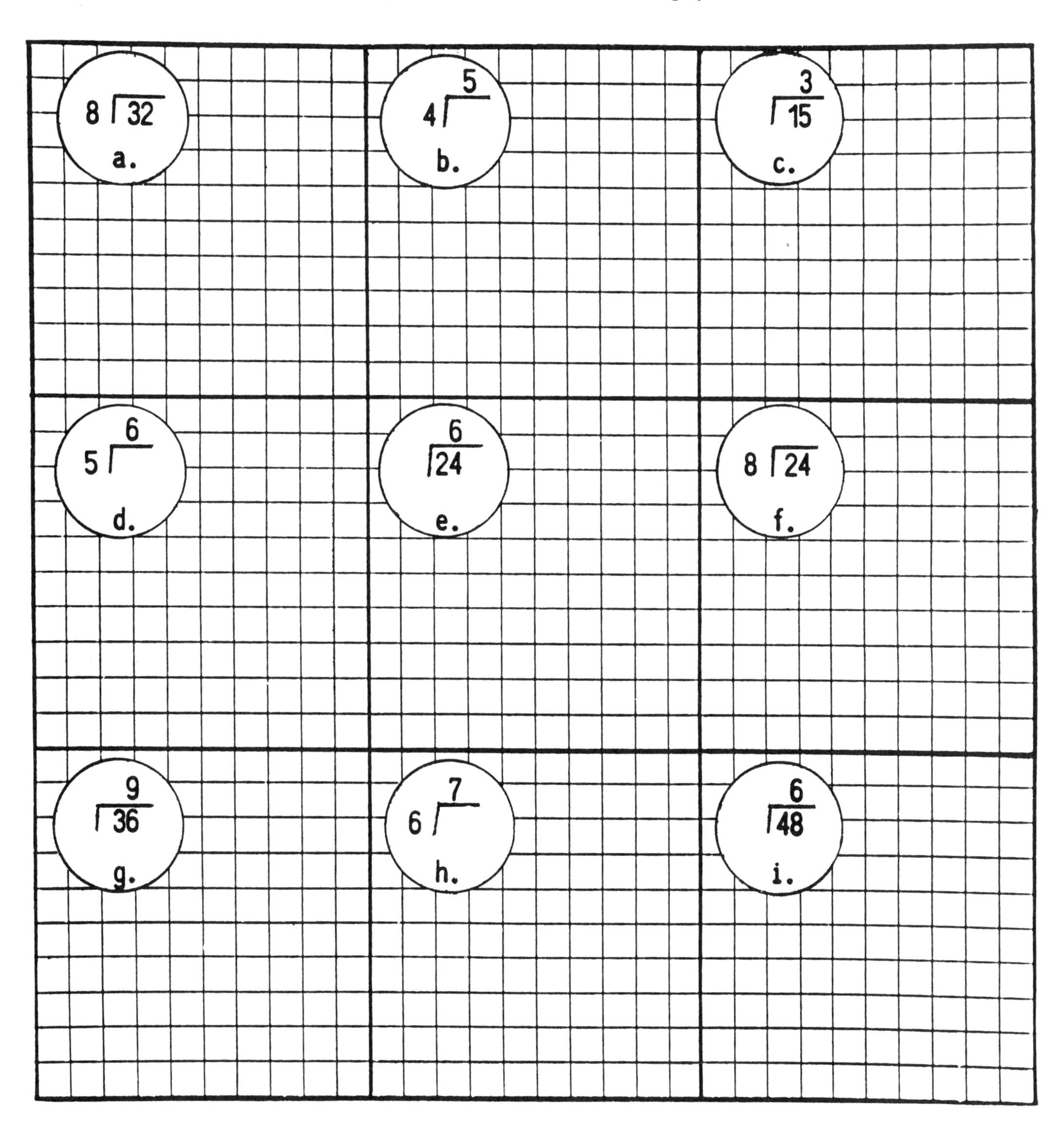

Answers: (cont.)

2. Drawings are made for the top three exercises; the remaining answers will be abbreviated.

a.

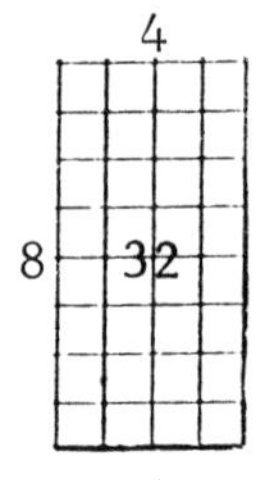

or

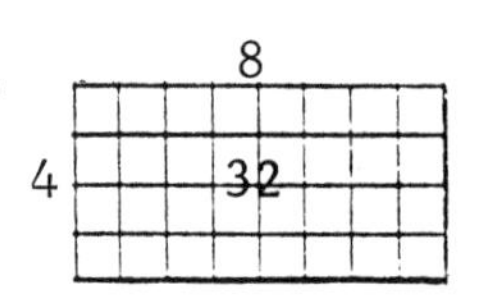

b.

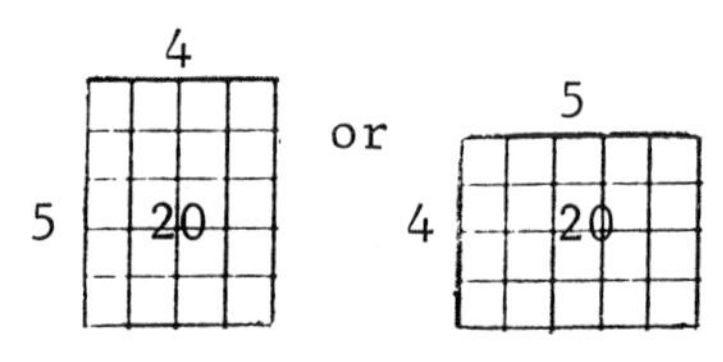

c.

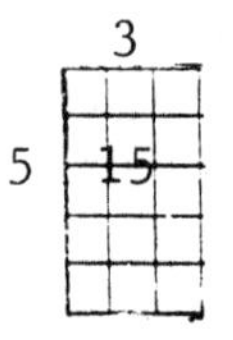

or

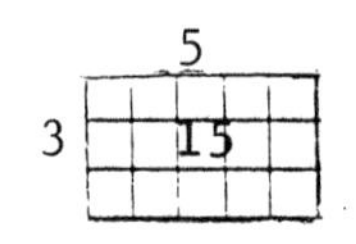

d. 5 by 6--30 squares e. 4 by 6--24 squares f. 8 by 3--24 squares

g. 4 by 9--36 squares h. 6 by 7--42 squares i. 8 by 6--48 squares

REMAINDERS

1. Take 19 tiles. Build a rectangle that is 6 tiles high. You don't have to use all the tiles, but use as many as you can.

   . Your rectangle is 6 by _____.

   . Your rectangle uses ____ tiles in all.

   . How many tiles remain? ______

2. Take 22 tiles. Try to build a rectangle that is 5 tiles high.

   . It is 5 by ______.

   . It uses _____ tiles in all.

   . _______ tiles remain.

3. Take 26 tiles. Try to build rectangles - 4 tiles high.
   - 5 tiles high.
   - 6 tiles high.

   Record your results.

Remainders

Mathematics teaching objectives:

- . Demonstrate by using rectangles that division involving two whole numbers does not always result in a whole number answer.
- . By using tile and grid paper, determine quotient and remainder when dividing a two-digit number by a single-digit number.

Problem-solving skills that might be emphasized:

- . Make and use drawings or models.
- . Describe situations using mathematical expressions and vice versa.

Materials needed:

- . 46 tiles for every 2 pupils

Comments and suggestions:

- . Introduce this lesson to the class using an overhead projector. Continue to work along with the class through page 147. Most pupils should be able to proceed through pages 149 and 151 independently after they have been introduced to one or two problems on page 149.
- . Observe and possibly assist pupils so they make the transitions from the drawings to mathematic notation and vice versa.

Answers:

1. 19 tile. Three different rectangles can be made with a dimension of 6: 6 by 1, 6 by 2, and 6 by 3. In each case not all the tile is used. The largest rectangle--6 by 3--contains the most tile, 18 tile, leaving only 1 remaining.

2. 22 tile. Four different rectangles can be made with a dimension of 5 5 by 1, 5 by 2, 5 by 3, 5 by 4. The largest rectangle--5 by 4--contains 20 tile, leaving a remainder of 2 tile.

3. 26 tile.
   4 tile high: Largest rectangle--4 by 6; 24 tile used, 2 not used.
   5 tile high: Largest rectangle--5 by 5; 25 tile used, 1 not used.
   6 tile high: Largest rectangle--6 by 4; 24 tile used, 2 not used.

4. Complete the division problems suggested by each drawing below.

a. 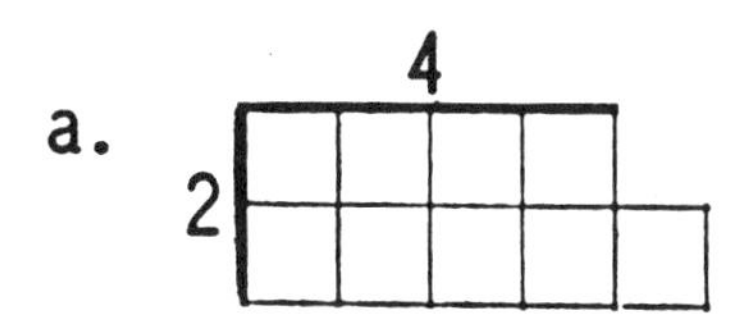

$2\overline{)9}$ Remainder ____

b. 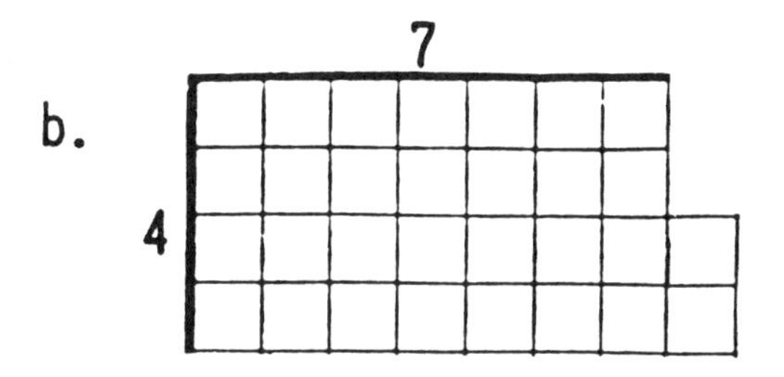

$\overline{)30}$ Remainder ____

c. 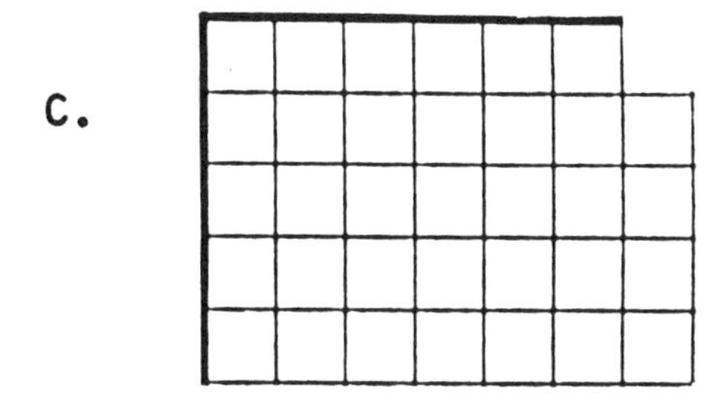

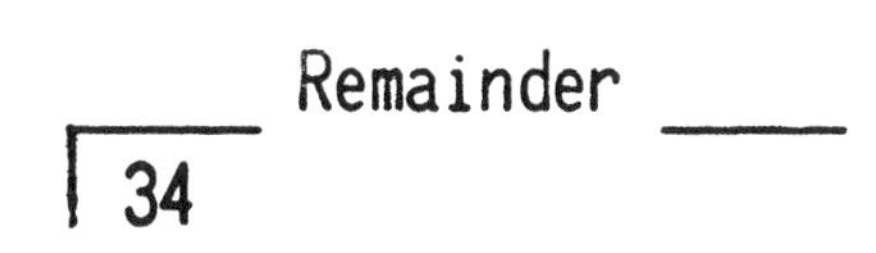

Remainder ____

d.

$3\overline{)}$ Remainder ____

e. 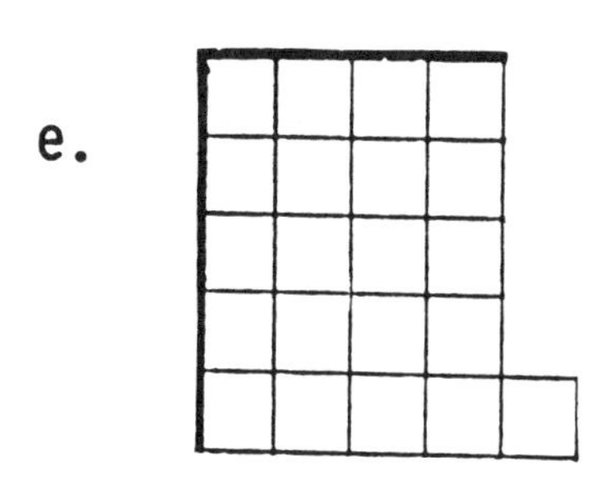

$\overline{)}$ Remainder ____

Remainders

Answers:

4.

a. $\begin{array}{r} 4 \\ 2\overline{)\;9} \end{array}$ remainder 1

b. $\begin{array}{r} 7 \\ 4\overline{)\;30} \end{array}$ remainder 2 or $\begin{array}{r} 4 \\ 7\overline{)\;30} \end{array}$ remainder 2

c. $\begin{array}{r} 6 \\ 5\overline{)\;34} \end{array}$ remainder 4 or $\begin{array}{r} 5 \\ 6\overline{)\;34} \end{array}$ remainder 4

d. $\begin{array}{r} 5 \\ 3\overline{)\;17} \end{array}$ remainder 2

e. $\begin{array}{r} 5 \\ 4\overline{)\;21} \end{array}$ remainder 1 or $\begin{array}{r} 4 \\ 5\overline{)\;21} \end{array}$ remainder 1

5.

a. $\begin{array}{r} 6 \\ 4\overline{)\;27} \end{array}$ remainder 3

or

b. $\begin{array}{r} 4 \\ 8\overline{)\;35} \end{array}$ remainder 3

or

c. $\begin{array}{r} 6 \\ 7\overline{)\;46} \end{array}$ remainder 4

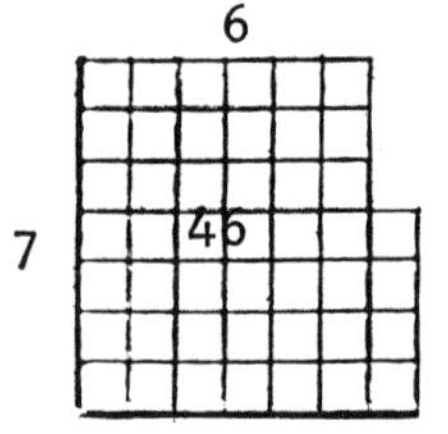

or

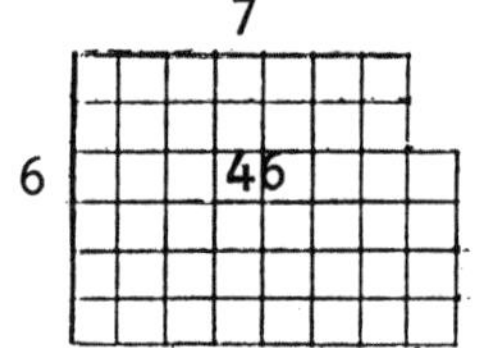

d. $\begin{array}{r} 5 \\ 6\overline{)\;31} \end{array}$ remainder 1

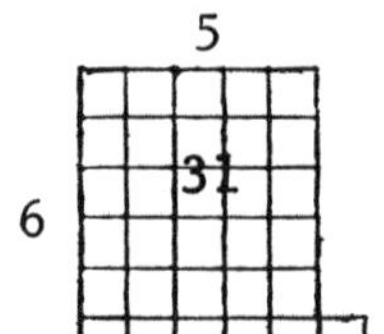

or

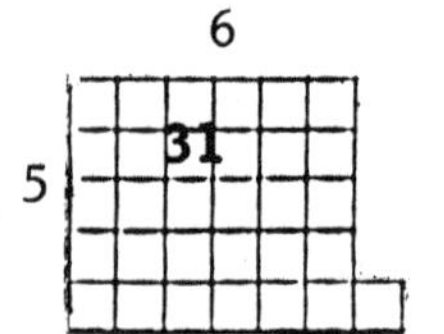

5. Use tile to solve the problems below.

   Record your results on squared paper.

   Complete the written problem.

a. $4\overline{)27}$ Remainder ____

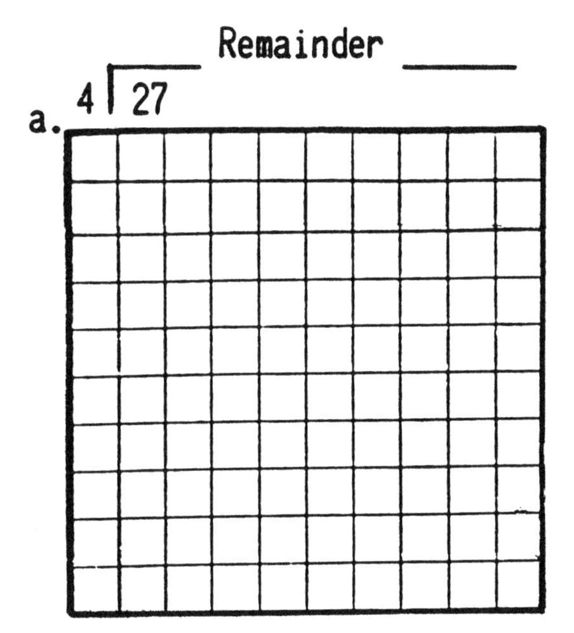

b. $8\overline{)35}$ Remainder ____

c. $7\overline{)46}$ Remainder ____

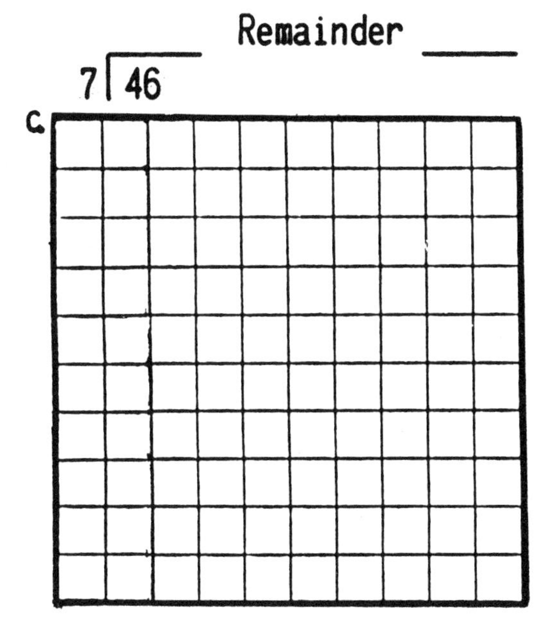

d. $6\overline{)31}$ Remainder ____

WRITTEN RECORDS

Use tile. Solve $4\overline{)29}$

Record on squared paper.

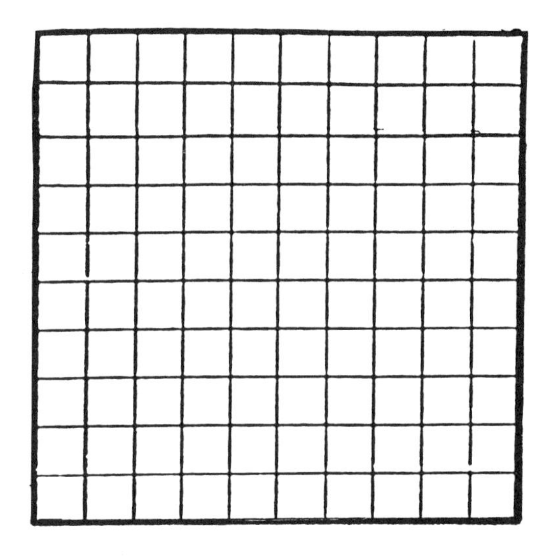

This problem can be written

$$\begin{array}{r} 7 \\ 4\overline{)29} \\ -28 \\ \hline 1 \end{array} \quad \text{Remainder } 1$$

Can you explain the written record? Discuss.

1. Complete the written record for each drawing below.

a. 6 / 4

$$\begin{array}{r} 4\overline{)26} \\ -24 \\ \hline \end{array}$$

Remainder ____

b. 7 / 3

$3\overline{)22}$

Remainder ____

c.

Remainder ____

SM 81

Written Records

Mathematics teaching objectives:

. Practice determining quotient and remainders, first by using grid paper and then by using the written record only.

Problem-solving skills that <u>might</u> be emphasized:

. Make and use drawings or models.

. Describe situations using mathematical expressions and vice versa.

Materials needed:

. 29 tiles per pupil

Comments and suggestions:

. Introduce this lesson by working along with the class as they do page 153. Most pupils should be able to proceed through pages 155-15 independently.

. Observe and possibly assist pupils as they make the transition from the drawings to mathematical notation and vice versa.

. The amount of practice work provided here should enable pupils to associate a division algorithm with an appropriate geometric model. The next step is to provide them with the drill and practice needed for attaining mastery. Use the text for the necessary material along with appropriate games.

Answers:

1\. a. $4\overline{)26}$ = 6 remainder 2; $26 - 24 = 2$

b. $3\overline{)22}$ = 7 remainder 1; $22 - 21 = 1$

c. $3\overline{)29}$ = 9 remainder 2; $29 - 27 = 2$

or $9\overline{)29}$ = 3 remainder 2; $29 - 27 = 2$

Pupils should be aware of both interpretations.

2. Use the squared paper. Solve the problems below.
   Make complete written records.

a. $5\overline{)26}$ Remainder ____
   -25

b. $6\overline{)41}$ Remainder ____

c. $6\overline{)39}$ r ____

d. $5\overline{)41}$ r ____

e. $3\overline{)25}$ r ____

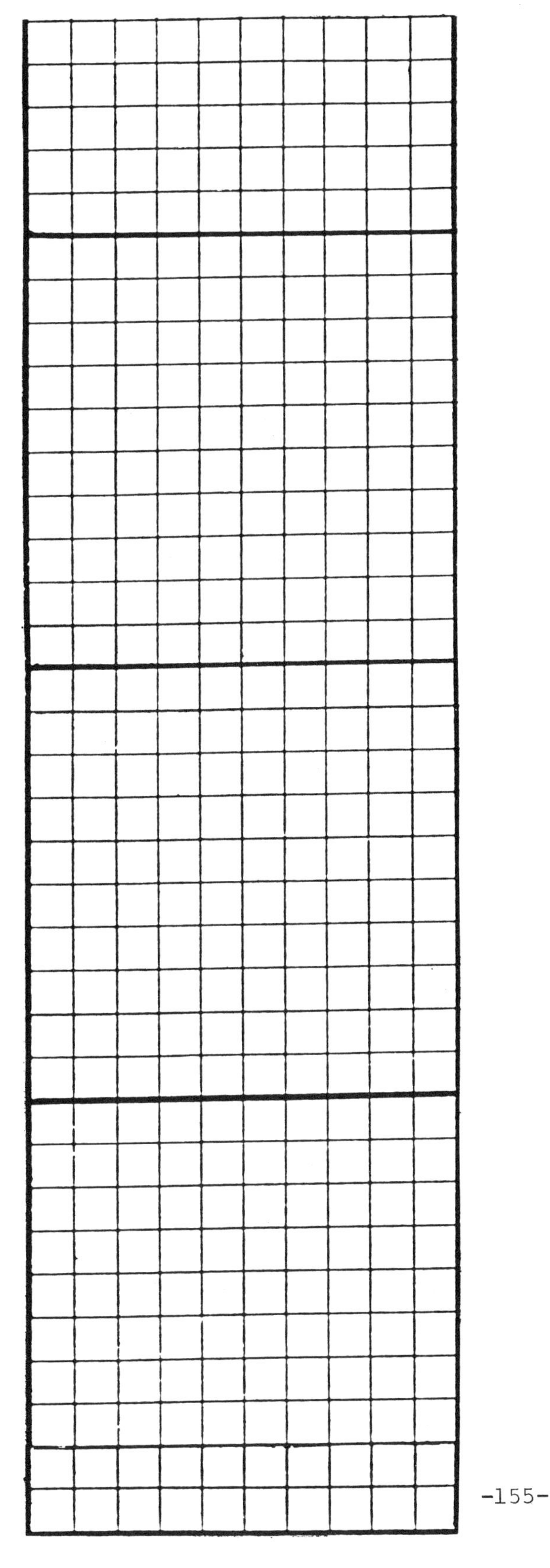

Written Records

Answers:

2.

a. $$\begin{array}{r} 5 \text{ remainder } 1 \\ 5\,\overline{)\,26} \\ -25 \\ \hline 1 \end{array}$$

b. $$\begin{array}{r} 6 \text{ r } 5 \\ 6\,\overline{)\,41} \\ -36 \\ \hline 5 \end{array}$$

c. $$\begin{array}{r} 6 \text{ remainder } 3 \\ 6\,\overline{)\,39} \\ -36 \\ \hline 3 \end{array}$$

d. $$\begin{array}{r} 8 \text{ r } 1 \\ 5\,\overline{)\,41} \\ -40 \\ \hline 1 \end{array}$$

e. $$\begin{array}{r} 8 \text{ r } 1 \\ 3\,\overline{)\,25} \\ -24 \\ \hline 1 \end{array}$$

Each record should be accompanied by an appropriate drawing. Two possible drawings are shown for e

Other variations are possible. Pupils should be aware that different correct drawings are possible.

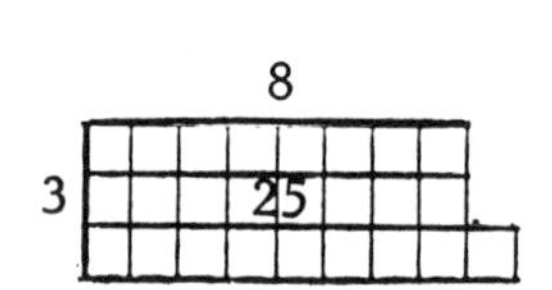

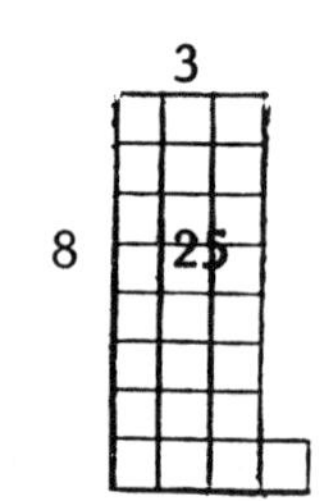

3.

a. $$\begin{array}{r} 7 \text{ r } 3 \\ 6\,\overline{)\,45} \\ -42 \\ \hline 3 \end{array}$$

b. $$\begin{array}{r} 4 \text{ r } 2 \\ 9\,\overline{)\,38} \\ -36 \\ \hline 2 \end{array}$$

c. $$\begin{array}{r} 4 \text{ r } 4 \\ 6\,\overline{)\,28} \\ -24 \\ \hline 4 \end{array}$$

d. $$\begin{array}{r} 5 \text{ r } 6 \\ 8\,\overline{)\,46} \\ -40 \\ \hline 6 \end{array}$$

If pupils have demonstrated they have mastered the symbolic form and choose to write only the quotient and remainder, they should be encouraged to do so.

3. Use the special squared paper below.
   Solve these problems.

a. $6\overline{)45}$ r ____

b. $9\overline{)38}$ r ____

c. $6\overline{)28}$ r ____

d. $8\overline{)46}$ r ____

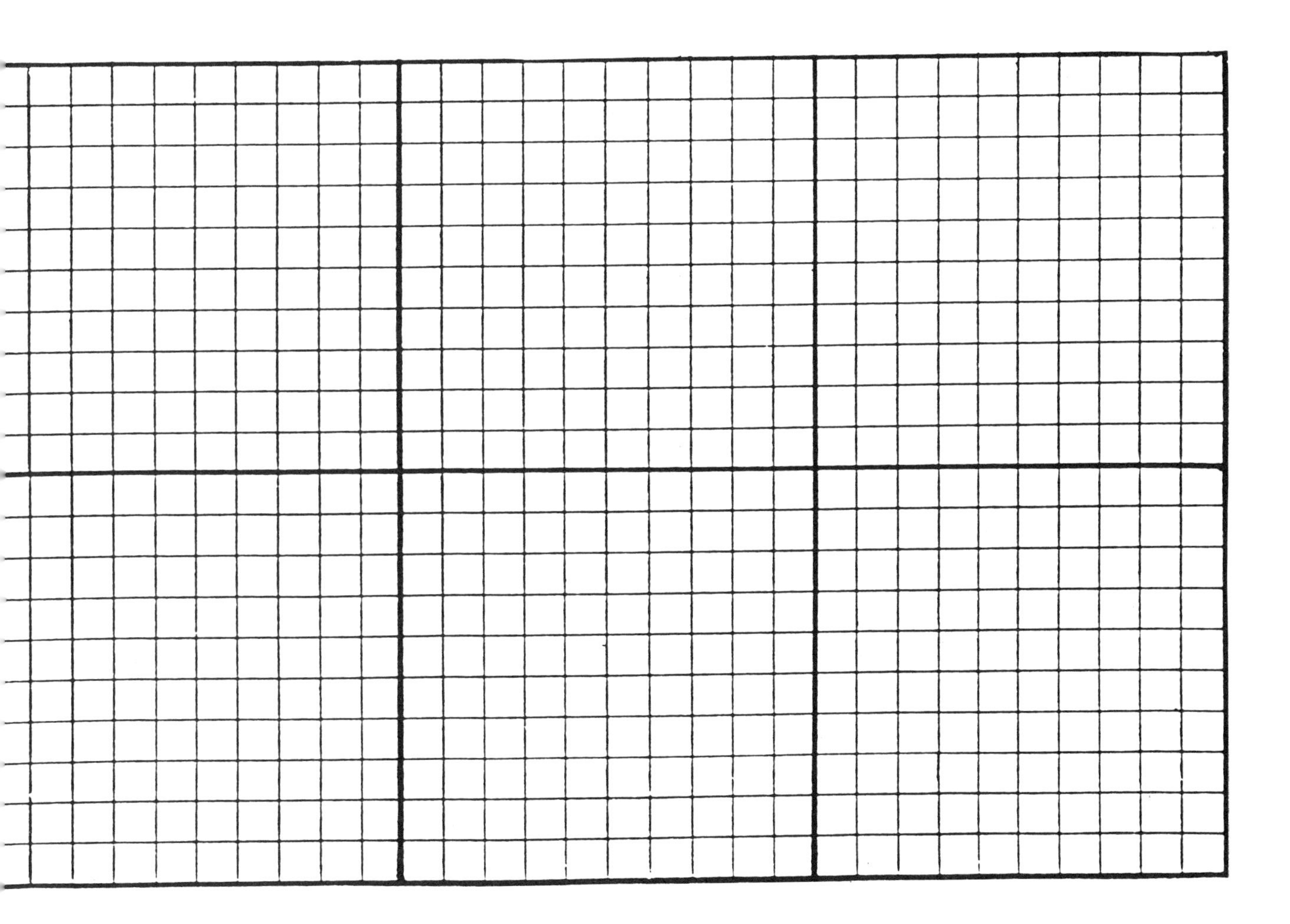

MANY NUMBER SENTENCES

1.a. Here are a few number sentences the *3* by *5* rectangle suggests:

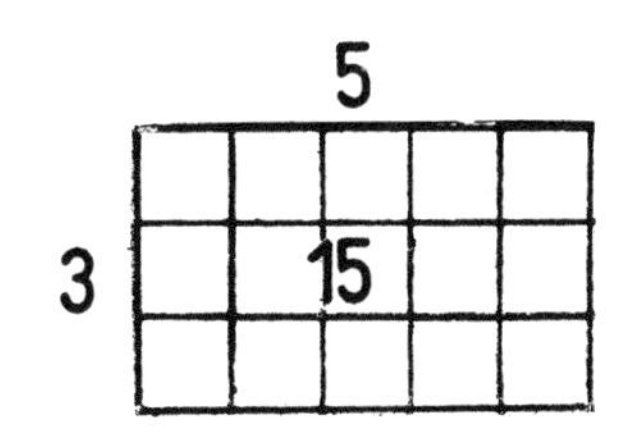

15 ÷ ____ = 5   5 x 3 = ____   3 x ____ = 15

b. What are other number sentences that match the rectangle?

Discuss your ideas.

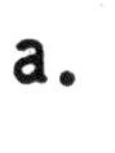

2. Write as many different multiplication and division sentences as you can for each rectangle below.

a. 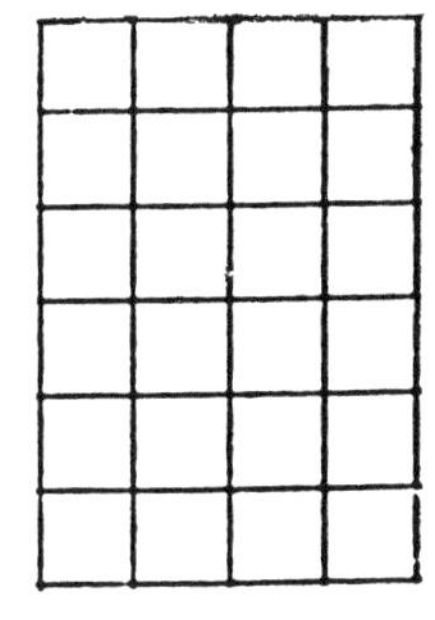

b. 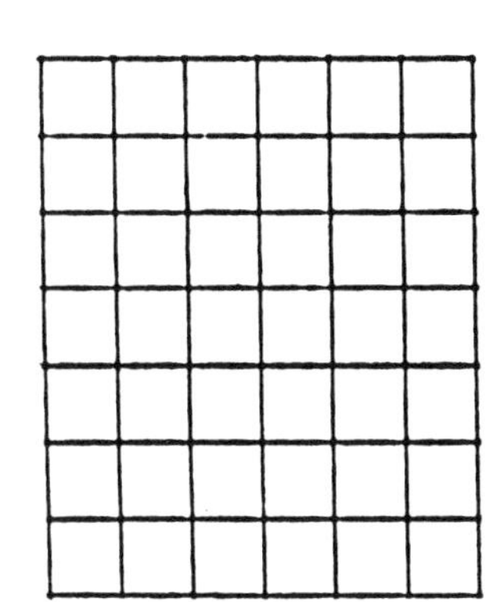

c. 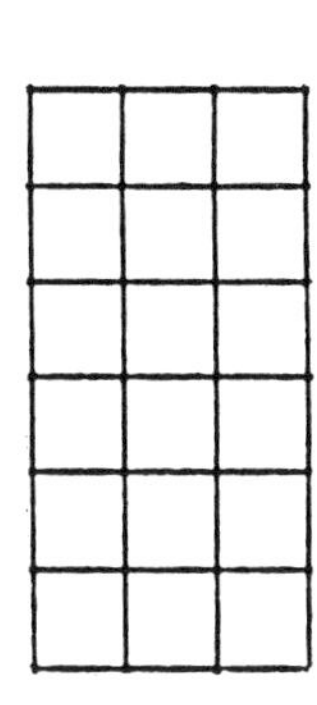

Many Number Sentences

Mathematics teaching objectives:

- Write the multiplication and division sentences associated with the dimensions and number of square units in a rectangle.
- Develop vocabulary - number sentence.

Problem-solving skills that might be emphasized:

- Make and/or use drawings.
- Translate a situation into mathematic notation.
- Make a systematic listing of possibilities.

Materials needed:

- None

Comments and suggestions:

- Introduce the class to the term number sentence. Point out that the 5 by 3 rectangle can suggest both division and multiplication number sentences.
- A distinction should be made between sentences with all necessary numbers given and those with one number missing. The term open sentence might be given as the expression for the "number missing" sentences.

Answers:

1. a. 3; 15; 5

   b. 16 number sentences match the 3 by 5 rectangle and can be associated with with the fact, 3 x 5 = 15:

15 ÷ 3 = 5	15 ÷ 5 = 3	5 x 3 = 15	3 x 5 = 15
__ ÷ 3 = 5	__ ÷ 5 = 3	__ x 3 = 15	__ x 5 = 15
15 ÷ __ = 5	15 ÷ __ = 3	5 x __ = 15	3 x __ = 15
15 ÷ 3 = __	15 ÷ 5 = __	5 x 3 = __	3 x 5 = __

2. During the class discussion, attention should be given to the systematic nature of the listing of number sentence possibilities.

   a. 4 by 6 rectangle: 4 x 6 = 24 and the other 15 sentences.

   b. 7 by 6 rectangle: 7 x 6 = 42 and the other 15 sentences.

   c. 6 by 3 rectangle: 6 x 3 = 18 and the other 15 sentences.

   Note: If pupils suggest that 5 x 3 = 15 is a different sentence than 15 = 5 x 3, let them have "their day in court!" If such variations are allowed, there are 32 rather than 16 sentences.

Extension: Which number facts suggest fewer than 16 number sentences? One possibility: 6 x 6 suggests 8 number sentences.

STORY PROBLEMS AND NUMBER SENTENCES

Write a number sentence to match each problem below.
Answers are <u>not</u> needed.

1. Jan paid 72¢ for 4 apples.
   How much did each apple cost?

2. Maria earns a quarter each time she weeds the garden.
   One month she weeded the garden 9 times.
   How much money did she earn?

3. Manuel baked 6 trays of cookies.
   Each tray had a dozen cookies.
   How many cookies did Manuel bake?

4. John walks 60 blocks to and from school each week.
   How many blocks does he walk each day?

5. Lee's football team scored 4 touchdowns.
   Each touchdown counted 6 points.
   How many touchdown points did Lee's team get?

Story Problems And Number Sentences

Mathematics teaching objectives:

- . Write number sentences for simple story problems.
- . Write stories for simple number sentences.

Problem-solving skills that might be emphasized:

- . Translate a situation into mathematical expressions.
- . Invent a problem situation for a mathematical expression.

Material needed:

- . None

Comments and suggestions:

- . Present this lesson after the preceding lesson, "Many Number Sentences."
- . Tell pupils they are not expected to get the answers for the problems. Writing number sentences does not require answers.
- . Work through two or three problems with the class. Make a point of writing sentences without the answers. Mention that equations without answers are often called open sentences. Let pupils work the other translation problems independently.
- . Help pupils get started on problem 11 by giving them examples of story problems which fit one or two of the number sentences. Encourage pupils to be imaginative in making up their stories.
- . Have pupils compare their story problems and equations with other class members as a class or in small groups.

Answers:

Comment on problems 1-10: There are several number sentences which are good translations for each story problem. Give pupils an opportunity to defend their translations.

1. $72 \div 4 = \_\_\_$; $72 \div \_\_\_ = 4$; $4 \times \_\_\_ = 72$

   $4\overline{)72}$ (One could argue that this is not a sentence. However this is not the time to be that critical.)

2. $9 \times 25 = \_\_\_$; $25 \times 9 = \_\_\_$

   $25 + 25 + 25 + 25 + 25 + 25 + 25 + 25 + 25 = \_\_\_$

3. $6 \times 12 = \_\_\_$; $12 \times 6 = \_\_\_$

   $12 + 12 + 12 + 12 + 12 + 12 = \_\_\_$

4. $60 \div 5 = \_\_\_$; $5 \times \_\_\_ = 60$

   $5\overline{)60}$

6. Oscar spends 20 minutes each day walking the dog.
   How many minutes a week does he walk the dog?

7. Bob put 48 stamps in his stamp book.
   He put 12 stamps on each page.
   How many pages did he fill?

8. In the summer Greta practices her piano lessons 2 hours a day.
   How many hours would she practice during the month of July?

9. Joey counted the wheels on his toy car collection.
   There were 168 wheels.
   How many cars were in his collection?

10. Mike has $12.40 in his dime collection.
    How many dimes does he have?

11. Write your own story problems for each of these.

    a. $25 + 75 =$ ______

    b. $128 \div 4 =$ ______

    c. $3723 - 1932 =$ ______

    d. $6 \times 298 =$ ______

Answers: (cont.)

5. $4 \times 6 = \_\_\_$; $6 \times 4 = \_\_\_$

$6 + 6 + 6 + 6 = \_\_\_$

6. $20 \times 7 = \_\_\_$; $7 \times 20 = \_\_\_$

$20 + 20 + 20 + 20 + 20 + 20 + 20 = \_\_\_$

7. $48 \div 12 = \_\_\_$; $48 \div \_\_\_ = 12$

$12 \overline{)48}$

8. $2 \times 31 = \_\_\_$; $31 \times 2 = \_\_\_$

9. $168 \div 4 = \_\_\_$

$168 \div \_\_\_ = 4$

Pupils may use 5 wheels instead of 4, spare tire included.

or

They may choose to think of a 3-wheeled car. If they do, make adjustments in the sentences accordingly.

10. $\$12.40 \div .10 = \_\_\_$

$1240 \div 10 = \_\_\_$

$10 \overline{)1240}$

11. a.-d. Answers will vary.

Grade 4

V. FRACTION CONCEPTS

V. FRACTION CONCEPTS

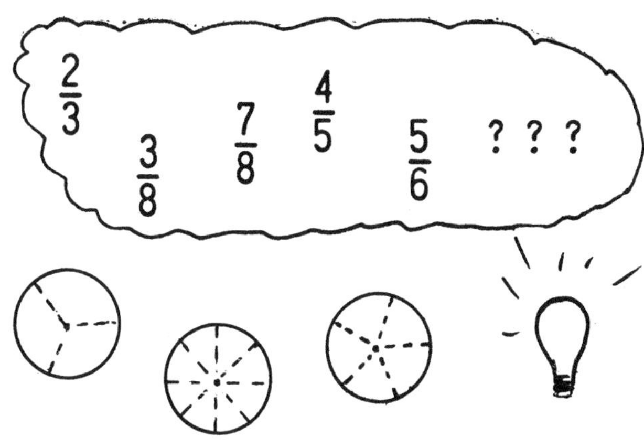

It seems perfectly sensible to many upils to add fractions straight across. hey have forgotten, or did not learn, he meaning for fraction addition. When sked the answer for 2 apples plus 3 pples and then asked the answer for -tenths plus 3-tenths, pupils usually nswer 5-tenths. In words they do fine ut in symbols they make up rules.

Pupils need much work with meanings of symbols and operations before they an be expected to use the symbols and operations with understanding. They eed to be experienced in working with a model so they can return again and gain to the model when they forget what to do. Research* indicates that he region model, using a circle or rectangle as a whole, should be mastered efore a set model or number-line model for fractions is used. The fourth rade seems an appropriate place for extensive work with the region model.

The lessons in this section use circular, square and rectangular regions s units. Diagrams and cut-outs of these regions are used to build background for developing fraction concepts and operations. Word names like -fourths are emphasized prior to using the symbol name like $\frac{3}{4}$. Activities re included to show the importance of comparing the size of the units efore comparing the size of the fractions. For example, $\frac{1}{2}$ of a small pizza s certainly smaller than $\frac{1}{2}$ of a large pizza. No work is done with formal lgorithms.

he First Seven Lessons

The activities are sequenced from concepts of naming fractions through nformal work with the concept of addition. Each lesson is designed to ake full use of the fraction pieces as a manipulative to better understand he concepts.

A time is eventually reached when pupils will not feel the need to use he fraction pieces. As one fourth-grade girl said, "I'll use them when I

* As discussed in DEVELOPING COMPUTATIONAL SKILLS, NCTM 1978 Yearbook.

need them." You as a teacher should encourage use of the pieces. At any time during an activity, pupils should be able to demonstrate the solution to a problem.

Because of slight inaccuracies in cutting, pupils will sometimes get false results. What is called an "exact covering" may be slightly off. Having pupils work together when answers differ is a partial solution to this problem

On pages 169-174, masters are provided for the circle pieces. A thermofax master can be used to ditto the circles onto construction paper. Four circles can be placed on each sheet so eight sheets, per color, are needed for a class of 32 pupils. The circles are to be cut out by the pupils themselves as part of their first lesson. The class time needed will be about 30 minutes. An envelope is needed for each pupil to store the pieces. It's helpful to have several spare pieces to replace those that get lost. About 8 extra white circles (wholes) are needed for the "Fraction Cover-Up Game 2."

A set of transparent circle fraction pieces is very helpful for teacher demonstrations on the overhead projector. Colored pieces can be produced using the Diazo process if such a machine is available. Or pieces can be colored with felt pens.

The Last Three Lessons

These lessons use as units square and rectangular as well as circular regions. The emphasis is more on making drawings than on cut-outs. The focus is on working with units of different sizes and on making comparisons. Lessons of this type are often not included in the usual presentations of fractions to pupils.

Current fourth-grade mathematics texts include exercises using colored area or region diagrams for fractions. These could be used nicely with this section. If it is your wish to use additional exercises involving other models for fractions, we would recommend that you provide the necessary background as recommended by your text.

FRACTION PATTERNS

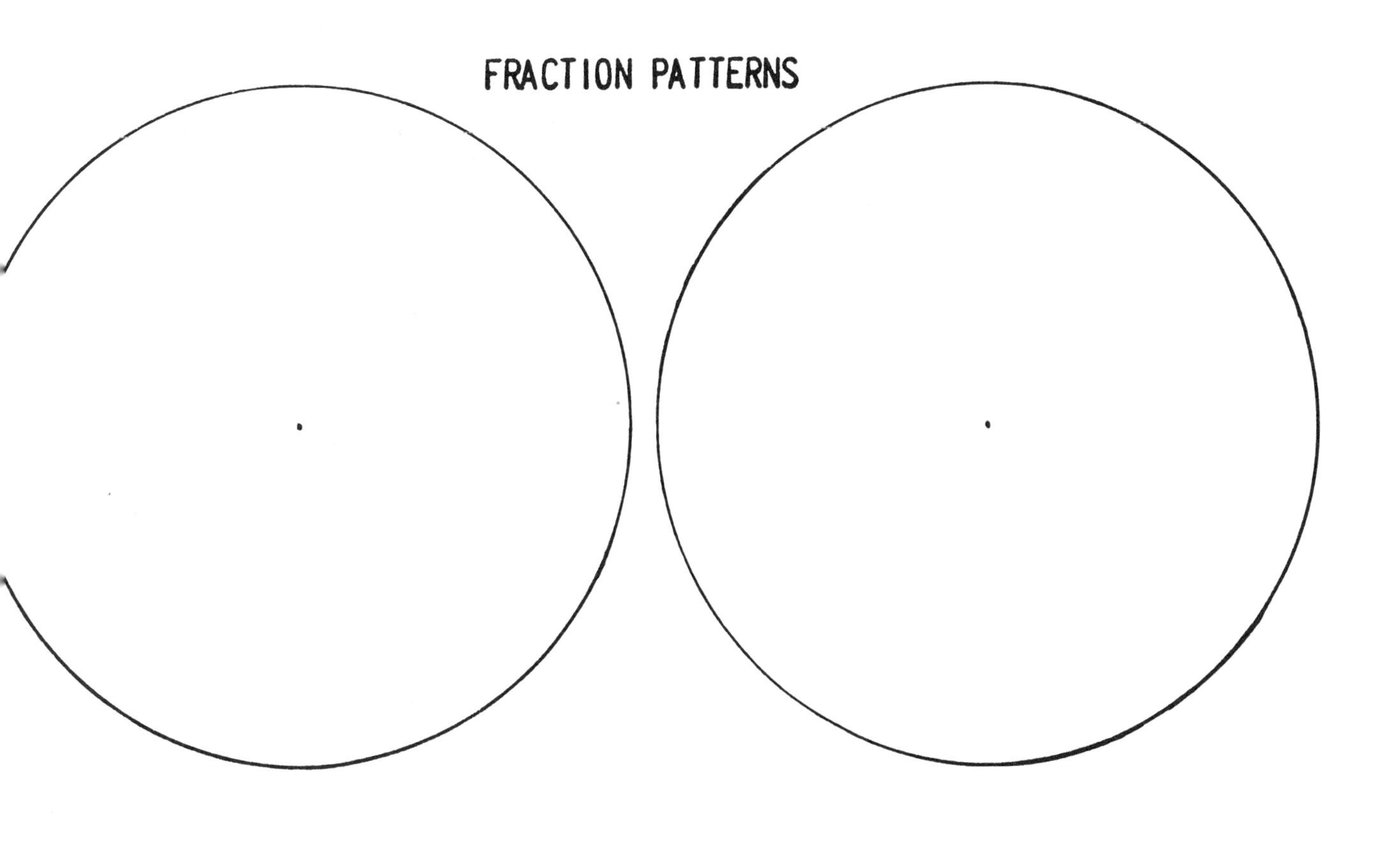

Wholes - White

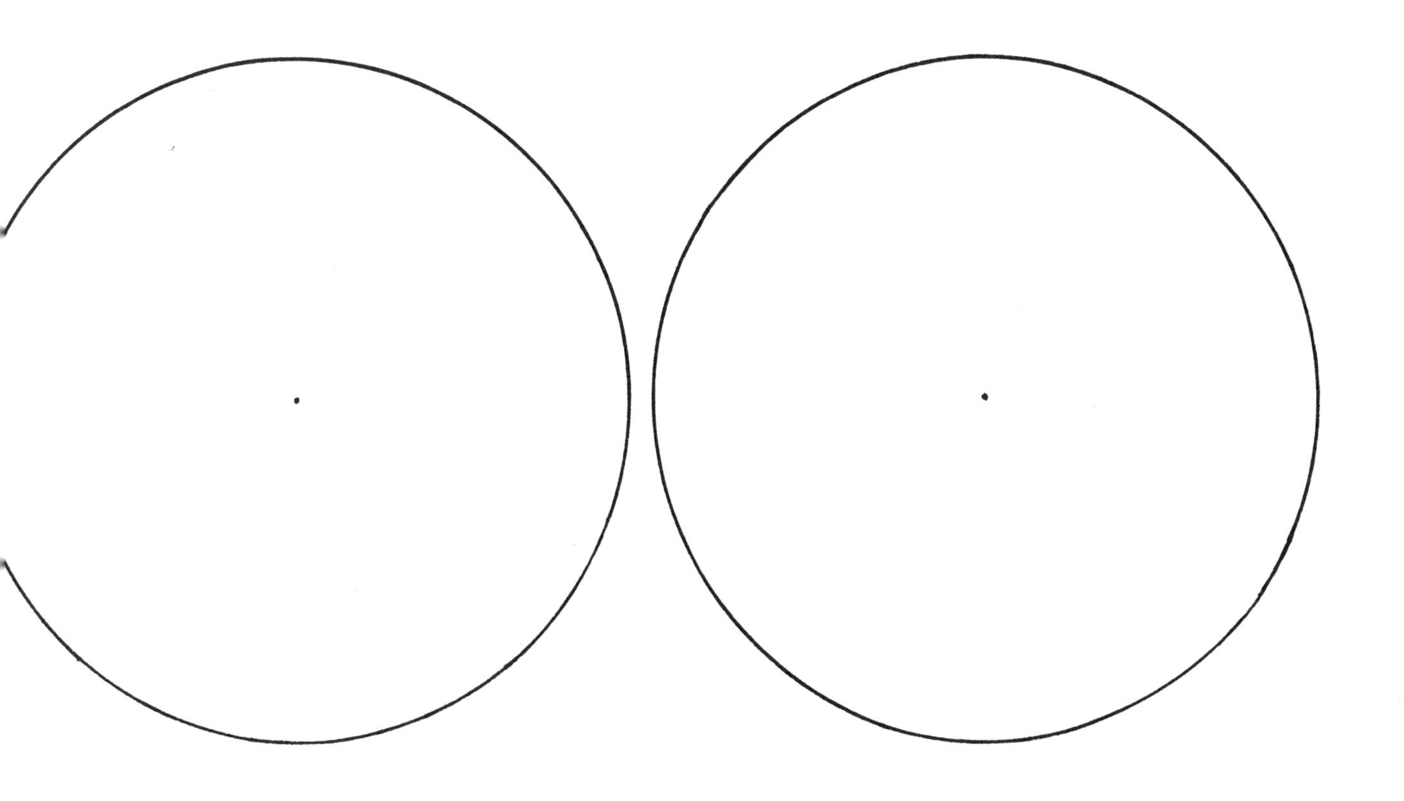

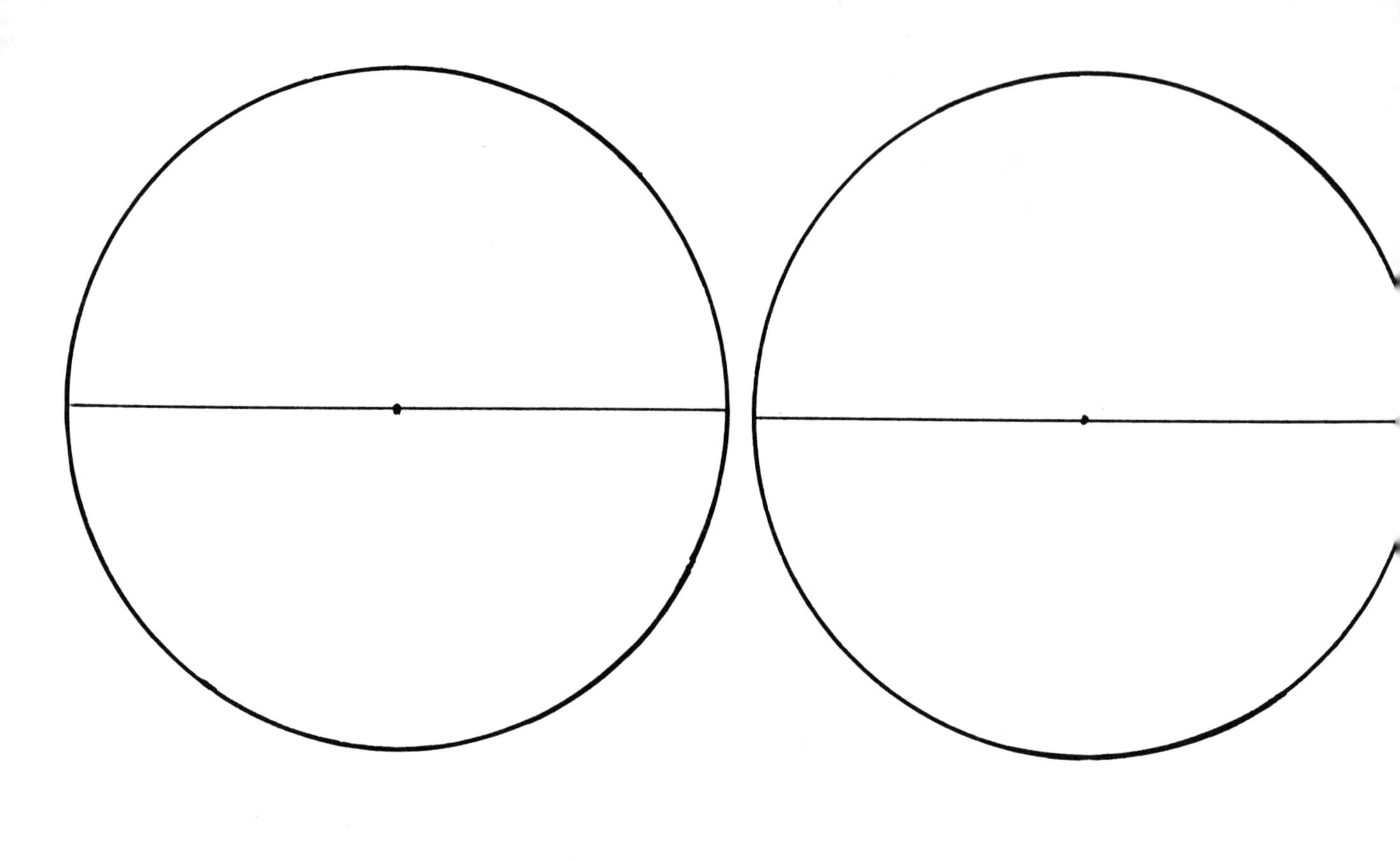

Halves - Yellow

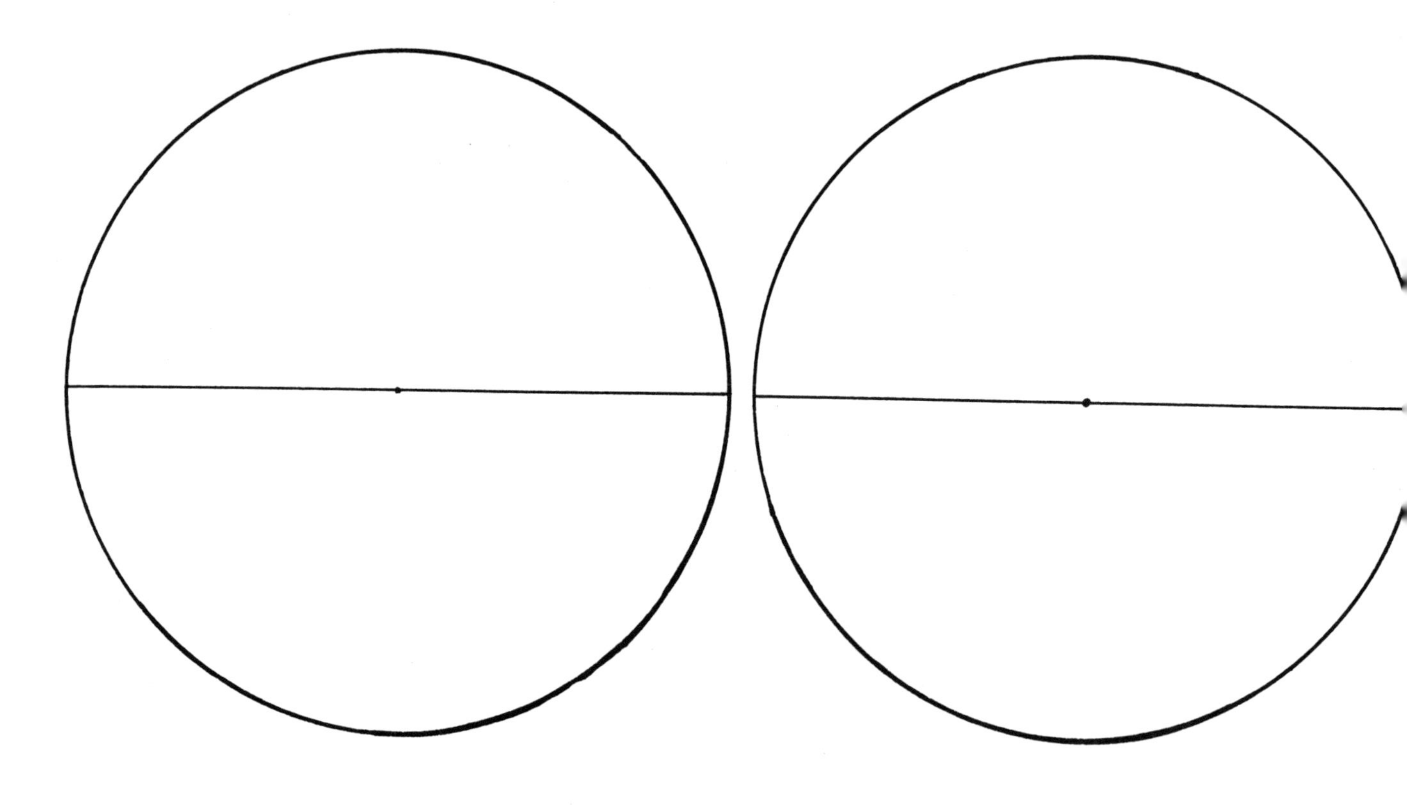

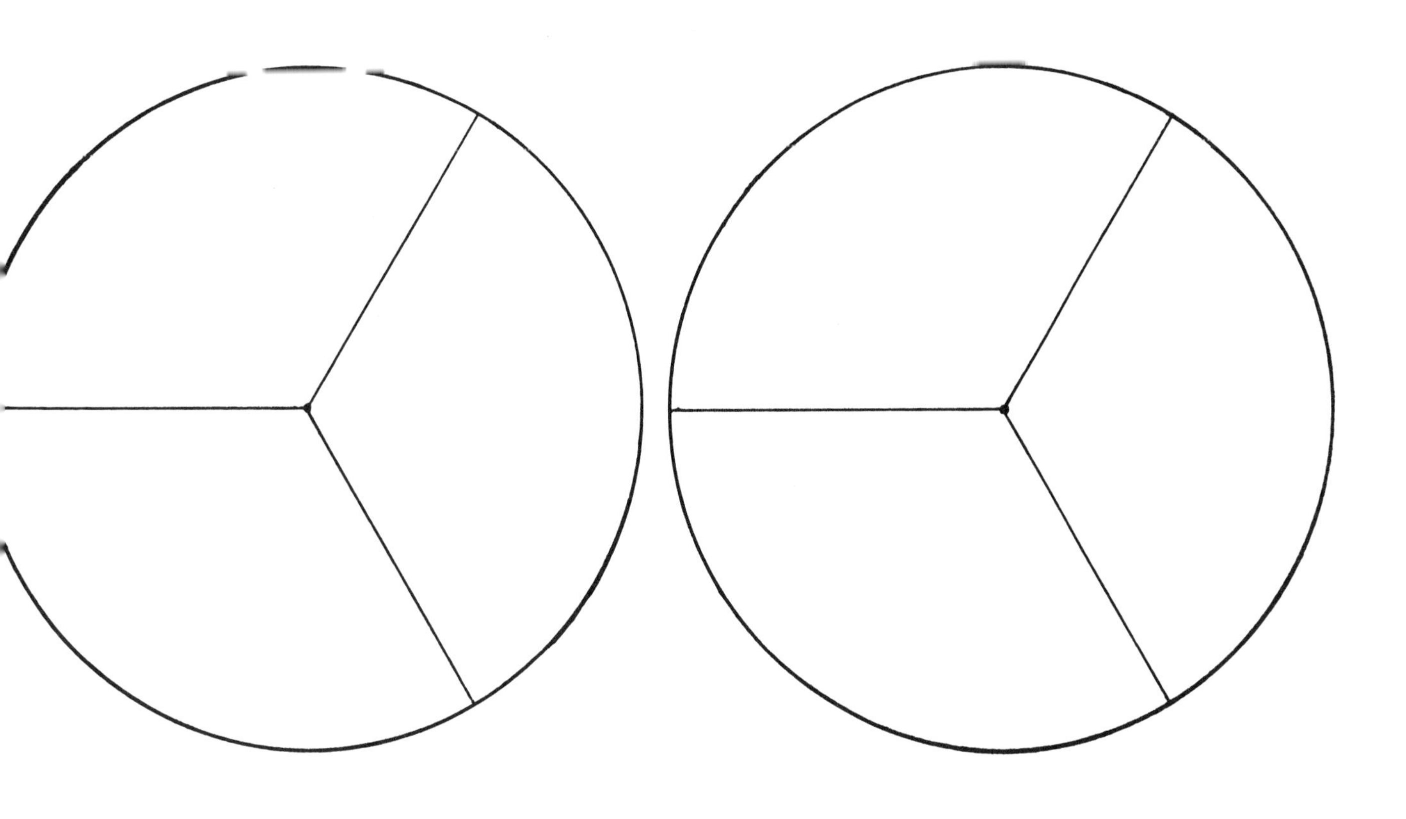

Thirds - Green

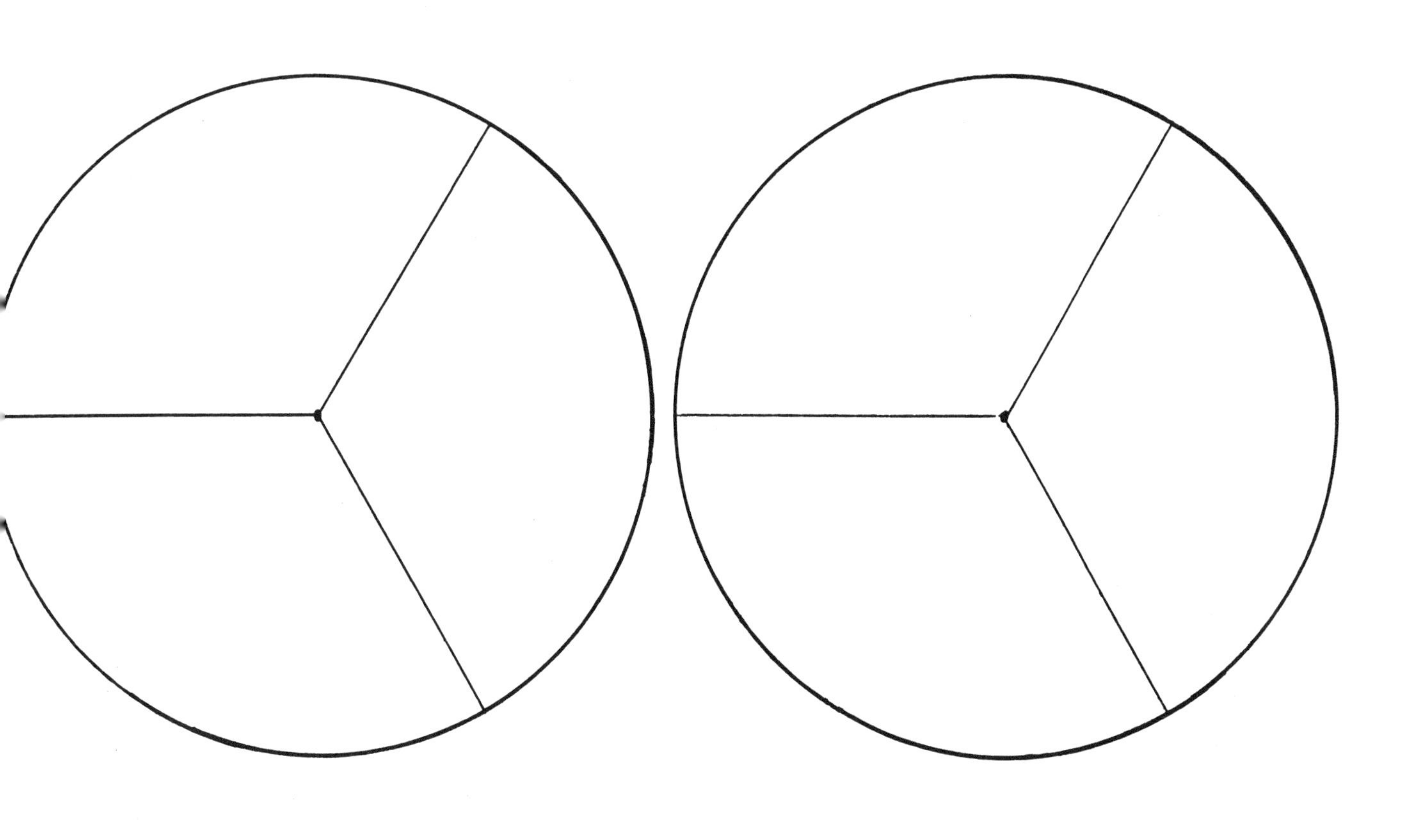

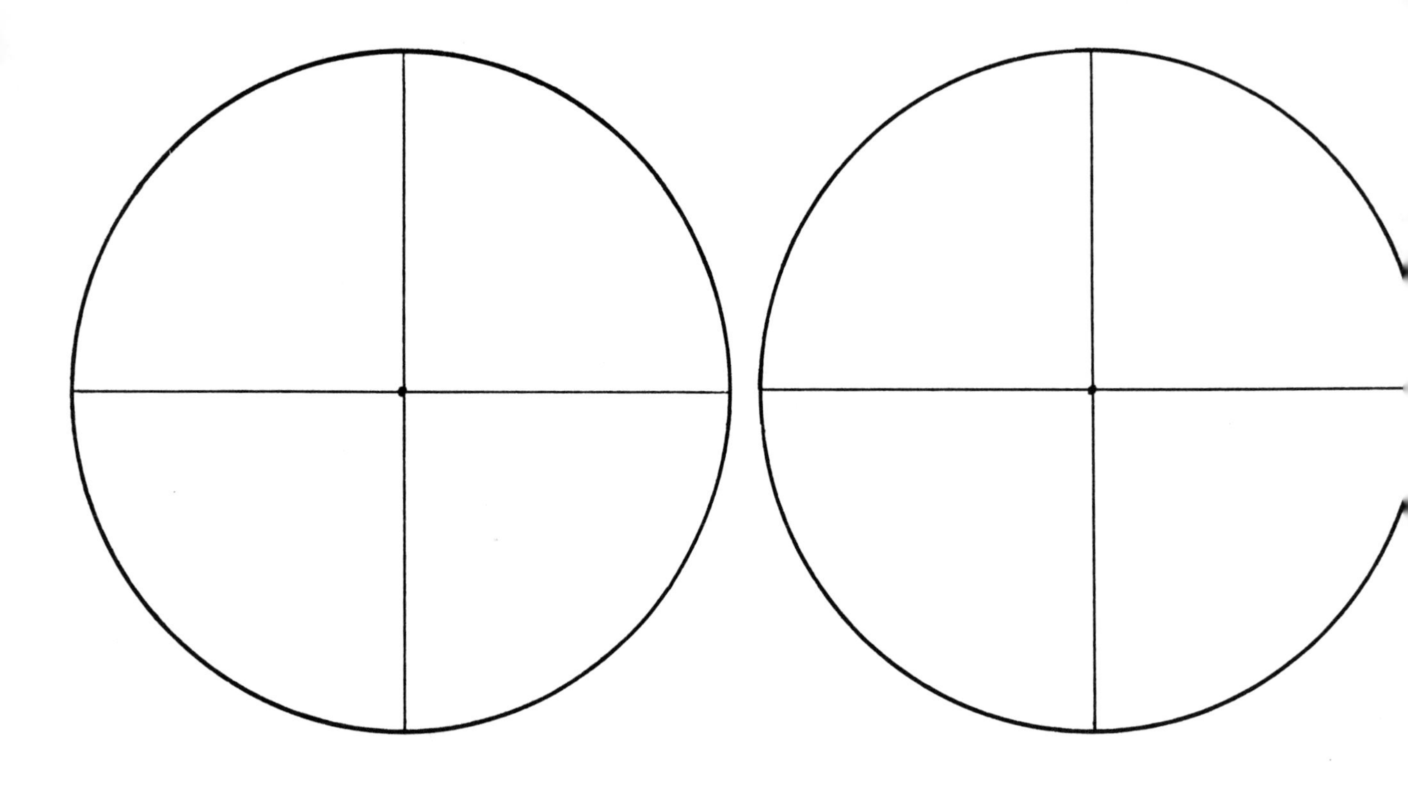

Fourths - Light Blue

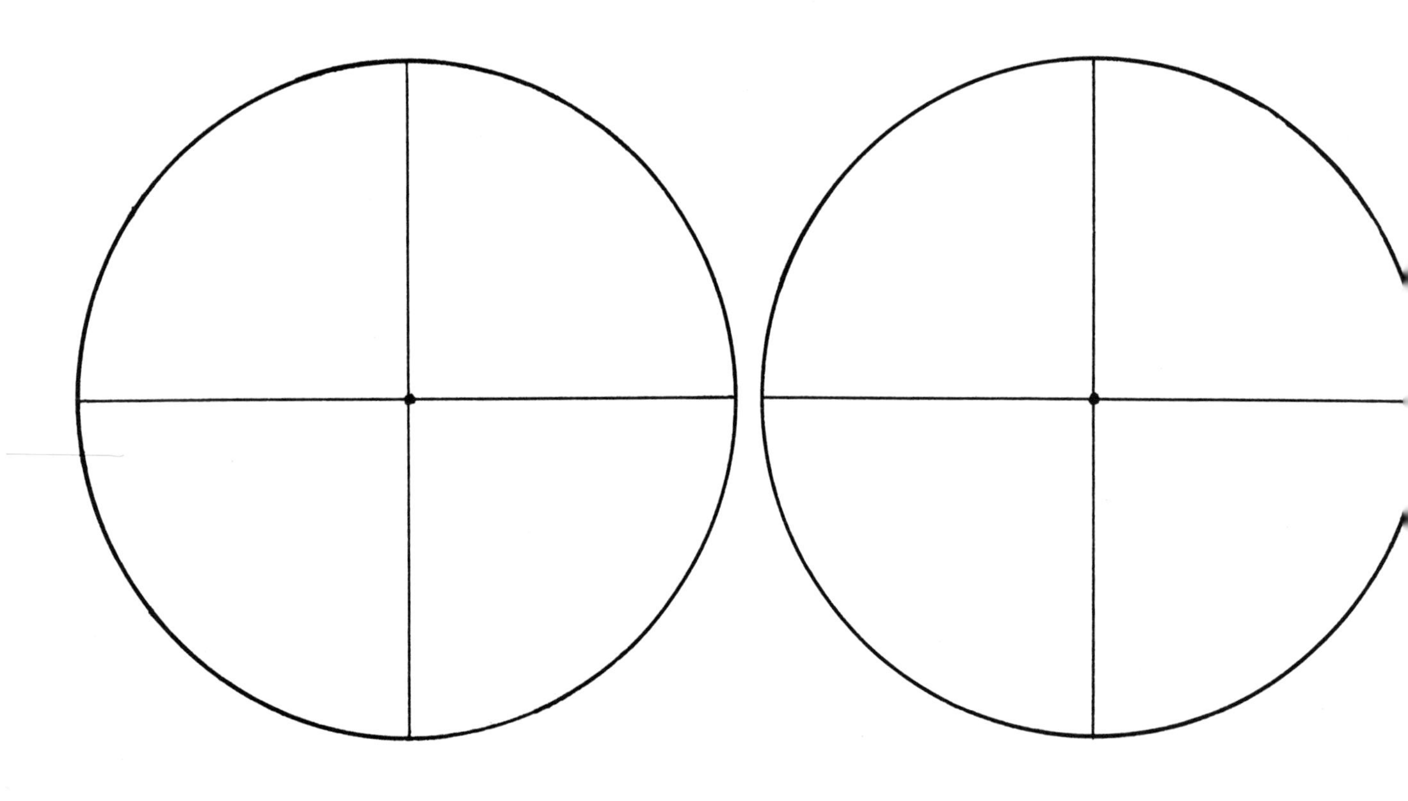

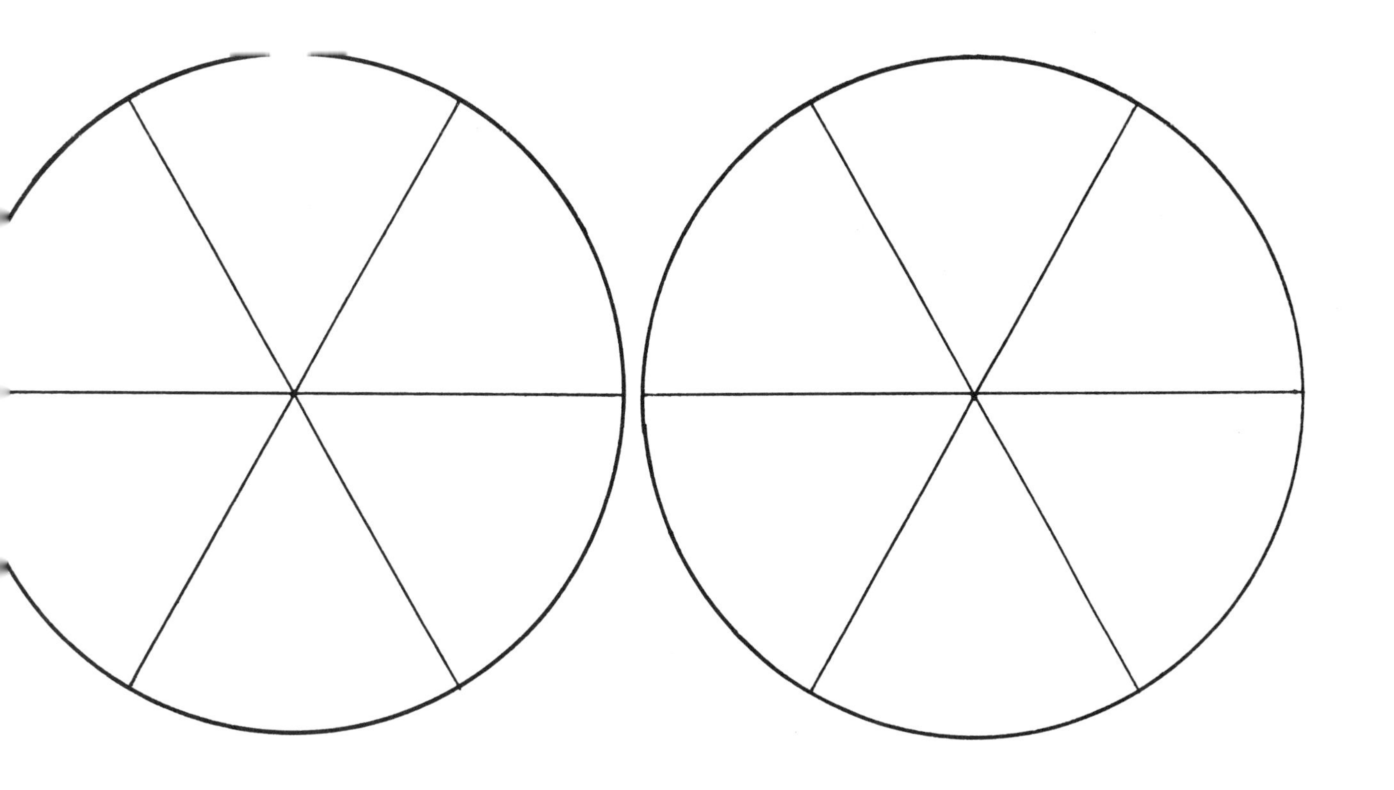

Sixths - Pink

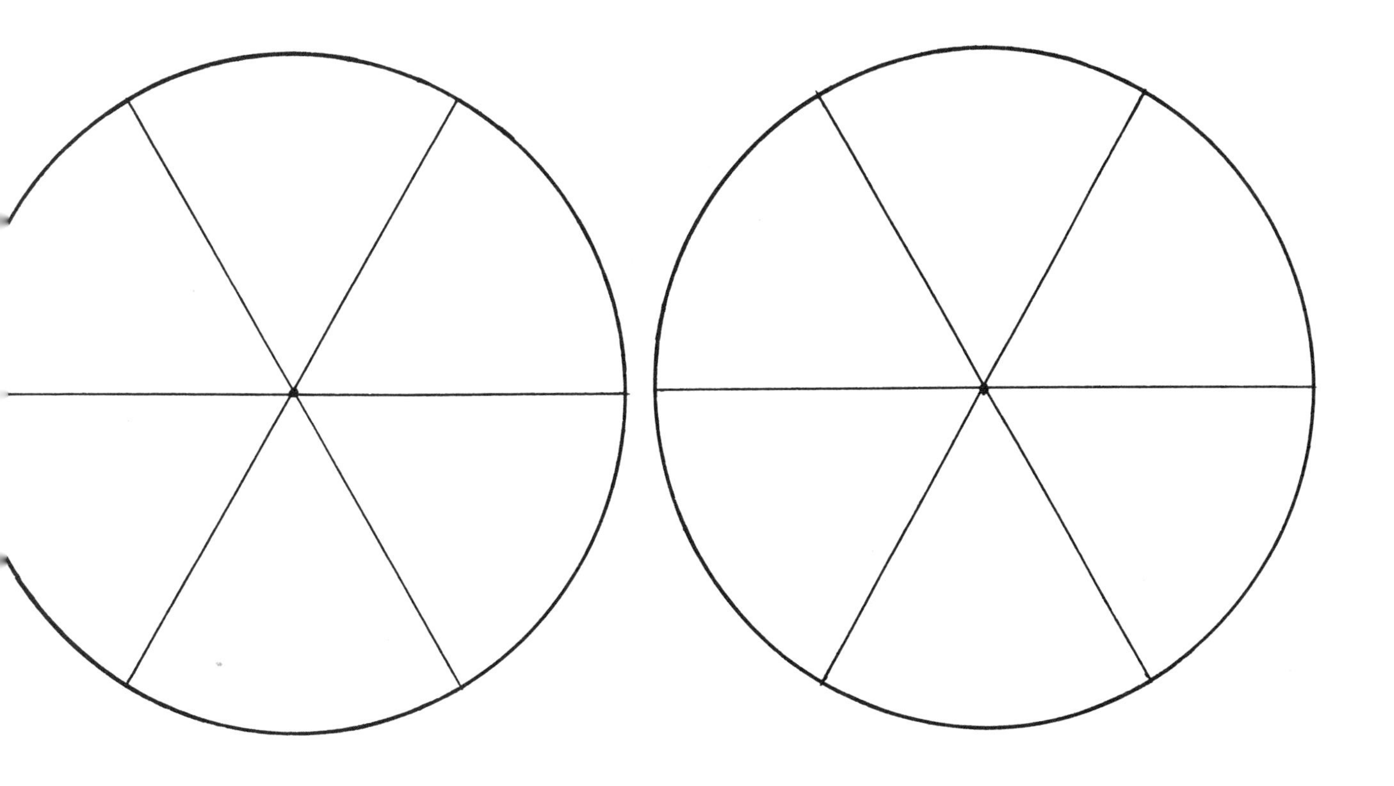

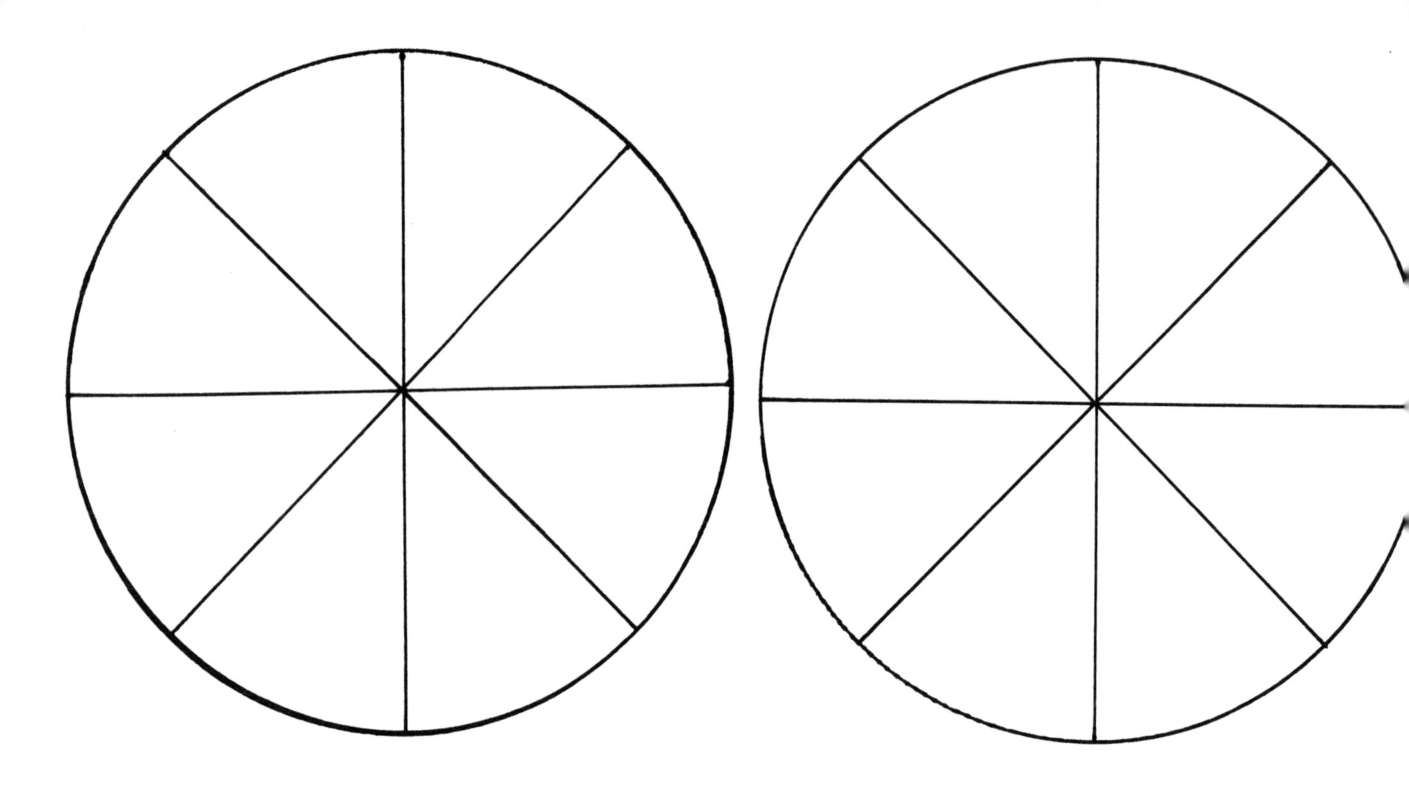

Eighths - Dark Blue

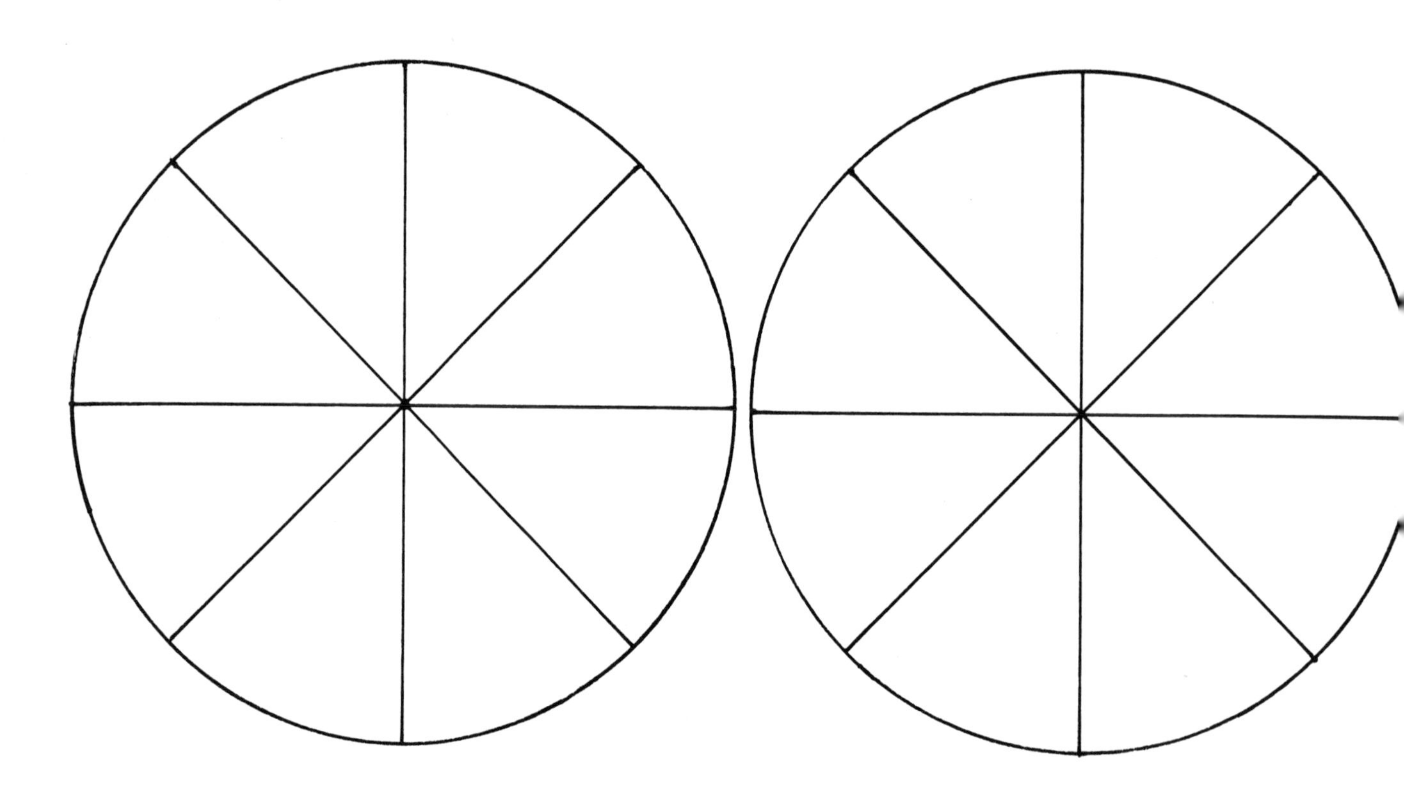

CUT-UPS

Needed: Construction paper circles
Scissors
One envelope

1. Cut around the outside of each circle and discard the scraps.

   How many different-colored circles did you make? ____________

2. Cut each circle into the pieces marked on top.

   What is the color of the smallest piece? ____________

   What is the color of the largest piece? ____________

3. Take one piece of each color.

   Place these pieces in order from smallest to largest.
   Write the color names in order below.

   dark blue ________ ________ ________ ________ white

4. Complete the chart below.

Color	Number of pieces in one whole circle
dark blue	
	6
	4
white	

5. If you have time, use the pieces to make an interesting design or pattern.

At the end of the class, put all pieces in the envelope.

Cut-Ups

Mathematics teaching objectives:

- Piece fractional parts of circles together to make a whole circle
- Order fractional parts of a circle according to size.

Problem-solving skills pupils might use:

- Use a physical model.
- Use a table.
- Look for patterns.

Materials needed:

- Circle fraction patterns reproduced on construction paper
- Scissors
- Envelope in which to "store" pieces

Comments and suggestions:

- After pupils cut out each circle, remind them that all the circle (or pies) are the same size.
- After they cut each circle into the pieces suggested, ask them to find pieces of the pies which are smaller than a piece of a given color; larger than that piece. Repeat the exercise with pieces o different colors.
- Let pupils work problems 3, 4, and 5 on their own.
- No reference should be made in this lesson to the fractional name for the pieces. Pupils will be given the opportunity to make thi discovery in the next lesson.

Answers:

1. 6

2. Smallest piece- dark blue
   Largest piece- white

3. dark blue pink light blue green yellow whit

4.

Color	Number of pieces in one whole circle
dark blue	8
pink	6
light blue	4
green	3
yellow	2
white	1

COVER-UPS

Needed: Envelope of circle and circle pieces

1. Cover the white circle with
   a. green pieces. How many are needed?
   b. yellow pieces. How many are needed?
   c. light blue pieces. How many are needed?

2. a. The green piece is called one-third. Why?
   b. The yellow piece is called one-half. Why?
   c. The dark blue piece is called one-eighth. Why?

3. The white piece is one whole. Which color shows:
   a. one-sixth? ________________
   b. one-fourth? ________________
   c. one-third? ________________

4. Write the word name, like one-sixth, for one piece of each color.
   a. one pink ________________
   b. one dark blue ________________
   c. 1 light blue ________________
   d. 1 green ________________
   e. 1 yellow ________________
   f. 1 white ________________

Cover-Ups

Mathematics teaching objectives:

- . Name certain parts of a whole as fractions.
- . Relate word names to fraction names (unit fractions).

Problem-solving skills pupils *might* use:

- . Use a physical model.
- . Make and use a table.
- . Look for patterns.

Materials needed:

- . Envelope of circle fraction pieces

Comments and suggestions:

- . Pupils are introduced to both a "word name" (like one-eighth) and a number name (like $\frac{1}{8}$) for the pieces. Most pupils should be able, by noticing patterns, to match the number names with the word names in problem 5 without any help.
- . Work problems 1 and 2 as a teacher-directed class activity. Let the complete the sheet independently.
- . As pupils complete the lesson, pair them up. Have one pupil close her/his eyes while the other pupil hands her/him a fraction piece. By touch, the first pupil tries to decide what the piece is. Pupils then reverse roles.
- . It is helpful to post on the bulletin board (or chalkboard) a list of color names and fraction words (half, third, fourth, etc.) to be used as a reference for spelling and as an aid to the memory.

Answers:

1. a. 3 b. 2 c. 4 3. a. pink b. light blue c. green

4. a. one-sixth b. one-eighth c. one-fourth
 d. one-third e. one-half f. one whole

5. Finish the chart below:

Color	Number of Pieces To Make 1 Whole	Word Name For 1 Piece	Fraction Number Name For 1 Piece
dark blue		one-eighth	$\frac{1}{8}$
	6		$\frac{1}{6}$
light blue			
	3		
		one-half	

Put all fraction pieces back in the envelope.

Answers: (cont.)

5.

Color	Number of pieces to make 1 whole	Word name for 1 piece	Fraction Number name for 1 piece
Dark blue	8	one-eighth	$\frac{1}{8}$
Pink	6	one-sixth	$\frac{1}{6}$
Light blue	4	one-fourth	$\frac{1}{4}$
Green	3	one-third	$\frac{1}{3}$
Yellow	2	one-half	$\frac{1}{2}$

SAME COLOR/MANY PIECES

Needed: Circle fraction pieces

1. Use pieces of the same color to make complete circles. You should have 5 different circles.

   Write the fraction word name for

   a. two pinks __________

   b. three pinks __________

   c. 4 pinks __________

   d. 5 pinks __________

2. Write the fraction word name for

   a. 3 light blue ____________________

   b. 5 dark blue ____________________

   c. 2 green ____________________

   d. 3 dark blue ____________________

3. Finish this chart.

Fraction Color Name	Fraction Number Name
one dark blue	
two dark blue	$\frac{2}{8}$
three dark blue	
______ dark blue	$\frac{4}{8}$
______ dark blue	$\frac{5}{8}$
six dark blue	
seven dark blue	

Put all fraction pieces back in the envelope.

Same Color/Many Pieces

Mathematics teaching objectives:

- Relate fraction word names to fraction names (other than unit fractions).
- Practice writing fraction word names for parts of a whole.

Problem-solving skills pupils <u>might</u> use:

- Use a physical model.
- Look for and use patterns.

Materials needed:

- Envelope of circle fraction pieces

Comments and suggestions:

- With the different circles pieced together before them, pupils should be expected to answer questions 1 and 2 without help.

- Challenge the pupils to answer question 3 by looking for patterns in the partially filled table.

- During class discussion you might extend the activity by asking word and number names for

  6 pinks, 7 pinks (6 sixths, $\frac{6}{6}$; 7 sixths, $\frac{7}{6}$)

  2 yellows, 3 yellows (2 halves, $\frac{2}{2}$; 3 halves, $\frac{3}{2}$)

  3 green, 4 green (3 thirds, $\frac{3}{3}$; 4 thirds, $\frac{4}{3}$)

  etc.

  Such questions prevent pupils from concluding that the numerator of a fraction must be less than the denominator.

- This lesson takes about 20 minutes.

Answers:

1. a. two-sixths b. three-sixths c. four-sixths d. five-sixths
2. a. three-fourths b. five-eighths c. two-thirds d. three-eighths

3.

Fraction Color Name	Fraction Number Name
	$\frac{1}{8}$
	$\frac{3}{8}$
four	
five	
	$\frac{6}{8}$
	$\frac{7}{8}$

WHICH FRACTION IS LARGER?

Needed: Circle fraction pieces

1. Use pieces of the same color to make complete circles. You should have 5 colored circles and the whole white circle.

2. Use one piece of each color. Lay one on top of the other to decide which is larger. Circle the larger one.

   a. one half or one third
   b. 1 sixth or 1 eighth
   c. $\frac{1}{3}$ or $\frac{1}{4}$
   d. $\frac{1}{2}$ or $\frac{1}{6}$
   e. $\frac{1}{8}$ or $\frac{1}{3}$
   f. $\frac{1}{4}$ or $\frac{1}{6}$

3. Use fraction pieces to decide which is larger. Circle the larger one.

   a. 1 third or 2 fourths
   b. 1 yellow or 3 dark blue
   c. 2 thirds or 3 fourths
   d. 1 yellow or 2 pink
   e. $\frac{2}{3}$ or $\frac{7}{8}$
   f. $\frac{1}{2}$ or $\frac{5}{8}$
   g. $\frac{5}{6}$ or $\frac{3}{4}$
   h. $\frac{3}{8}$ or $\frac{1}{2}$

4. Suppose you had many other circle fraction pieces. Decide which would be larger and circle it.

   a. 1 eighth or 1 tenth
   b. 4 sixths or 4 fifths
   c. $\frac{5}{9}$ or $\frac{5}{10}$
   d. $\frac{6}{9}$ or $\frac{6}{12}$
   e. $\frac{8}{10}$ or 1
   f. $\frac{5}{9}$ or 1

Put all fraction pieces back in the envelope.

Which Fraction Is Larger?

Mathematics teaching objectives:

- Recognize size differences of various fractional parts of the same whole unit.

Problem-solving skills pupils *might* use:

- Make a physical model.
- Look for and use patterns.

Materials needed:

- Envelope of circle fraction pieces

Comments and suggestions:

- If transparent fraction pieces are available, work through problem with the class using the overhead projector.
- With the different circles pieced together before them, pupils should be expected to answer problems 2 and 3 *without* referring to a "crutch" such as

  1 green piece - one-third - $\frac{1}{3}$

  1 yellow piece - one-half - $\frac{1}{2}$

  etc.
- Let pupils "try their luck" on problem 4 without your assistance. See how many use the pattern:
  - The larger the fraction number name - the smaller the piece.
  - The greater the bottom number of a unit fraction - the smaller the fraction.
- This activity takes about 20 minutes.

Answers:

1. a. one-half b. one-sixth c. $\frac{1}{3}$ d. $\frac{1}{2}$ e. $\frac{1}{3}$ f. $\frac{1}{4}$

2. a. 2 fourths b. 1 yellow c. 3 fourths d. 1 yellow
   e. $\frac{7}{8}$ f. $\frac{5}{8}$ g. $\frac{5}{6}$ h. $\frac{1}{2}$

3. a. 1 eighth b. 4 fifths c. $\frac{5}{9}$ d. $\frac{6}{9}$ e. 1 f. 1

FRACTION COVER-UP GAME - 1

1. Read together the directions for the game below.

Players:	One banker (does not play game) Three players
Materials:	One envelope of fraction pieces for each player One special die marked $\frac{1}{8}$, $\frac{1}{8}$, $\frac{1}{6}$, $\frac{1}{4}$, $\frac{1}{3}$, $\frac{1}{2}$ One score sheet for each player
Directions:	. Each player takes one whole from the envelope of fraction pieces and give remaining pieces to banker. . Player one - roll the die. - ask banker for the fraction piece named by the roll of the die. - place that piece on the one whole piece. . Player two and other players - in turn, do the same. . Any time you do not want the fraction piece named by the roll of the die, you may pass that turn. . Play until all players completely and exactly cover their own one whole piece. . Score game as follows: $\frac{1}{2}$ point for first player to cover 1 whole. $\frac{1}{3}$ point for second player to cover 1 whole. $\frac{1}{4}$ point for third player to cover 1 whole.

2. Play several games. Take turns being banker. Record the name of the banker and the results of each game on the special score sheet.

Take back your own fraction pieces. Put them back in your envelope.

Fraction Cover-Up Game - 1

Mathematics teaching objectives:

. Match fraction number names to fractional parts of a whole.

Problem-solving skills pupils *might* use:

. Use a physical model.

Materials needed:

. Envelope of circle fraction pieces for each player.

. Special die whose faces are marked $\frac{1}{8}$, $\frac{1}{8}$, $\frac{1}{6}$, $\frac{1}{4}$, $\frac{1}{3}$, $\frac{1}{2}$. (One die per 4 pupils is needed.)

. One score sheet for each player (page 185)

Comments and suggestions:

. Discuss the basic rules for the Fraction Cover-Up Game as a class.

. Ask pupils to form groups of 4 players and to decide as groups who will be first banker. After pupils have formed their groups and readied a space to play the game, distribute the dice needed for the game.

. Require pupils to *verbalize* their requests to the banker: "Please give me a one-fourth piece." This is another way for pupils to practice.

. At the completion of 8 games, pupils should be encouraged to determine as a group who earned the most points. If pupils ask help in doing this, "hint" that the circle fraction pieces might be of use in totaling points earned.

. As you circulate among the groups as they play the game, you will likely observe pupils using various strategies. Suggest that pupils mention such strategies during the discussion after the game.

SPECIAL SCORE SHEET FOR FRACTION COVER-UP GAME

Game 1	Game 2
________ banker	________ banker
________ $\frac{1}{2}$ point	________ $\frac{1}{2}$ point
________ $\frac{1}{3}$ point	________ $\frac{1}{3}$ point
________ $\frac{1}{4}$ point	________ $\frac{1}{4}$ point
Game 3	**Game 4**
________ banker	________ banker
________ $\frac{1}{2}$ point	________ $\frac{1}{2}$ point
________ $\frac{1}{3}$ point	________ $\frac{1}{3}$ point
________ $\frac{1}{4}$ point	________ $\frac{1}{4}$ point
Game 5	**Game 6**
________ banker	________ banker
________ $\frac{1}{2}$ point	________ $\frac{1}{2}$ point
________ $\frac{1}{3}$ point	________ $\frac{1}{3}$ point
________ $\frac{1}{4}$ point	________ $\frac{1}{4}$ point
Game 7	**Game 8**
________ banker	________ banker
________ $\frac{1}{2}$ point	________ $\frac{1}{2}$ point
________ $\frac{1}{3}$ point	________ $\frac{1}{3}$ point
________ $\frac{1}{4}$ point	________ $\frac{1}{4}$ point

Who scored the most points in all? ________________ Explain.

ALL THE SAME

Needed: Circle fraction pieces

1, Find out how many light blue pieces cover one yellow piece exactly. Record your finding.

    ________ light blue cover ________ yellow

2. Find out how many pink pieces cover the 1-half piece exactly. Record.

    ________ pink cover 1 half.

3. How many dark blue cover 1-half exactly. Record.

    ________ eighths cover 1 half.

4. Take the $\frac{1}{2}$ piece. Cover exactly with light blue pieces. Record.

    $\frac{1}{2}$ equals ______

5. Take the $\frac{1}{2}$ piece. Cover with sixths. Record.

    $\frac{1}{2}$ = ________

6. Use the $\frac{1}{3}$ piece. Find an exact covering. Record.

    $\frac{1}{3}$ = ________

7. Use the $\frac{1}{4}$ piece. Find an exact covering. Record.

    $\frac{1}{4}$ = ________

8. Find and record these exact coverings:

    $\frac{2}{3}$ = ________ $\frac{3}{4}$ = ________

Put all fraction pieces back in the envelope.

All The Same

Mathematics teaching objective:

- Discover equivalent fractions

Problem-solving skills pupils *might* use:

- Use a physical model.
- Guess and check.

Materials needed:

- Envelope of fraction pieces

Comments and suggestions:

- Pupil accuracy in making the coverings is very important

Answers:

1. 2 light blue cover 1 yellow.
2. 3 pink cover 1 half.
3. 4 eighths cover 1 half.
4. $\frac{1}{2}$ equals $\frac{2}{4}$.
5. $\frac{1}{2} = \frac{3}{6}$
6. $\frac{1}{3} = \frac{2}{6}$
7. $\frac{1}{4} = \frac{2}{8}$
8. $\frac{2}{3} = \frac{4}{6}$ $\qquad$ $\frac{3}{4} = \frac{6}{8}$

FRACTION COVER-UP GAME - 2

Needed: One envelope of fraction pieces for each pupil
One special Fraction Cover-Up Game die

Play some Fraction Cover-Up Games with three other players. Make these changes in the directions:

. This time, use a "fewest pieces" rule. Whenever possible, trade two or more pieces with the banker for one piece the same size.

. Play until each player exactly covers 2 whole pieces. Record results below.

Game 1	Game 2
____________ banker	____________ banker
____________ $\frac{1}{2}$ point	____________ $\frac{1}{2}$ point
____________ $\frac{1}{3}$ point	____________ $\frac{1}{3}$ point
____________ $\frac{1}{4}$ point	____________ $\frac{1}{4}$ point
Game 3	**Game 4**
____________ banker	____________ banker
____________ $\frac{1}{2}$ point	____________ $\frac{1}{2}$ point
____________ $\frac{1}{3}$ point	____________ $\frac{1}{3}$ point
____________ $\frac{1}{4}$ point	____________ $\frac{1}{4}$ point
Game 5	**Game 6**
____________ banker	____________ banker
____________ $\frac{1}{2}$ point	____________ $\frac{1}{2}$ point
____________ $\frac{1}{3}$ point	____________ $\frac{1}{3}$ point
____________ $\frac{1}{4}$ point	____________ $\frac{1}{4}$ point
Game 7	**Game 8**
____________ banker	____________ banker
____________ $\frac{1}{2}$ point	____________ $\frac{1}{2}$ point
____________ $\frac{1}{3}$ point	____________ $\frac{1}{3}$ point
____________ $\frac{1}{4}$ point	____________ $\frac{1}{4}$ point

Fraction Cover-Up Game - 2

Mathematics teaching objective:

. Get informal experiences with equivalent fractions and mixed numbers.

Problem-solving skills pupils *might* use:

. Use a physical model.

. Guess and check.

Materials needed:

. Envelope of circle fraction pieces

. One special die (used in "Fraction Cover-Up Game-1") for each group of 4 pupils.

. About 6 extra "whole pieces" (white circles)

Comments and suggestions:

. Briefly review rules of "Fraction Cover-Up Game-1" played previously Note the two changes in the rules to be used with this game (Game-2)

. Circulate as pupils work on the activity. Be certain pupils are verbalizing their requests to the banker, i.e. "I have two-fourths to trade for one-half "

. Allow time for pupils to talk about the strategies they used.

ROUND PIZZAS AND SOME COOKIES

Paul's Pizza Parlor sells three sizes of pizza. A smaller picture of each size is given below.

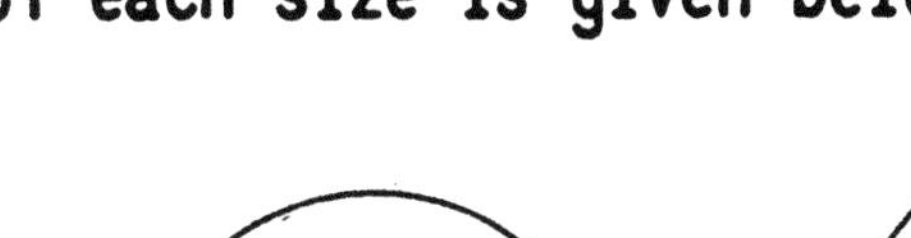

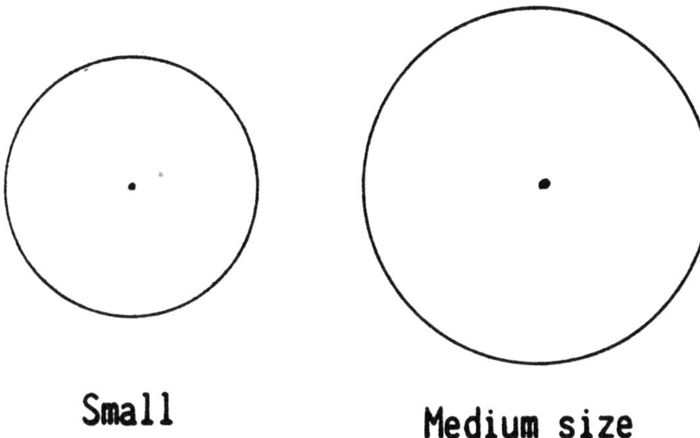

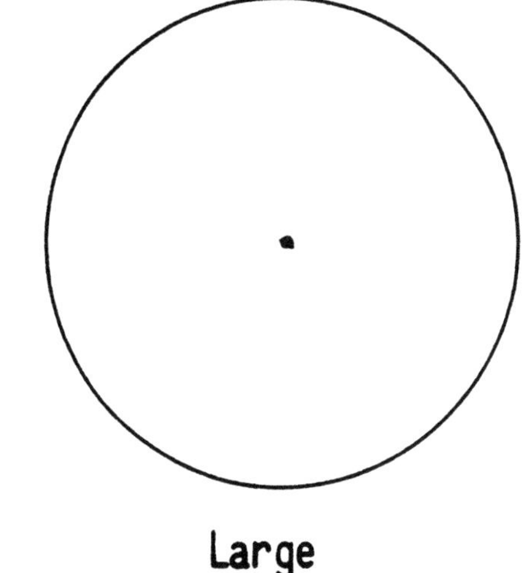

Small   Medium size   Large

1. Show where to cut each pizza in half.

2. Use the drawings below. Mark the places to cut to show fourths.

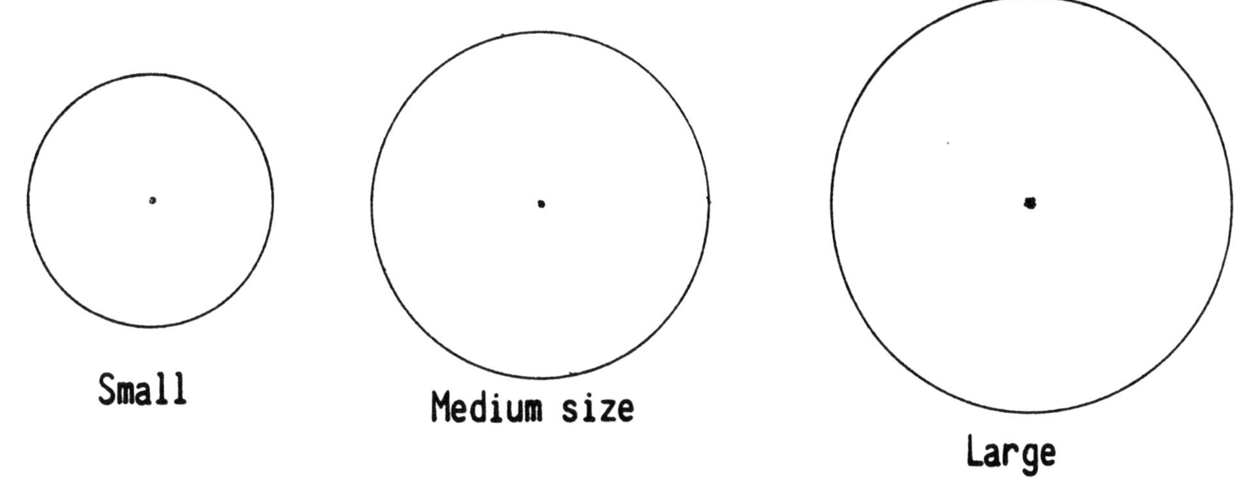

Small   Medium size   Large

3. Sometimes $\frac{1}{4}$ can be greater than $\frac{1}{2}$. Show how this is possible.

4. Is this true of the fourths and halves shown above? Prove your answer by cutting out the pieces.

5. Each picture shows $\frac{1}{4}$ of a cookie.

   $\frac{1}{4}$

   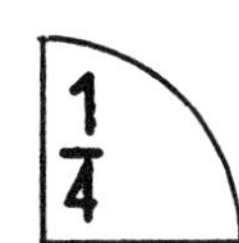

   a. In each case, draw the whole cookie. Be as careful as you can.

   b. Which cookie is the larger?

Round Pizzas And Some Cookies

Mathematics teaching objectives:

- Compare fractional parts when units of different sizes are given.
- Draw the whole circle when a fractional part of it is given.

Problem-solving skills pupils _might_ use:

- Make and use a drawing or model.
- Make explanations based upon drawings.

Materials needed:

- Ruler
- Scissors

Comments and suggestions:

- Let pupils discover that the size of a fractional part depends upon the size of the unit. For example, $\frac{1}{2}$ of a large unit will be greater than $\frac{1}{2}$ of a smaller unit. This idea needs to be emphasized often.
- Let pupils work independently after working problems 1 and 2 as a class activity.
- Use large demonstration models of pizzas to show the relative sizes of $\frac{1}{2}$.

Answers:

1. Pupils' drawings.
2. Pupils' drawings.
3. One-fourth of a large pizza can be greater than one-half of a small pizza. The size of fractional parts depends upon the size of the unit.
4. Yes. A fourth of the large pizza is bigger than a half of the small one.
5. a. Pupils' drawings.
   b. The first cookie.

ound Pizzas And Some Cookies

. Each picture shows $\frac{1}{3}$ of a cookie

a. Draw 3 thirds of each cookie.

b. Which whole is the biggest?

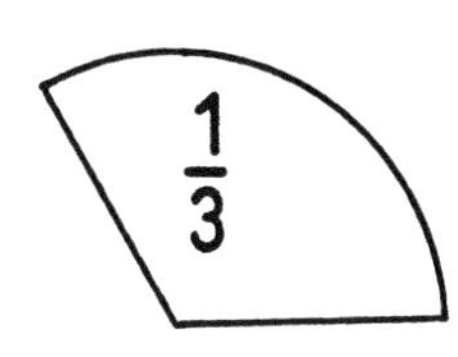

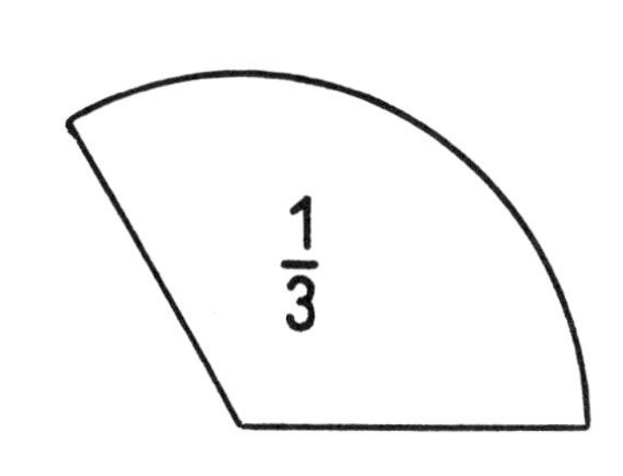

. Which is the biggest:

$\frac{1}{8}$ of the big cookie or $\frac{1}{2}$ of the small cookie?

Cutting them up may help you decide.

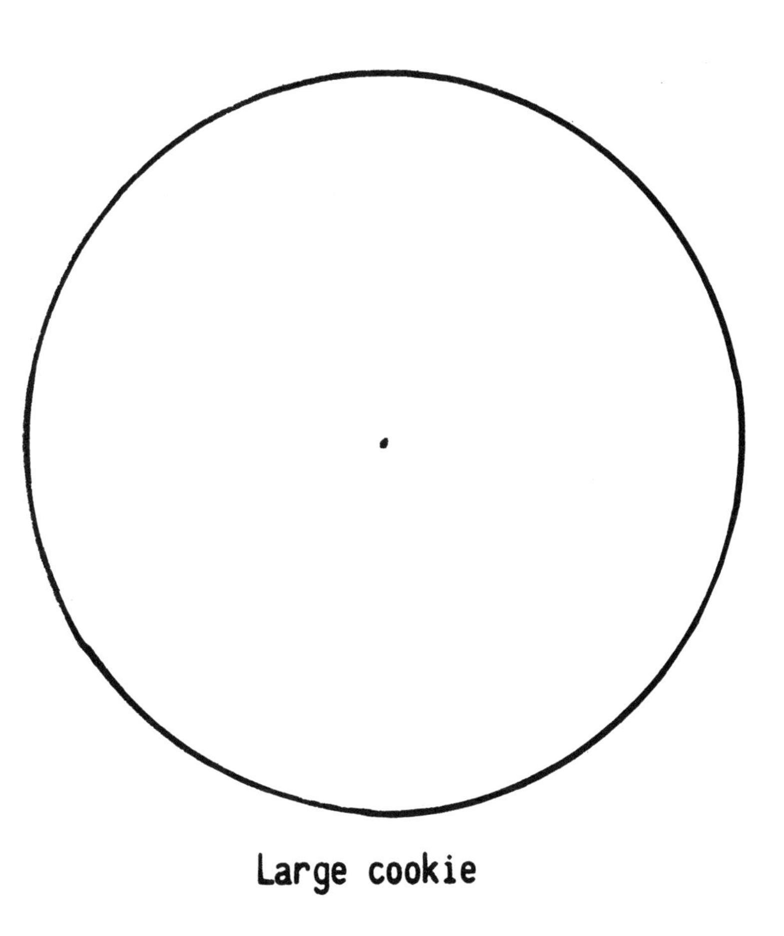

Large cookie

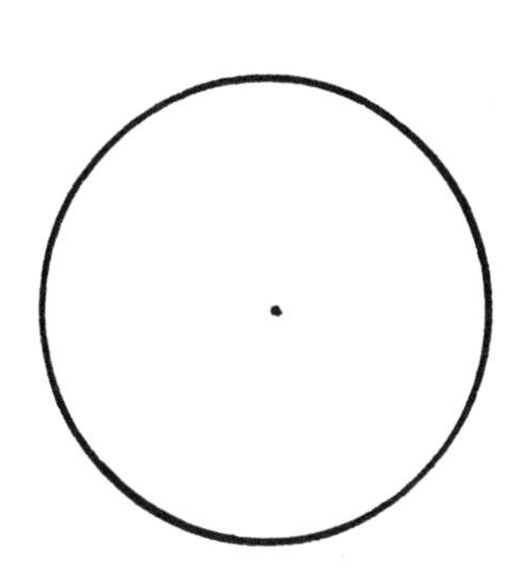

Small cookie

Answers: (cont.)

6. a. Pupils' drawings.

   b. The second cookie.

7. $\frac{1}{8}$ of the large cookie.

SQUARE PIZZAS

Some pizzas are square. Smaller pictures of three different sizes are given below.

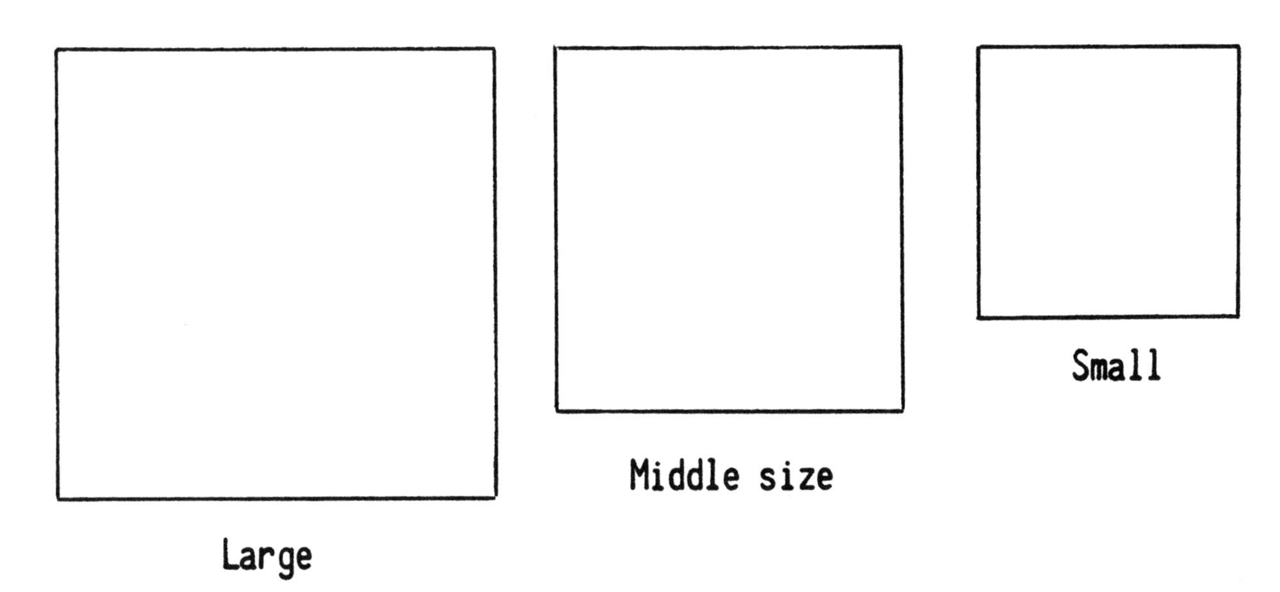

1. Show how to cut each pizza in half.

2. Use the drawings below. Show how to cut each pizza in fourths.

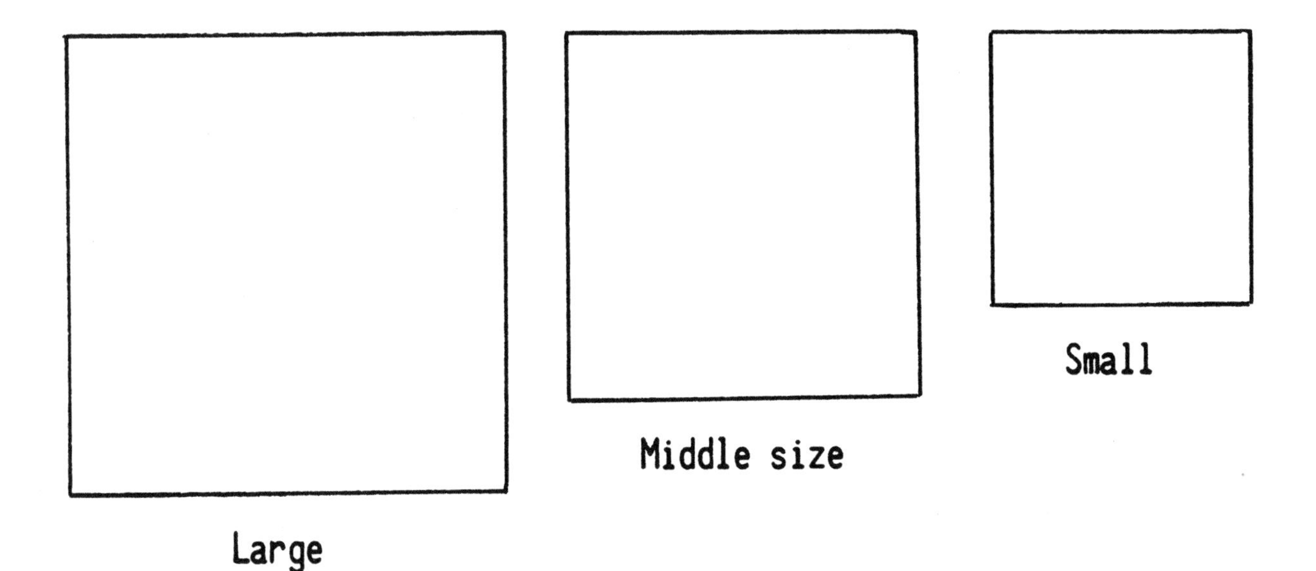

3. Sometimes $\frac{1}{2}$ is smaller than $\frac{1}{4}$. Show how this is possible.

Square Pizzas

Mathematics teaching objectives:

. Compare fractional parts when unit squares of different sizes are giv

. Draw the whole square when a fractional part of it is given.

Problem-solving skills pupils <u>might</u> use:

. Make and use a drawing.

. Make explanations based upon drawings.

Materials needed:

. Ruler

Comments and suggestions:

. Remind pupils that the sizes of fractional parts of a square unit depend upon the size of the unit.

. Use large demonstration models of square pizzas when comparing halves and fourths.

. Share with the class the various ways pupils divide a square in half.

Answers:

1. Pupils' drawings.

2. Pupils' drawings.

3. One-half of a small square can be greater than one-fourth of a large square.

4. Pupils' drawings.

5. The pizza in part (a). (Discuss with the class. Is this statement true? If a single cut is made, it always goes through the center of the square.)

6. Pupils drawings.

4. In each case a part of a square pizza is drawn. For each one, draw the whole pizza.

a. 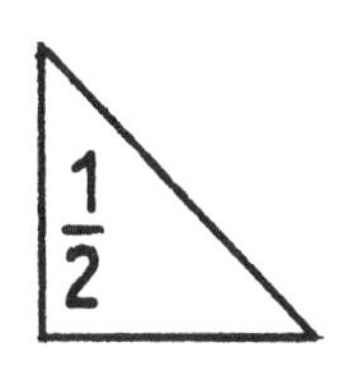

b. 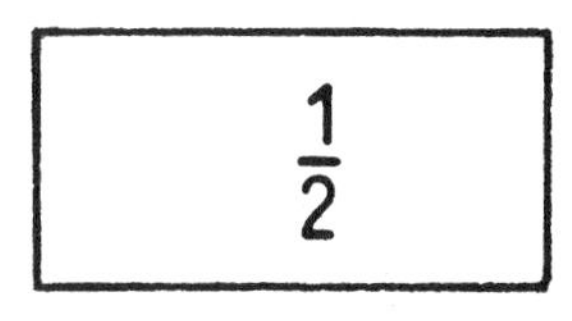

c. 

d. 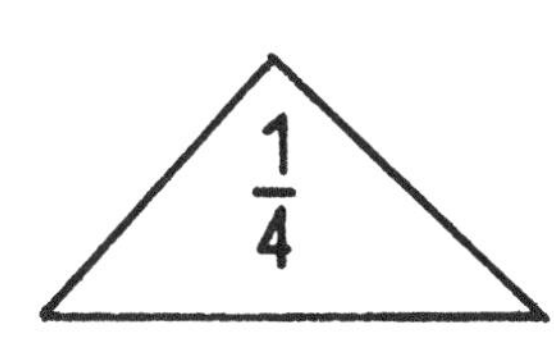

e. 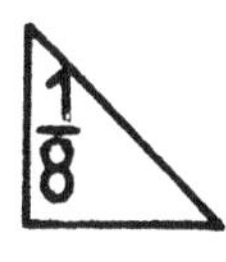

f. $\frac{1}{3}$

5. In problem 4, which of the whole squares is smallest?

6. The drawings show two different ways to divide a square in half. Make drawings to show other ways to divide a square in half. Use the back of the paper.

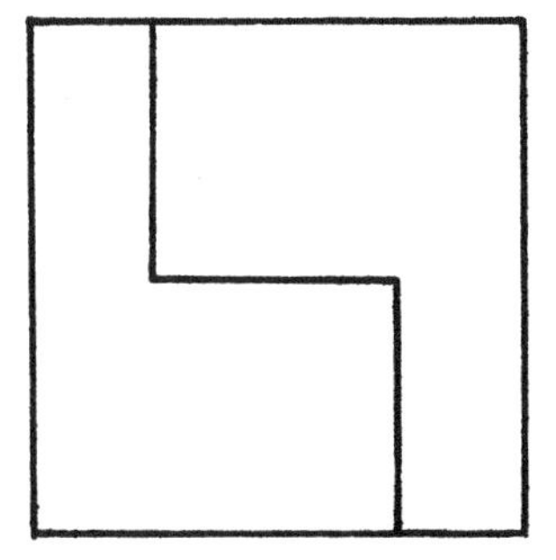

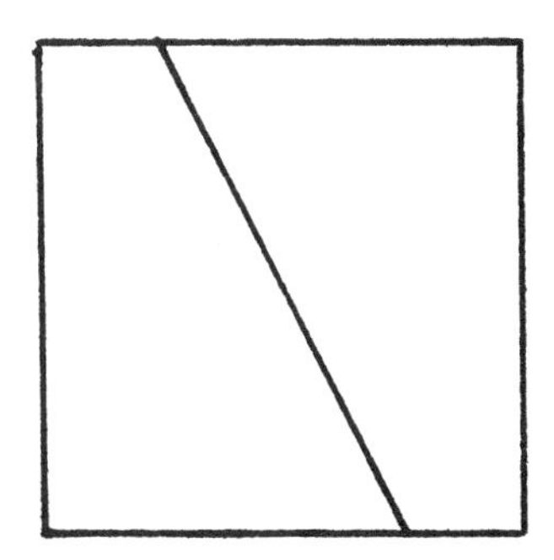

A PIECE OF CAKE

1. Pictures of three rectangular cakes are shown. Which would be larger:

   $\frac{1}{4}$ of the large cake?

   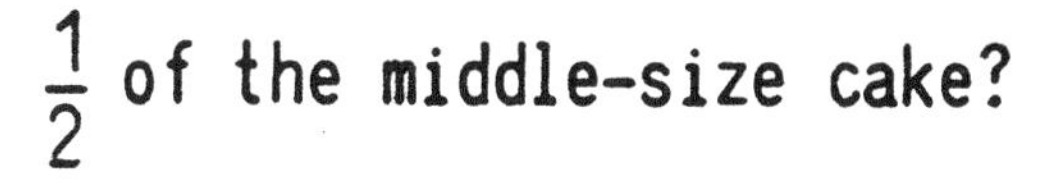

   $\frac{1}{2}$ of the middle-size cake?

   the entire small cake?

   Cut out the "cakes." Check your answer.

2. Small pictures of different size cakes are shown below. Show how to divide each of them in eighths? Which would be larger? Check your answers by cutting, tracing, or measuring.

a. $\frac{1}{4}$ of B or $\frac{1}{8}$ of D?

c. $\frac{7}{8}$ of A or $\frac{1}{2}$ of D?

b. all of A or $\frac{1}{2}$ of C?

d. $\frac{1}{4}$ of C or $\frac{1}{2}$ of B?

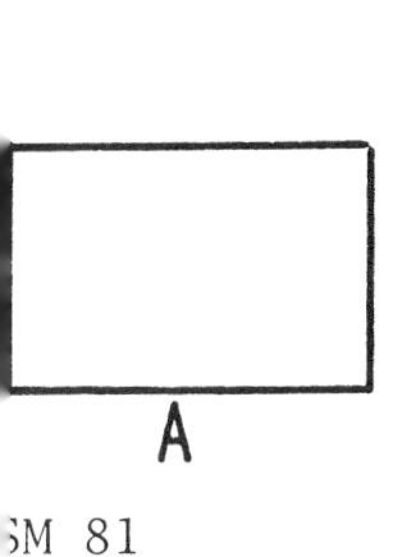

A

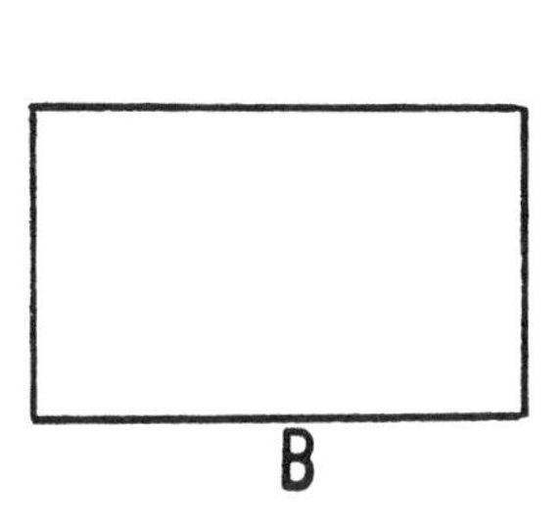

B

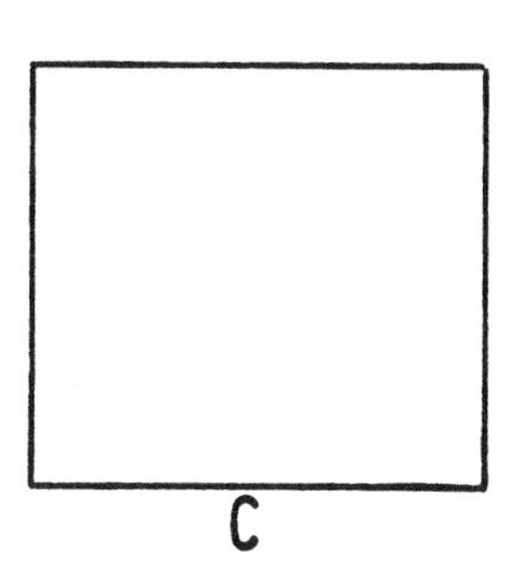

C

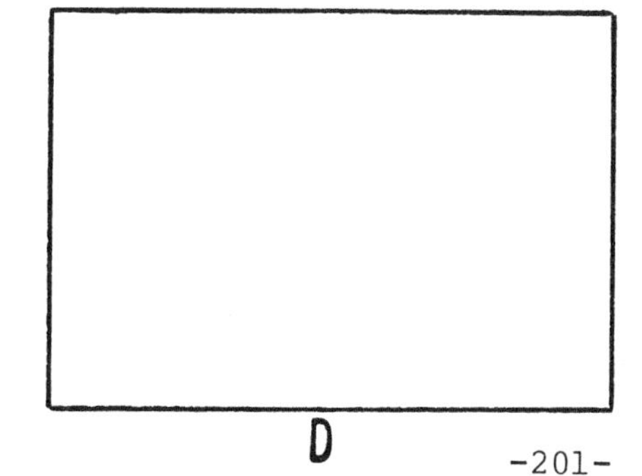

D

A Piece Of Cake

Mathematics teaching objectives:

- Compare fractional parts when unit rectangles of different sizes are given.
- Draw the whole rectangle when a fractional part of it is given.

Problem-solving skills pupils *might* use:

- Make and use a drawing.
- Guess and check.
- Make explanations based upon drawings.

Materials needed:

- Ruler
- Scissors

Comments and suggestions:

- Develop procedures through class discussion for working problems 1 and 2.
- Use large demonstration models for comparing halves and fourths.
- Direct the discussion to help pupils "discover" in problem 3 that the unit can be a rectangle of different shapes. This was not true when the unit was a circular or square region.

Answers:

1. $\frac{1}{2}$ of middle-size cake.

2. a. $\frac{1}{8}$ of D

   b. $\frac{1}{2}$ of C

   c. $\frac{1}{2}$ of D

   d. $\frac{1}{2}$ of B

Piece Of Cake (cont.)

. In each case, a part of a rectangular cake is shown. For each one, draw the whole cake.

a. $\frac{1}{2}$

b. $\frac{1}{2}$

c. $\frac{1}{4}$

d. $\frac{1}{4}$

e. $\frac{1}{3}$

f. $\frac{1}{5}$

g. $\frac{1}{8}$

h. $\frac{3}{4}$

. In problem 3, which whole cake is larger? Describe how you could "prove" your answer.

. One-third of a cake is "left over" from a party.

$\frac{1}{3}$ of a cake

a. Show how to divide this in half.

b. Make an outline of the whole cake.

c. What part of the cake would half of the "left over" be?

. Three boys want to share two cakes.

a. Show how to divide the two cakes into three equal parts.

b. About how much of a cake would each boy get?

1 cake	1 cake

Answers: (cont.)

3. Pupils drawings. (Have pupils compare their drawings with a a partner.

4. The cake in part (d). Compare the drawings of the whole cakes.

5. a. and b. Pupils drawing. Have pupils compare their drawing wit a class member.

   b. $\frac{1}{6}$

6. a. Pupils' drawing.

   b. $\frac{2}{3}$

Grade 4

VI. TWO-DIGIT MULTIPLICATION

VI. TWO-DIGIT MULTIPLICATION

One important topic of fourth-grade mathematics is two-digit multipli-
ation. Usually, much work is done with learning and practicing this
lgorithm. The algorithm should be more meaningful if pupils have "seen"
wo-digit multiplication with a model.

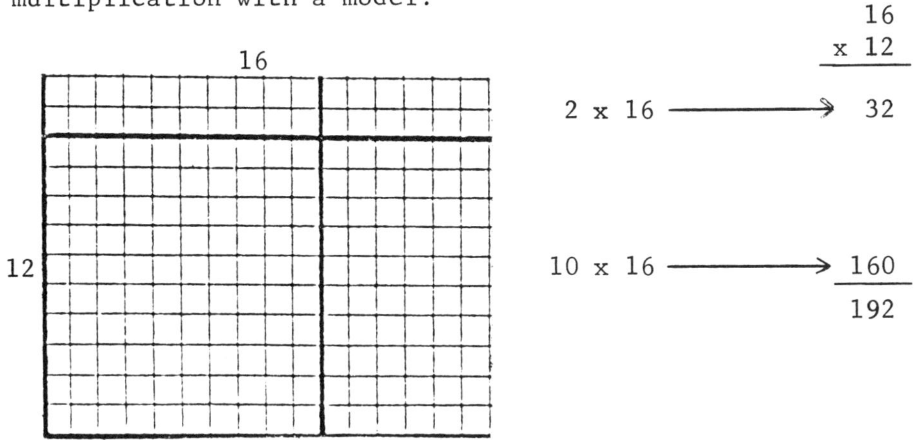

The instructional development for teaching the multiplication algorithm begins
ith a concrete phase--finding products by drawing rectangles on special
rid paper. The problem-solving aspect in this section is concentrated
argely in the lessons for this instructional phase. These lessons are
ased upon the model used in the <u>Multiplication And Division Concepts And
ectangles</u> section (see pages 115 -164). It is assumed that pupils al-
eady have some skill in using algorithms based upon a place value model
or multiplying by a single-digit and by two-digit multiples of ten.
owever these skills are reviewed using the rectangle model. This latter
odel then serves as a vehicle for developing two-digit multiplication.

In the second instructional phase pupils are directed to develop
fficient procedures for counting the small squares in a rectangle in
ayers and blocks involving multiples of ten. The written record for
hese procedures results in the multiplication algorithm. During this
hase the commutative and associative properties for multiplication and
he distributive property are used implicitly in non-verbal and subtle
ays. For example, pupils are encouraged to think of 3 x 16 or $\begin{array}{r} 16 \\ \times\ 3 \\ \hline \end{array}$ as
sixteens or as 16 threes. Such flexibility should help

those pupils who seem to find it easier to change interpretations in the "middle of the stream." For example, in $\begin{array}{r} 23 \\ \times\ 17 \\ \hline \end{array}$ pupils might find it more natural to think of the first partial product as 7 twenty-threes and for the second partial product as 23 tens.

The final instructional phase involves drill and practice with the algorithm The final lessons in this section make a start on this phase. Supplementary exercises from the class text or other sources will be needed to provide additional practice. For additional comments see page 250.

Story problems are scattered throughout the section. Emphasis is placed upon translating situations into mathematical expressions and also upon inventing story problems to match given mathematical expressions. However, pupils will need more practice with such problems. Most current mathematics texts are a good source for such problems.

The section was designed to be used in sequence. Some supplementary activities will be needed but you will want to check to be certain they are developmentally consistent with the presentation given here.

The instructional development given here was adapted from:

Robert W. Wirtz, DRILL AND PRACTICE AT THE PROBLEM-SOLVING LEVEL. Curriculum Development Associates, 1973.

A supply of squared paper with a special grid will need to be duplicated for this section. (See page 211.)

The outline of lessons for this section along with a few notes follows:

ecommended ays On he Lesson		page
1	"Written Records" - a first step toward using the multiplication algorithm.	243
1	"Multiplication Without A Drawing" - a second step toward using the algorithm.	247
1	"Sum Of Two Smaller Products" - practice using the algorithm.	249
1	"Story Problem"	253
12		

SQUARED PAPER MASTER 2

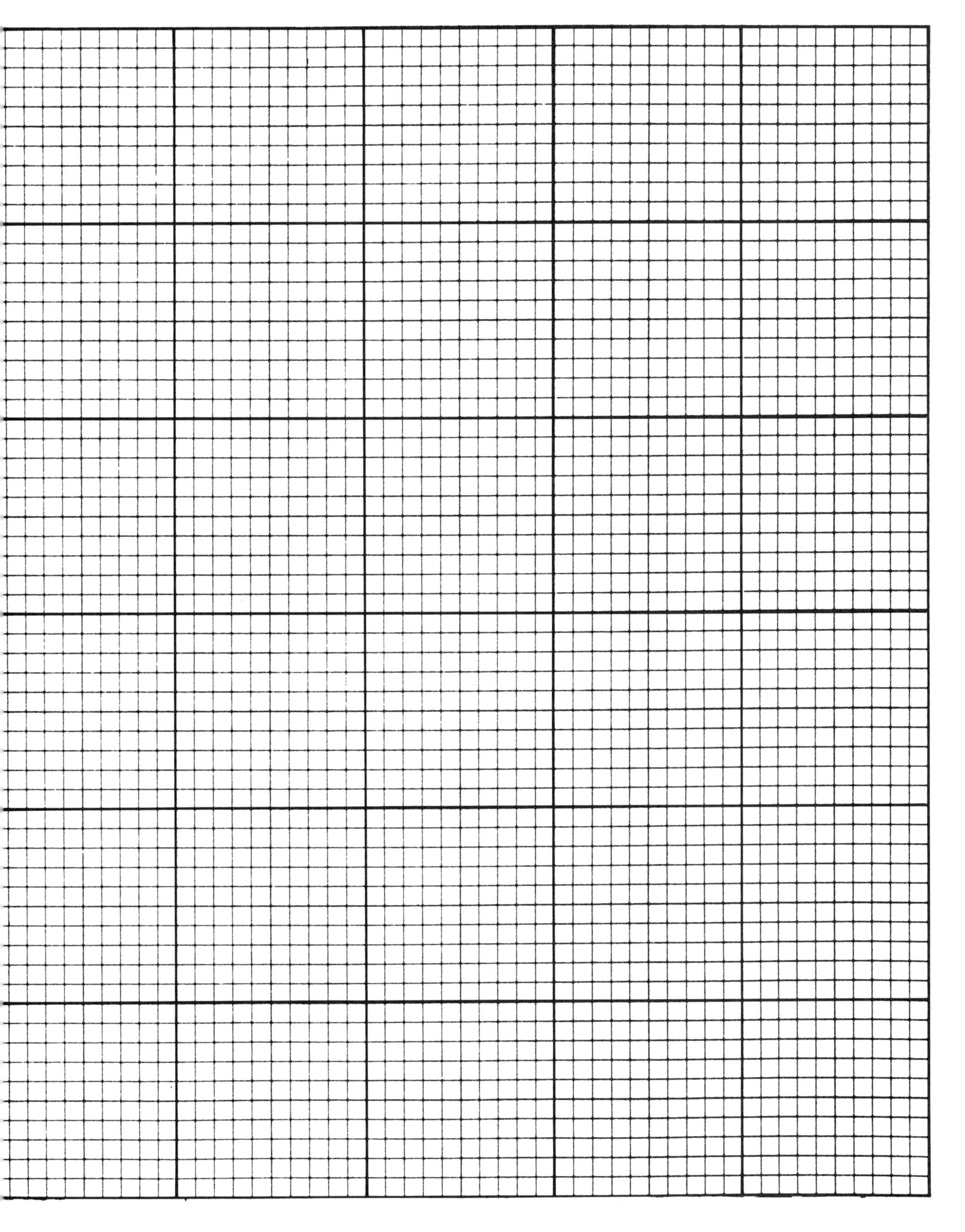

HOW MANY SMALL SQUARES?

1. How many small squares are inside each rectangle below? Record your answer below.

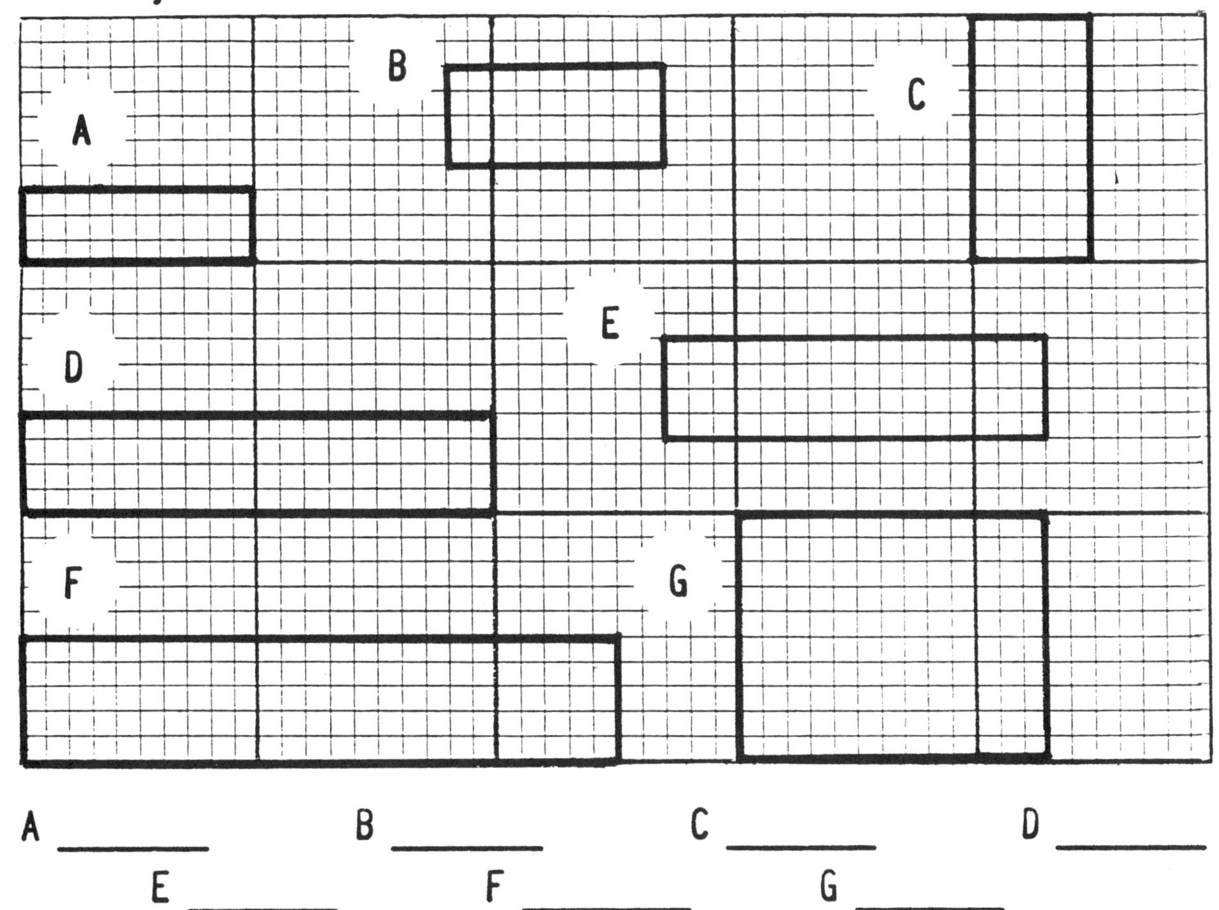

A ________ B ________ C ________ D ________

E ________ F ________ G ________

Which were easiest to find? Why?

2. Use a sheet of special squared paper. Make the rectangles needed to complete the chart below.

	Dimensions of the Rectangle	Number of Small Squares Inside
a.	4 by 10	
b.	7 by 10	
c.	7 by 30	
d.	10 by 10	
e.	12 by 10	
f.	10 by 12	
g.	30 by 4	

Which rectangle was the easiest to make? Why?

How Many Small Squares?

Mathematics teaching objectives:

. Use rectangles to give meaning to multiplication by 10.

. Practice multiplying by 10.

Problem-solving skills pupils _might_ use:

. Make and use a drawing.

. Break a problem into manageable parts.

. Describe situations using mathematical expressions and vice versa.

. Generalize from examples.

Materials needed:

. A supply of special squared paper (see pupil page 211)

. A transparent copy of pupil page 213 for use on the overhead

Comments and suggestions:

. Spend two days on this lesson. Work problems 1-3 the first day.

. Discuss this special squared paper with the class. Pupils should notice that the little squares come in 10 by 10 blocks or batches. In each of these blocks there are 100 small squares.

. Let pupils work on problem 1 independently and then discuss how the heavy lines help in getting some answers rather quickly.

. Have pupils complete problem 2. Some pupils may need a review of the expression, _number sentence_, for problem 3.

. Start the second days work by discussing the word _product_. The term will be used throughout this section.

. Help pupils get started with problem 4. Notice the different placement of 10 in parts (a)-(d). See the comments with the answers on page 216.

. Let pupils work independently with the remaining problems. If pupils have difficulties with problems 5 and 6 you may need to provide additional work with multiplication where one of the numbers is 10 or 100.

. Pupils need practice going back and forth from the problem situation to the mathematical expression. More of this will be done throughout this section.

(Answers are given on next page...)

3. Look at problem 1. This number sentence $3 \times 10 = \square$ is for Rectangle A. It tells how to find the number of small squares in the rectangle. Other ways to show this are

   $10 \times 3 = \square$ $\quad$ $\begin{array}{r} 10 \\ \times\ 3 \\ \hline \end{array}$ $\quad$ $\begin{array}{r} 3 \\ \times\ 10 \\ \hline \end{array}$

   Write how to find the number of small squares for

   a. Rectangle B ____________
   b. Rectangle C ____________
   c. Rectangle D ____________
   d. Rectangle E ____________
   e. Rectangle F ____________
   f. Rectangle G ____________

4. Use the special squared paper. Make rectangles for finding these answers. These answers are called <u>products</u>.

   a. $17 \times 10 = \square$
   b. $10 \times 23 = \square$
   c. $\begin{array}{r} 17 \\ \times\ 10 \\ \hline \end{array}$
   d. $\begin{array}{r} 10 \\ \times\ 23 \\ \hline \end{array}$
   e. Can rectangles be used to solve every multiplication problem? Explain.

5. Find these products. You may draw rectangles if you like.

   a. $18 \times 10 = \square$
   b. $24 \times 10 = \square$
   c. $10 \times 19 = \square$
   d. $\begin{array}{r} 32 \\ \times\ 10 \\ \hline \end{array}$
   e. $\begin{array}{r} 43 \\ \times\ 10 \\ \hline \end{array}$
   f. $\begin{array}{r} 10 \\ \times\ 52 \\ \hline \end{array}$
   g. $98 \times 10 = \square$
   h. $123 \times 10 = \square$
   i. $10 \times 239 = \square$
   j. $12 \times 100 = \square$
   k. $100 \times 27 = \square$

How Many Small Squares?

Answers:

1. a. 30 b. 36 c. 50 d. 80 e. 64

   f. 125 g. 130

   h. Probably pupils will say A, C and D are the easiest. One dimension of these rectangles is either 10 or 20. The heavy lines help you count by tens. However, accept all reasonable answers.

2. a. 40 b. 70 c. 210 d. 100 e. 120

   f. 120 g. 120

   Pupils will probably say the 10 by 10 rectangle is easiest to make because of the heavy grid lines.

3. Only one possible answer is given for each part.

   a. 4 x 9 = ☐

   b. 5 x 10 = ☐

   c. 20 x 4 = ☐

   d. 4 x 16 = ☐

   e. 25 x 5

   f. 10 x 13

4. a. 170 (plus drawing)

   b. 230 (plus drawing)

   c. 170 (plus drawing)

   d. 230 (plus drawing)

   e. Yes. The number of small squares in one layer of the rectangle multiplied by the number of layers is equal to the number of small squares inside the rectangle.

   Comment: Notice there are only two different rectangles. Review the idea that the dimensions of a rectangle may be stated in different orders; e.g. a 17 by 10 rectangle is the same as a 10 by 17 rectangle. Of course, this is also true for the answer of 10 x 17 and 17 x 10. (See page 125 in IV. Multiplication and Division Concepts and Rectangles.)

(Answers continued on the next page...

6. Describe a quick way for showing the products in Problem 5.

7. Tell how to do the problem. Write a number sentence <u>without</u> the answer.

   The dimensions of a rectangle are 32 by 46.
   How many small squares in the rectangle?

8. Write a rectangle story problem for 20 x 30 = ☐.

Answers: (cont.)

5. a. 180 d. 320 g. 980 j. 1200

   b. 240 e. 430 h. 1230 k. 2700

   c. 190 f. 520 i. 2390

   Comment: Generally, pupils interpret 18 x 10 as 18 tens and are quick to give the product 180. If the exercise is 10 x 18 they hesitate. To them ten eighteens is not as obvious as 180. Usually they switch t 18 tens before giving the product.

6. To multiply a number by 10, place a zero immediately to the right of the number.

7. 32 x 46 = ☐ or 46 x 32 = ☐

   Remind pupils they will learn how to find the answer to this problem before they finish this unit.

8. Answers will vary. The next lesson will show how the answer to the problem can be found by making a drawing.

LAYERS OF RECTANGLES

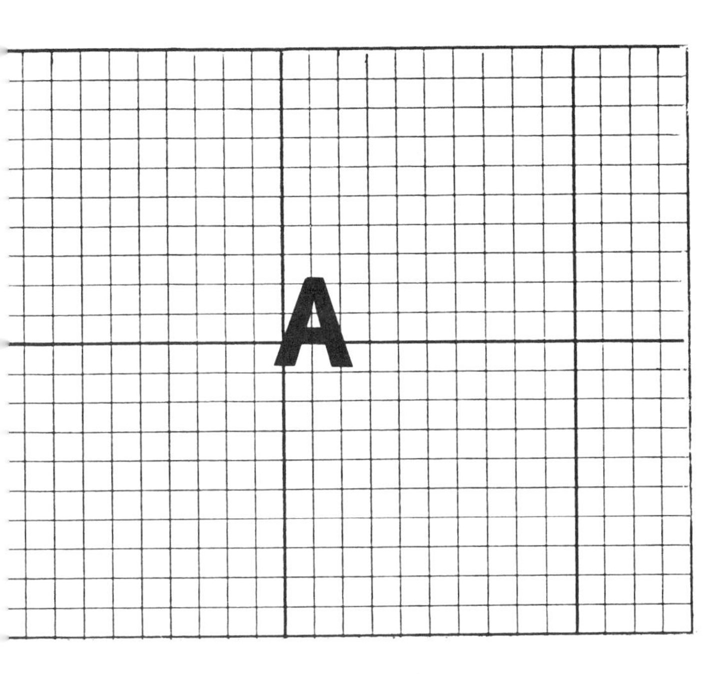

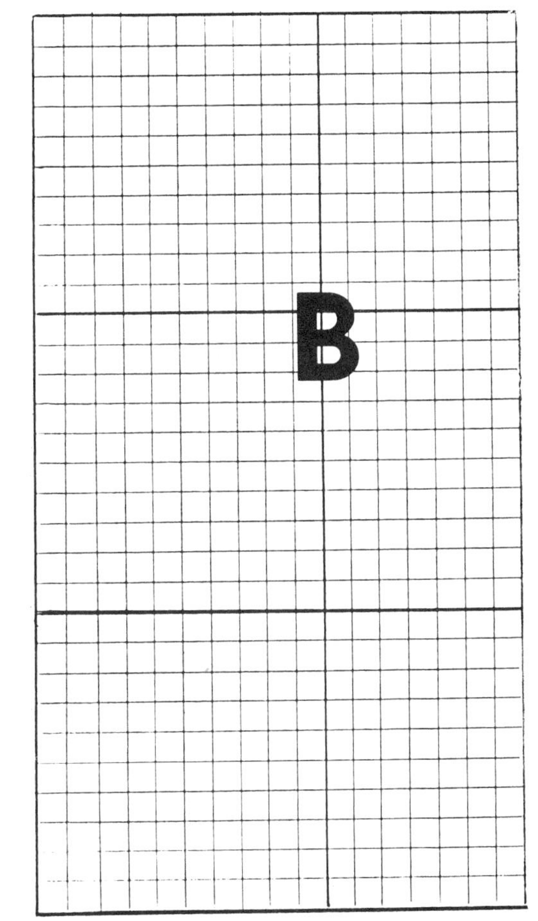

1. Rectangle A
   a. Dimensions? ____________
   b. Small Squares? __________

2. Rectangle B
   a. Dimensions? ____________
   b. Small Squares? __________

3. Which rectangle shows
   a. 20 x 24 ?
   b. $\begin{array}{r} 17 \\ \times 30 \\ \hline \end{array}$?
   c. 30 x 17 ?
   d. $\begin{array}{r} 24 \\ \times 20 \\ \hline \end{array}$?

4. Use special squared paper. Make a rectangle which shows
   a. $\begin{array}{r} 35 \\ \times 20 \\ \hline \end{array}$
   b. 30 x 20
   c. 20 x 36
   d. $\begin{array}{r} 26 \\ \times 30 \\ \hline \end{array}$

Layers Of Rectangles

Mathematics teaching objectives:

- Use rectangles to give meaning to multiplication by 10, 20, 30 . . .
- Use an algorithm for multiplying by 20, 30, 40 . . .
- Solve story problems.

Problem-solving skills pupils *might* use:

- Make and use a drawing.
- Break a problem into manageable parts.
- Invent problems for mathematical expressions.

Materials needed:

- A supply of special squared paper

Comments and suggestions:

- After pupils work several minutes independently, discuss with the class the method used in problem 5. Pupils may have their own ways to work the problem. Encourage them to compare their way with the method shown. Pupils may prefer multiplying by 2, then by 10. If so, this is an opportunity to discuss the property -

  All different orders for finding the product of the same three numbers result in the same final answer; e.g.

  $$5 \times 3 \times 2 = 30$$
  $$3 \times 2 \times 5 = 30$$
  $$5 \times 2 \times 3 = 30 \quad \text{etc.}$$

- Remind pupils that the multiplication problem suggested by a rectangle can be written in different ways; e.g. 3a and 3d. (Also see page 215.)
- Skill in multiplication by two-digit multiples of ten is needed in later lessons in this section.

Answers:

1. a. 20 by 24
   b. 480
2. a. 30 by 17
   b. 510
3. a. A
   b. B
   c. B
   d. A
4. a. 35 by 20 rectangle (drawing)
   b. 30 by 20 rectangle (drawing)
   c. 20 by 36 rectangle (drawing)
   d. 26 by 30 rectangle (drawing)

(Answers continued on the next page...)

5. Use the rectangles you made to show how:

   a. $\begin{array}{r} 35 \\ \times\ 20 \\ \hline \end{array}$ means $\begin{array}{r} 35 \\ \times\ 10 \\ \hline 350 \end{array}$ → $\begin{array}{r} 350 \\ \times\quad 2 \\ \hline 700 \end{array}$

   b. $\begin{array}{r} 20 \\ \times\ 30 \\ \hline \end{array}$ means $\begin{array}{r} 20 \\ \times\ 10 \\ \hline 200 \end{array}$ → $\begin{array}{r} 200 \\ \times\quad 3 \\ \hline 600 \end{array}$

6. Use the rectangles you made to explain:

   a. $\begin{array}{r} 36 \\ \times\ 20 \\ \hline \end{array}$ b. $\begin{array}{r} 26 \\ \times\ 30 \\ \hline \end{array}$

7. Find these products. Use your own way.

   a. $\begin{array}{r} 34 \\ \times\ 30 \\ \hline \end{array}$ b. 40 x 46 c. $\begin{array}{r} 73 \\ \times\ 50 \\ \hline \end{array}$ d. $\begin{array}{r} 42 \\ \times\ 40 \\ \hline \end{array}$

   e. 70 x 38 f. $\begin{array}{r} 84 \\ \times\ 80 \\ \hline \end{array}$ g. 26 x 60 h. $\begin{array}{r} 30 \\ \times\ 47 \\ \hline \end{array}$

8. Write the number sentence and then solve these story problems.

   a. Kay's school has 14 softball teams. Each team has 20 players. How many players are there in all?

   b. In the teachers' lunchroom there are 2 tables. One table seats 30 teachers and the other seats 16 teachers. How many teachers can be seated at the same time?

   c. Phillip charges 75¢ an hour to rake lawns. Last fall he worked 40 hours. How much money did he make?

Answers: (cont.)

5. Possible explanations:

   a. Each layer has 35 x 10 or 350 small squares. There are 2 layers. Therefore, 2 x 350 or 700 squares altogether.

   b. Each layer has 20 x 10 or 200 small squares. There are 3 layers. Therefore, 3 x 200 or 600 squares.

6. Possible explanations:

   a. Each layer has 36 x 10 or 360 small squares. There are 2 layers. Therefore, 2 x 360 or 720 squares.

   b. Each layer has 26 x 10 or 260 small squares. There are 3 layers. Therefore, 3 x 260 or 780 squares.

7. a. 1020   b. 1840   c. 3650   d. 1680

   e. 2660   f. 6720   g. 1560   h.* 1410

   * first rewrite the problem as → $\begin{array}{r} 47 \\ \underline{\times\ 30} \end{array}$

   If more practice is needed, select similar exercises from the adopted text.

8. a. 14 x 20 = ☐

   280 players

   b. 30 + 16 = ☐

   46 teachers

   c. 75¢ x 40 = ☐

   3000 or $30

THREE DIFFERENT WAYS

1.

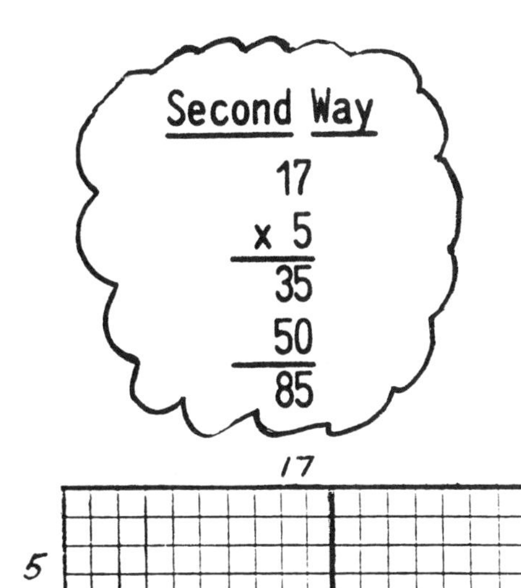

A Third Way

This rectangle shows that

5 x ____ = ____.

2. Use the special squared paper below. Solve these multiplication problems.

a. 3 x 17 = ____

b. 14 x 7 = ____

c. 3 x 23 = ____

d. 18 x 6

e. 26 x 3

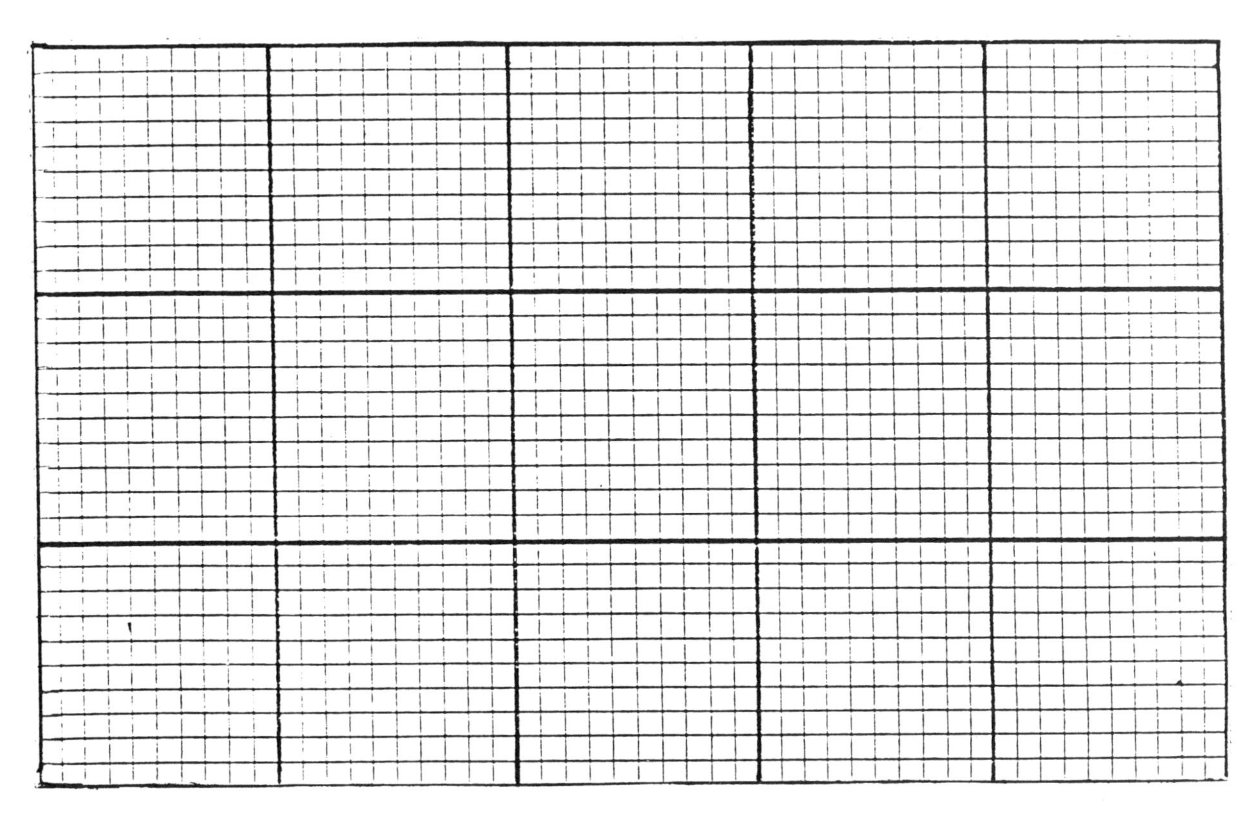

3. Use the "third way" to explain why the "second way" works.

Three Different Ways

Mathematics teaching objectives:

- Give an extended meaning for multiplying a two-digit number by a one-digit number.
- Provide readiness activities for area.
- Practice multiplying a two- or three-digit number by a single-digit number.

Problem-solving skills pupils might use:

- Make and use a drawing.
- Break a problem into manageable parts.
- Make evaluations.
- Invent problems for mathematical expressions and vice versa.

Materials needed:

- None

Comments and suggestions:

- Spend two days on this lesson. Work problems 1-6 the first day.
- Discuss problem 1. Let students work independently (individually or in pairs) on the problems in part two.
- Discuss problem 3 (see answers). Point out that pupils don't have to draw the rectangles for problem 4, just think and decide which are possible.
- Work problems 7-11 the second day. Emphasize that writing a number sentence does not mean find the answer. Pupils will not know how to get some of the answers. This is something they have yet to learn.

Answers:

1. 5 x 17 = 85

2. a. 51
   b. 98 d. 108 e. 78
   c. 69

3. Answers will vary. However discussion should center on questions like these -

   What are the dimensions of the rectangle on one side of the heavy vertical line?

   How many small squares are in this rectangle? Locate that number in the Second Way.

   What are the dimensions of the rectangle on the other side? etc.

4. Circle the problems below you could do on the squared paper.

a. 24 x 3

b. 66 x 5

c. 56 x 9

d. 34 x 9

e. $\begin{array}{r} 73 \\ \times\ 4 \\ \hline \end{array}$

f. $\begin{array}{r} 53 \\ \times\ 8 \\ \hline \end{array}$

g. $\begin{array}{r} 60 \\ \times\ 9 \\ \hline \end{array}$

h. $\begin{array}{r} 67 \\ \times\ 5 \\ \hline \end{array}$

5. Which of the problems above would take the.most squared paper?

6. Work all the examples in Problem 4. Use the first way shown in Exercise 1.

7. Tell how to find the number of small squares in these rectangles. Write a number sentence.

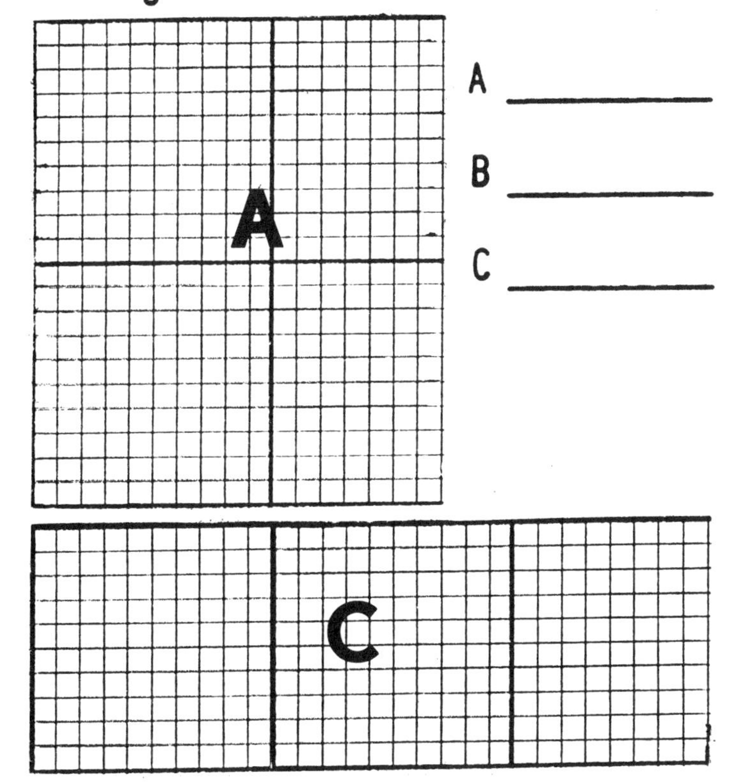

A __________

B __________

C __________

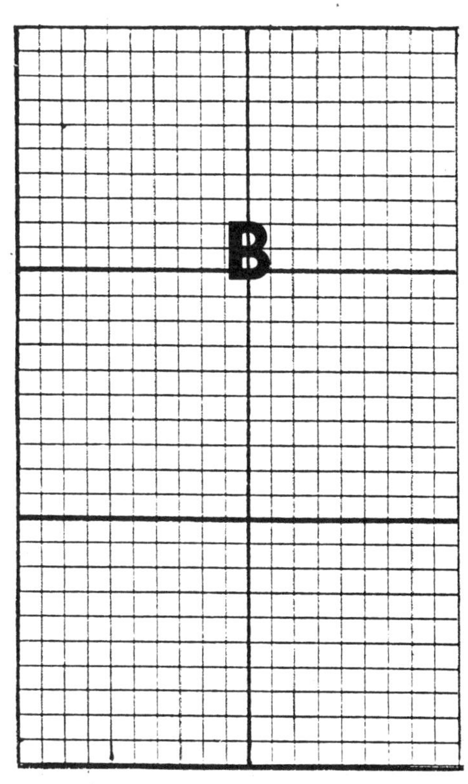

D. The dimensions of a rectangle are 27 by 32. __________

E. The dimensions of a rectangle are 235 by 317. __________

Answers: (cont.)

4. These problems should be circled.

   a. 24 x 3 c. 34 x 9

   (Pupils may have valid reasons for not circling them; there's no room on the squared paper without overlapping, etc.)

5. $\begin{array}{r} 60 \\ \times\ 9 \\ \hline \end{array}$ (Again, listen to pupil reasons for other answers.)

6. a. 72 e. 292

   b. 330 f. 424

   c. 504 g. 540

   d. 306 h. 335

7. A 17 x 20 = ☐ D 27 x 32 = ☐

   B 30 x 19 = ☐ E 235 x 317 = ☐

   C 10 x 18 = ☐

8. Answers will vary. Here are some examples:

   a. The dimensions of a rectangle are 14 by 27. How many small squares in the rectangle?

   b. The dimensions of a rectangle are 22 by 17. How many small squares in the rectangle?

9. a. 25 x 75¢ = ☐

   b. $2.39 – $1.45 = ☐

   Notice:
   A subtraction problem was included for the purpose of variety!

10. a. 2450 d. 4980 g. 2940

    b. 4320 e. 3160 h. 1440 j. 1980

    c. 3710 f. 2560 i. 4690

    (If you think more practice is needed, select suitable exercises from the class textbook.)

11. a. 490 squares long

    b. At least 9 sheets would be needed if they were glued together the "long" way.

    At least 10 sheets if they were glued together the "short" way.

8. Write a "rectangle" story problem for

   a. 14 x 27 =

   b. $\begin{array}{r} 17 \\ \times 22 \\ \hline \end{array}$

9. Write a number sentence to tell how to do these. Do not solve them.

   a. A dozen donut holes cost 75¢. How much will 25 dozen cost?

   b. Donuts cost $2.39 per dozen. Cookies cost $1.45 per dozen. How much more per dozen do donuts cost than cookies?

10. Work these. Use the first way shown on the first page of this lesson.

a.	b.	c.	d.	e.
$\begin{array}{r} 490 \\ \times 5 \\ \hline \end{array}$	$\begin{array}{r} 480 \\ \times 9 \\ \hline \end{array}$	$\begin{array}{r} 530 \\ \times 7 \\ \hline \end{array}$	$\begin{array}{r} 830 \\ \times 6 \\ \hline \end{array}$	$\begin{array}{r} 790 \\ \times 4 \\ \hline \end{array}$

f.	g.	h.	i.	j.
$\begin{array}{r} 320 \\ \times 8 \\ \hline \end{array}$	$\begin{array}{r} 980 \\ \times 3 \\ \hline \end{array}$	$\begin{array}{r} 160 \\ \times 9 \\ \hline \end{array}$	$\begin{array}{r} 670 \\ \times 7 \\ \hline \end{array}$	$\begin{array}{r} 990 \\ \times 2 \\ \hline \end{array}$

11. Suppose you were asked to solve 10-a by drawing a rectangle.

    a. How long would that rectangle be?

    b. How many sheets of special squared paper would be needed?

RECTANGLES

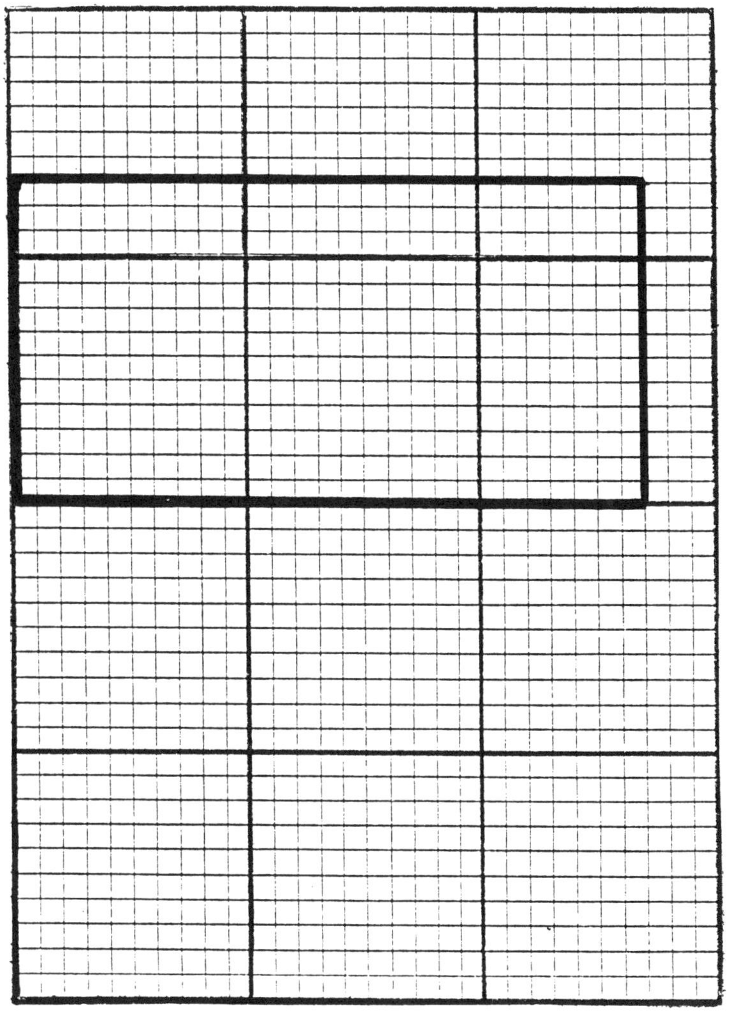

1. Kirby marked this rectangle on special squared paper.

   How many small squares does the rectangle fence in?

   Find out.

   Record. ________

2. Discuss and compare answers.

   Is it necessary to count the squares one by one?

   Did anyone use a "short-cut" instead of counting?

   Do the heavy lines on the special squared paper help in any way?

3. Use special squared paper.

   a. Draw a 12 by 16 rectangle. How many squares inside? ______
      What is the product of 12 and 16? ________

   b. Draw a 16 by 25 rectangle. How many squares inside? _______
      What is the product of 16 and 25? ______

   c. Draw a 21 by 13 rectangle. How many squares inside? ______
      What is the product of 21 and 13? ______

   d. Draw a 19 by 18 rectangle. How many squares inside? _______
      What is the product of 19 and 18? _______

Rectangles

Mathematics teaching objectives:

. Find the number of unit squares in a rectangle with two-digit dimensions.

Problem-solving skills pupils <u>might</u> use:

. Make and use a drawing.

. Break a problem into manageable parts.

Materials needed:

. A supply of special squared paper (see pupil page 211)

Comments and suggestions:

. Let pupils find the number of squares in problem 1 independently, then compare the answers. What methods did pupils use? Discuss the questions.

. Let pupils work the remainder of the sheet as seatwork. Allow pupils to compare their drawings and results with classmates. Pupils may find it easier to count squares if the outline of the rectangle is made with crayon.

. If pupils need more practice, try these on special squared paper: 14 by 23 rectangle; 28 by 23 rectangle.

. Suggest pupils put the "tens" at the bottom and the "units" at the top of the rectangle.

Answers:

1. 351 unit squares in the 13 by 27 rectangle.

2. The discussion should reveal that counting by tens and hundreds is much quicker than counting the unit squares one by one. Remind pupils that the purpose of the remaining lessons is to find short-cuts for counting squares in rectangles.

3. a. 12 by 16 rectangle - 192 small squares

   b. 16 by 25 rectangle - 400 small squares

   c. 21 by 13 rectangle - 273 small squares

   d. 19 by 18 rectangle - 342 small squares

TRY THIS

. Use the special squared paper below to solve this problem:

13 X 17 = _____

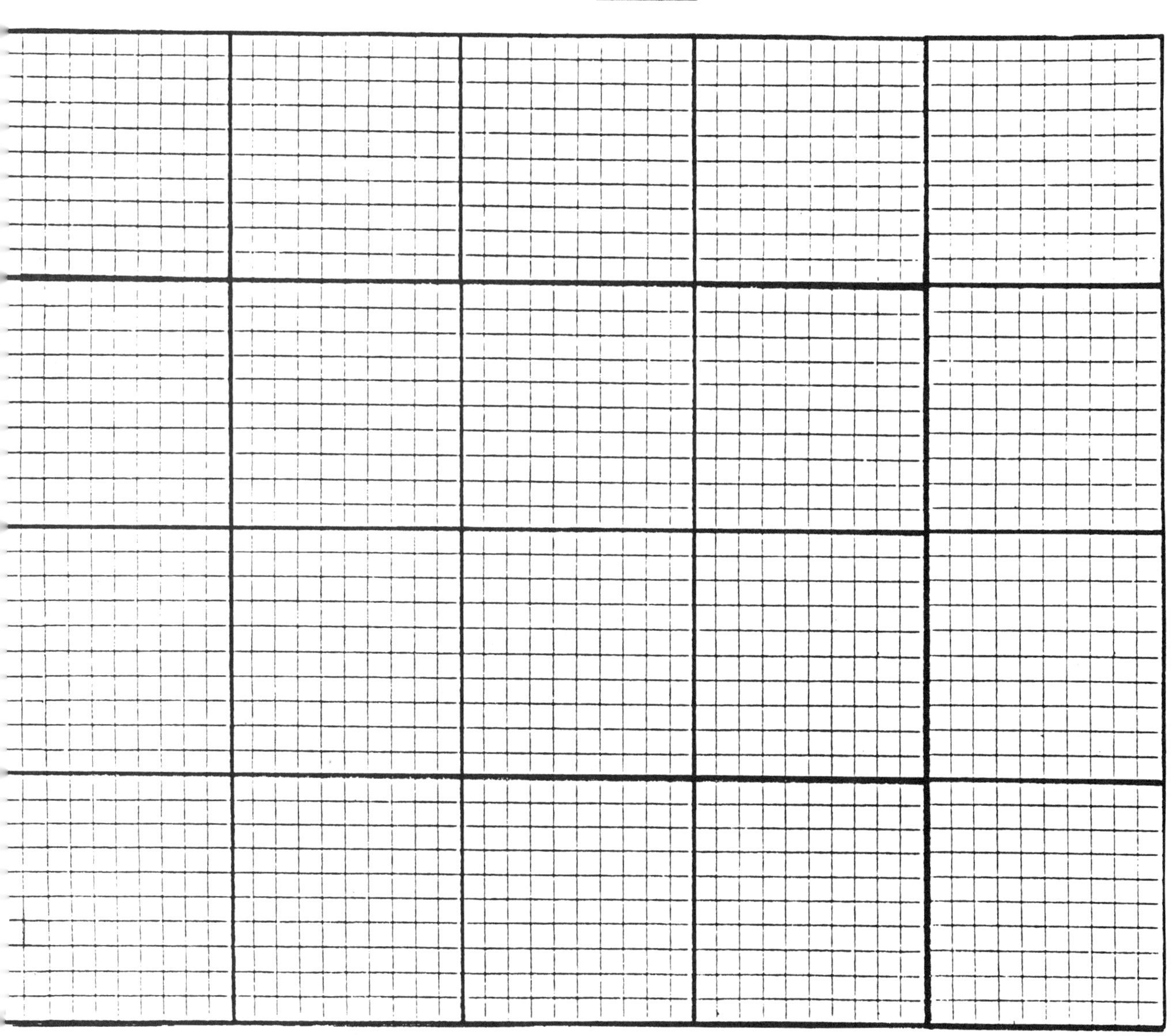

Discuss your results.

2. Try these: a. 16 x 23 = ____ b. 17 x 21 = ____

Try This

Mathematics teaching objective:

. Find the product of two-digit numbers by counting squares in a rectangle.

Problem-solving skills pupils might use:

. Make and use a drawing.

. Break a problem into manageable parts.

Materials needed:

. A supply of special squared paper (see pupil page 211)

Comments and suggestions:

. Pupils will be able to work the problems on page 231 without much initial instruction. By this time, a multiplication problem like 13 x 17 should suggest to them a 13 by 17 rectangle.

Note: The lessons so far have encouraged pupils to attach no special meaning to the order in which dimensions are given. For example, the first dimension in 25 by 14 may describe either dimension. The same has been true for the numbers in the indicated multiplication, 25 x 14. However in the next few lessons, a special meaning is given to each number because of its order. The first number is the height and the second the width. The special meaning helps teach the multiplication algorithm. Just as it is done in everyday usage, the terms length, height and width are used flexibly in the lessons in this section.

. Since page 233 is highly structured, pupils will be able to work it without much direct help. A closing discussion should include a comparison of answers and a discussion of any disagreements.

. As pupils continue with these lessons they will need to have developed skill in multiplying by a single-digit number. If pupils need more practice, select suitable exercises for them to do from the class text.

(Answers are given on the next page...)

Try This (cont.)

Study this rectangle.

3. What are its dimensions?
 14 by ____

How many squares does it enclose? ____

What multiplication problem does it show?
____ x ____ = ____

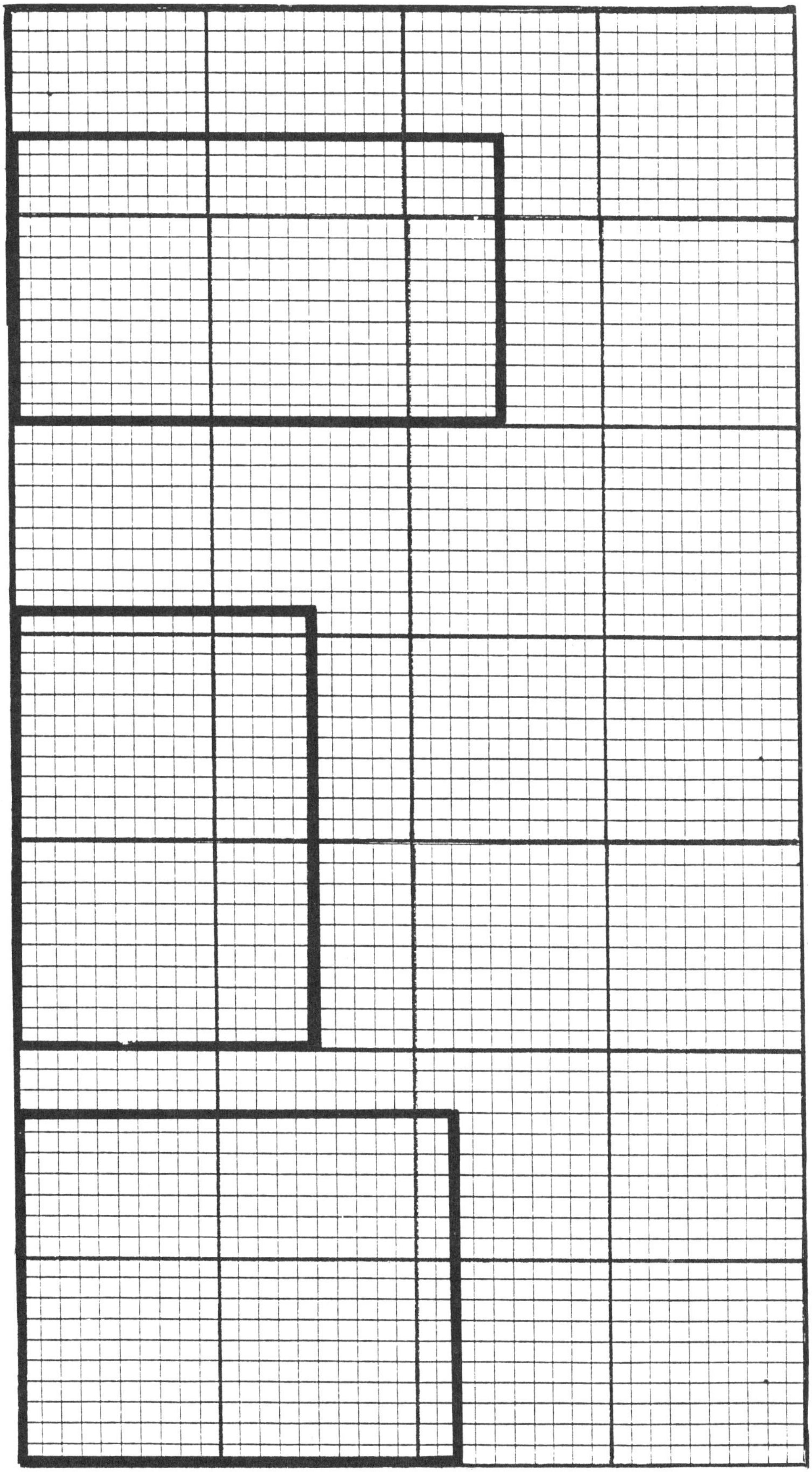

4. This rectangle is 21 by ____.
It shows that
____ x ____ = ____

5. This rectangle is ____ by ____.
It shows that
____ x ____ = ____

Try This

Answers:

1. $13 \times 17 = \underline{221}$ Drawings of appropriate rectangles should accompany each problem. Pupils can compare the way they made their rectangles.

2-a. $16 \times 23 = \underline{368}$

b. $17 \times 21 = \underline{357}$

3. 14 by 25 rectangle - 350 squares $14 \times 25 = 350$

4. 21 by 15 rectangle - 315 squares $21 \times 15 = 315$

5. 17 by 22 $17 \times 22 = 374$

BIG TIME MULTIPLICATION

Study this rectangle.

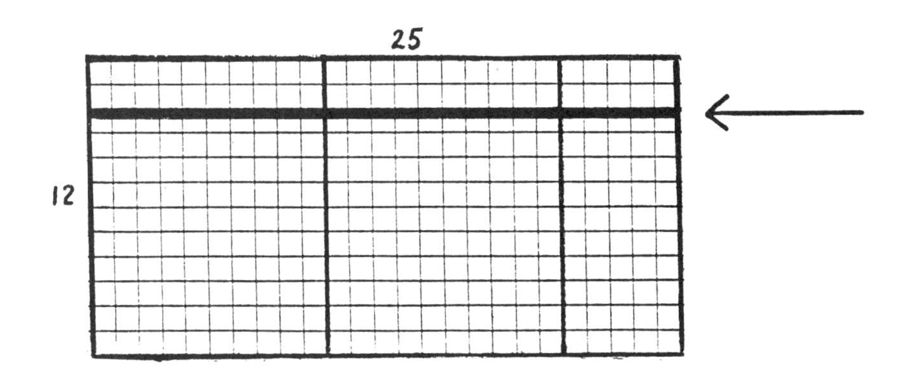

.a. Consider the part of the rectangle <u>above</u> the heavy line.

Its dimensions are 2 by ___ .

It shows that 2 x ___ = ___ .

b. Consider the part of the rectangle <u>below</u> the heavy line.

Its dimensions are 10 by ___ .

It shows that 10 x ___ = ___ .

c. How would you find the number of squares enclosed by the total rectangle?

What is the product of 12 and 25?

Big Time Multiplication

Mathematics teaching objective:

. Provide experience with a model for the multiplication algorithm for two-digit numbers.

Problem-solving skills pupils might use:

. Use a drawing.

. Break a problem into manageable parts.

Materials needed:

. Transparencies could be made for use at the overhead.

Comments and suggestions:

. The four pages provide meaning for the multiplication algorithm. Notice how the development on top of page 239 corresponds to This correspondence will be pointed out to pupils in the next activity.

$$\begin{array}{r} 26 \\ \underline{\times\ 14} \\ 104 \\ \underline{260} \\ 364 \end{array}$$

. You may want to make a transparency of page 235 and page 237 for discussion with the class. Most of the pupils should be able to do (b) on page 239 and all of problem 3 independently.

Answers:

1. a. Above the heavy line - a 2 by 25 rectangle: 2 x <u>25</u> = <u>50</u>

   b. Below the heavy line - a 10 by 25 rectangle; 10 x <u>25</u> = <u>250</u>

   c. Total number of small squares: 50 + 250 = 300

(Answers continued on next page ...)

. a. This large rectangle has dimensions of _____ by _____.

The part above the heavy line shows that

____ x ____ = ____.

The part below the heavy line shows that

10 x ____ = ____.

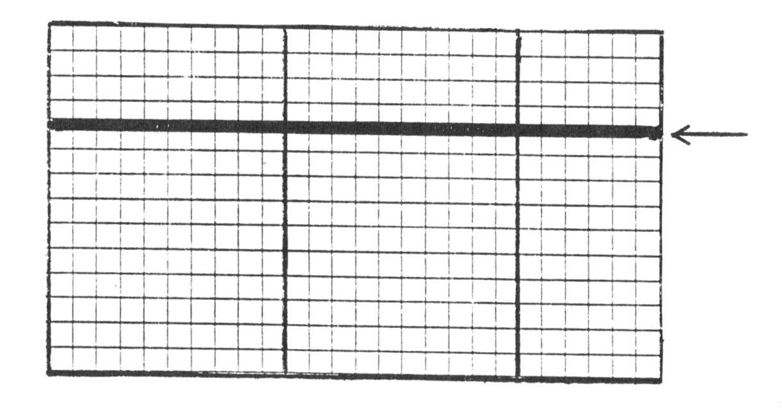

14 x 26 = __________

b. This large rectangle has dimensions of ____ by ____.

The part above the heavy line shows that

____ x ____ = ____.

The part below the heavy line shows that

____ x ____ = ____.

23 x ____ = ____.

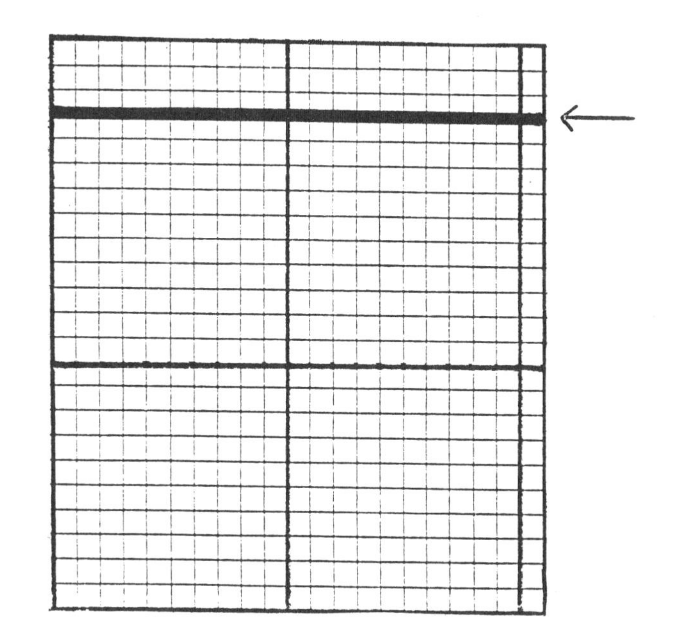

. Supply the missing information.

a.

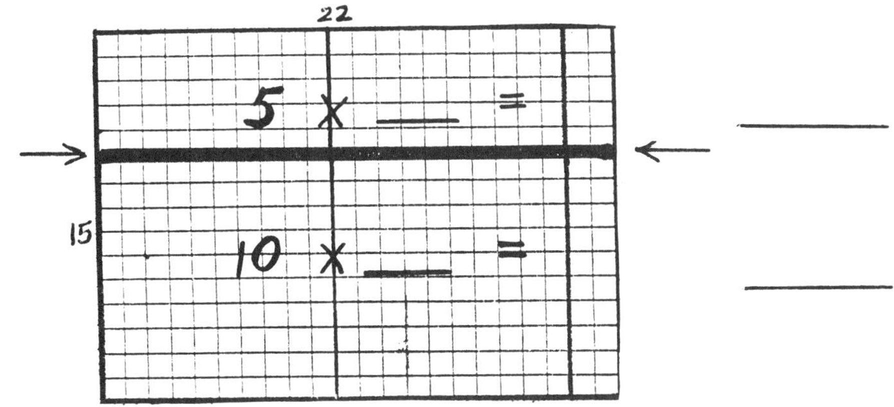

This rectangle shows that 15 x 22 =

Answers: (cont.)

2. a. Dimensions of large rectangle - 14 by 26

   Above line - 4 x 26 = 104

   Below line - 10 x 26 = 260

   Total - 14 x 26 = 364

   b. Dimensions of large rectangle - 23 x 21

   Above line - 3 x 21 = 63

   Below line - 20 x 21 = 420

   Total - 23 x 21 = 483

3. a. Above line - 5 x 22 = 110

   Below line - 10 x 22 = 220

   Total - 15 x 22 = 330

   b. Above line - 3 x 28 = 84

   Below line - 20 x 28 = 560

   Total - 23 x 28 = 644

   Point out that at least one of the two rectangles must have a height less than 10.

   c. 4 x 32 = 128

   10 x 32 = 320

   14 x 32 = 448

   d. 2 x 14 = 28

   30 x 14 = 420

   32 x 14 = 448

   e. The answers are the same. The two rectangles have the same dimensions. However, the record keeping is different. Point out that the numbers in a multiplication problem can be switched. Such switching should be made if the problem then becomes easier

   f. 6 x 24 = 144

   20 x 24 = 480

   26 x 24 = 624

b.

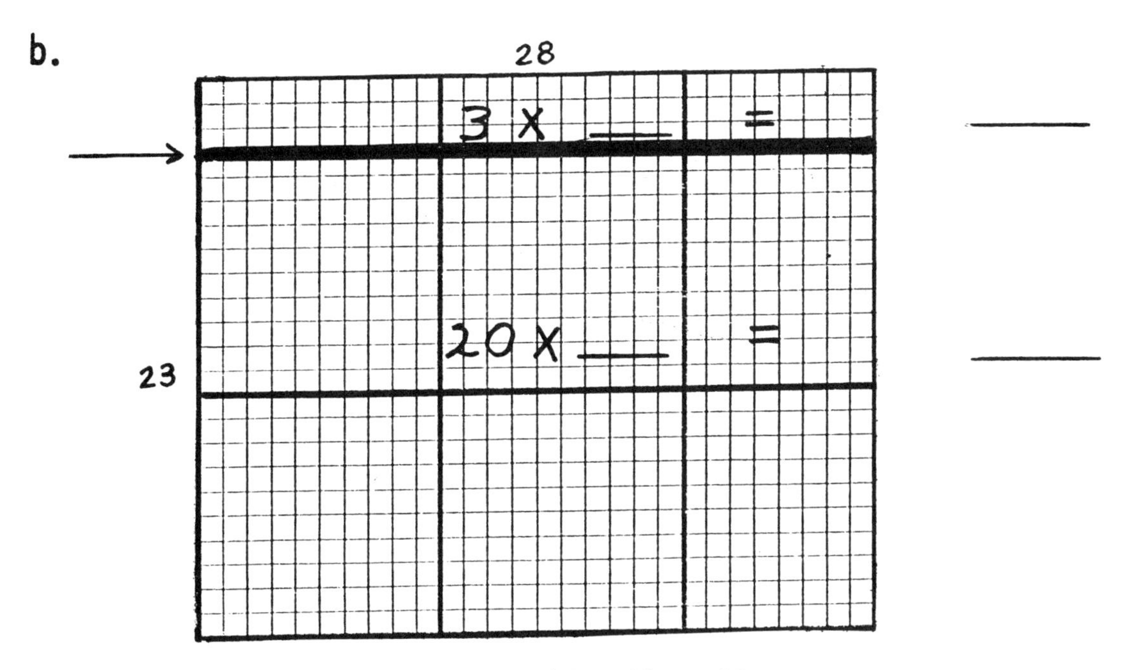

What is the product? 23 x 28 = ______

c.

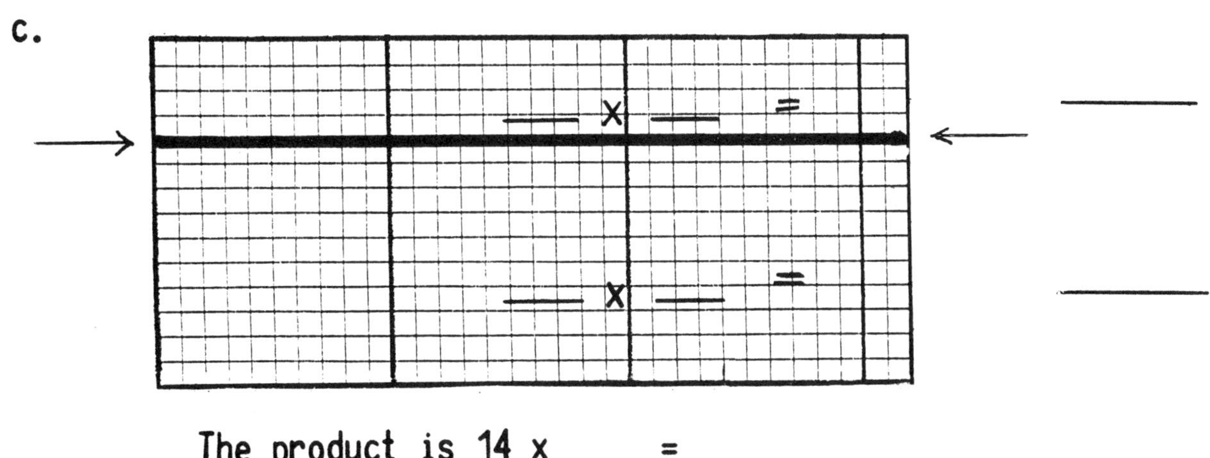

The product is 14 x ___ = ________

d.

___ x ___ = ___

___ x ___ = ___

The product is ___

32 x ___ =

e. Compare problems 3c and 3d. How are they alike? How are they different?

f.

___ x ___ = ___

___ x ___ = ___

The product is ___ x ___ = ___

1. The rectangle below shows this problem.

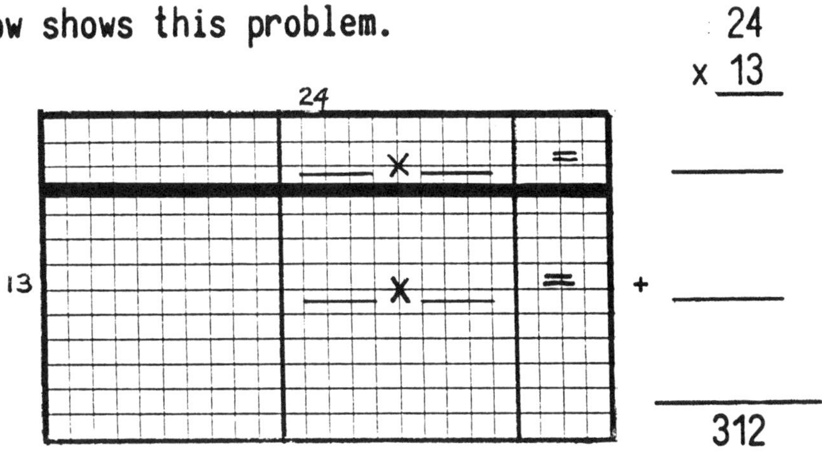

a. Fill in the blanks. Explain your work.

b. Find the product. Use the drawing below.

$$\begin{array}{r} 36 \\ \times\ 23 \\ \hline \end{array}$$

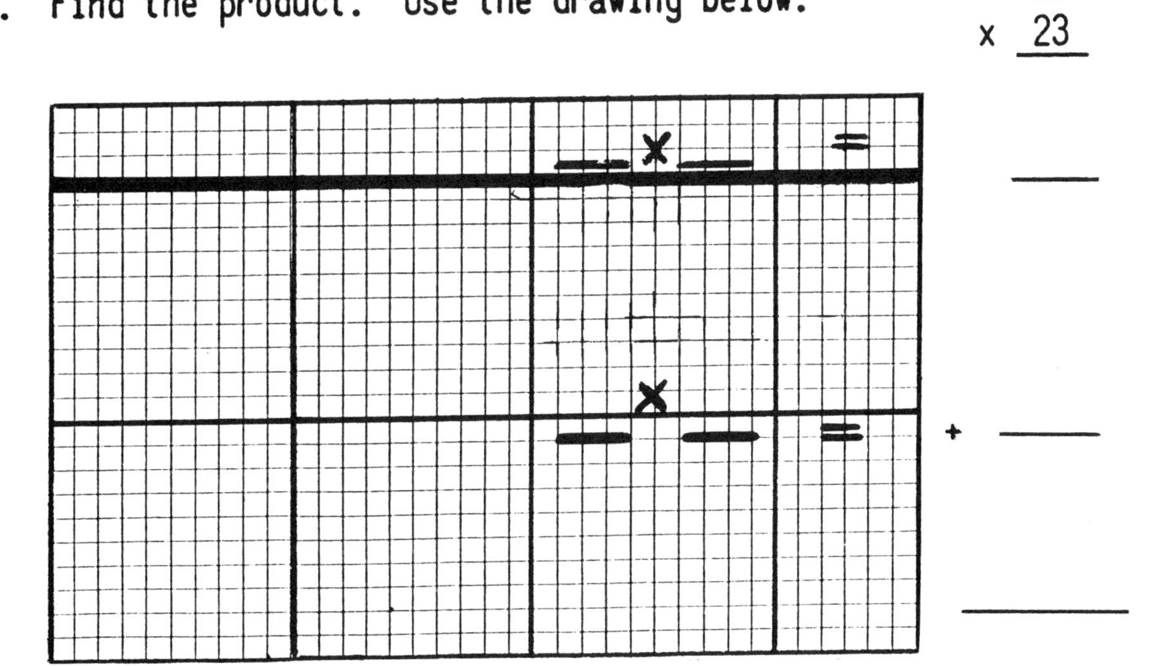

Written Records

Mathematics teaching objective:

. Use a model for the multiplication algorithm for two-digit numbers

Problem-solving skills pupils *might* use:

. Make and use a drawing or model.

. Break a problem into manageable parts.

. Invent problems for mathematical expressions and vice versa.

Materials needed:

. A blank transparency of the special graph paper (see page 211)

Comments and suggestions:

. Work 1(a) and (b) along with the whole class.

. Remind pupils that in the next four lessons the order a number is placed in the written record gives that number special meaning. Notice in 1(a) the 24 in $\begin{array}{r} 24 \\ \underline{\times\ 13} \end{array}$ is the length -- the other number is the height. This is done to help pupils learn a faster way to find a product.

. Pupils should be able to work problems 2, 3, and 4 independently.

. Problem 4 provides some computation practice which should prepare pupils for the next lesson.

Answers:

1. a.

$$\begin{array}{rr} & 24 \\ & \underline{\times\ 13} \\ 3 \times 24 = & 72 \\ 10 \times 24 = & \underline{240} \\ & 312 \end{array}$$

b.

$$\begin{array}{rr} & 36 \\ & \underline{\times\ 23} \\ 3 \times 36 = & 108 \\ 20 \times 36 = & \underline{720} \\ & 828 \end{array}$$

(Answers continued on next page...)

2. Use the special squared paper. Find these products.

a. $\begin{array}{r} 22 \\ \times\ 16 \\ \hline \underline{\qquad} \\ +\ \underline{\qquad} \\ \hline 352 \end{array}$

b. $\begin{array}{r} 25 \\ \times\ 21 \\ \hline \underline{\qquad} \\ +\ \underline{\qquad} \\ \hline \end{array}$

c. $\begin{array}{r} 16 \\ \times\ 32 \\ \hline \underline{\qquad} \\ +\ \underline{\qquad} \\ \hline \end{array}$

3. Use special squared paper. Draw a rectangle to show

a. $\begin{array}{r} 23 \\ \times\ 15 \\ \hline 115 \\ 230 \\ \hline 345 \end{array}$

b. $\begin{array}{r} 26 \\ \times\ 21 \\ \hline 26 \\ 520 \\ \hline 546 \end{array}$

4. Do these without squared paper. (A review.)

a. $\begin{array}{r} 35 \\ \times\ \ 6 \\ \hline \end{array}$

b. $\begin{array}{r} 35 \\ \times\ 10 \\ \hline \end{array}$

c. $\begin{array}{r} 28 \\ \times\ \ 9 \\ \hline \end{array}$

d. $\begin{array}{r} 28 \\ \times\ 20 \\ \hline \end{array}$

e. $\begin{array}{r} 53 \\ \times\ \ 7 \\ \hline \end{array}$

f. $\begin{array}{r} 53 \\ \times\ 30 \\ \hline \end{array}$

g. $\begin{array}{r} 76 \\ \times\ \ 8 \\ \hline \end{array}$

h. $\begin{array}{r} 76 \\ \times\ 50 \\ \hline \end{array}$

Answers: (cont.)

2\. a.

$$\begin{array}{r} 22 \\ \times\ 16 \\ \hline 132 \\ +\ 220 \\ \hline 352 \end{array}$$

b.

$$\begin{array}{r} 25 \\ \times\ 21 \\ \hline 25 \\ +\ 500 \\ \hline 525 \end{array}$$

c.

$$\begin{array}{r} 16 \\ \times\ 32 \\ \hline 32 \\ +\ 480 \\ \hline 512 \end{array}$$

Drawings may or may not accompany the pupils work, depending upon their degree of proficiency with the algorithm.

3\. a.

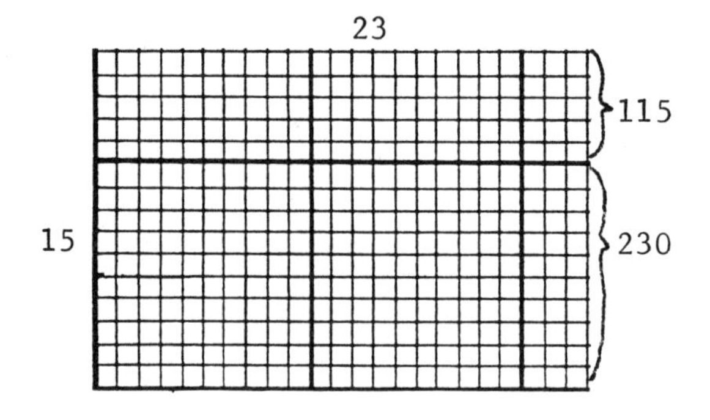

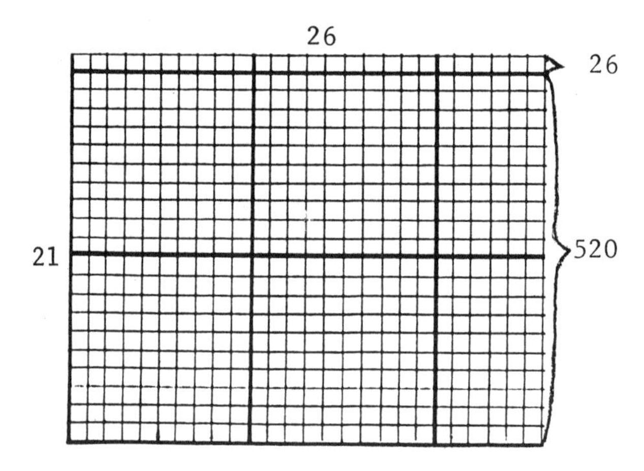

Notice the first number in the vertical expression is the dimension showing length The first number in the horizontal expression is the dimension showing the height.

4\. a. 210 b. 350 c. 252 d. 560

e. 371 f. 1590 g. 608 h. 3800

MULTIPLICATION WITHOUT A DRAWING

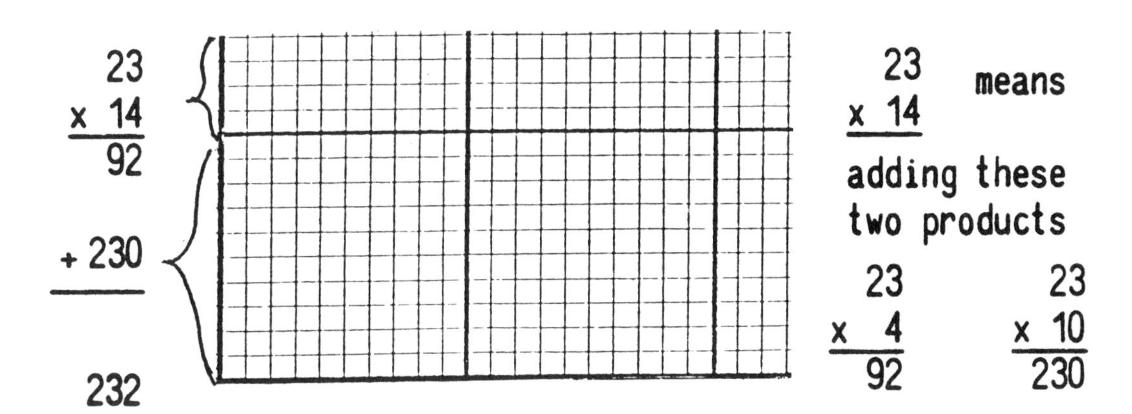

The drawing shows that the final product 322 is the sum of two smaller products 92 and 230 .

1. What two smaller products need to be added to get the final product?

   a. $\begin{array}{r} 26 \\ \times\ 15 \\ \hline \end{array}$ b. $\begin{array}{r} 16 \\ \times\ 27 \\ \hline \end{array}$ c. $\begin{array}{r} 57 \\ \times\ 32 \\ \hline \end{array}$ d. $\begin{array}{r} 93 \\ \times\ 48 \\ \hline \end{array}$

2. A short cut: $\begin{array}{r} 34 \\ \times\ 23 \\ \hline 102 \\ 680 \\ \hline 782 \end{array}$ Explain the shortcut.

3. a. $\begin{array}{r} 51 \\ \times\ 23 \\ \hline \end{array}$ b. $\begin{array}{r} 59 \\ \times\ 17 \\ \hline \end{array}$ c. $\begin{array}{r} 76 \\ \times\ 27 \\ \hline \end{array}$ d. $\begin{array}{r} 85 \\ \times\ 19 \\ \hline \end{array}$

   e. $\begin{array}{r} 92 \\ \times\ 28 \\ \hline \end{array}$ f. $\begin{array}{r} 87 \\ \times\ 36 \\ \hline \end{array}$ g. $\begin{array}{r} 69 \\ \times\ 25 \\ \hline \end{array}$ h. $\begin{array}{r} 44 \\ \times\ 33 \\ \hline \end{array}$

Multiplication Without A Drawing

Mathematics teaching objectives:

- Use an algorithm for two-digit multiplication.
- Explain the meaning for each step in the algorithm.

Problem-solving skills pupils *might* use:

- Make and use a drawing.
- Break a problem into manageable parts.
- Study the solution process.
- Explain how you solved a problem.

Materials needed:

- None

Comments and suggestions:

- Go over the introductory comments reviewing the correspondence between the rectangle and the algorithm.
- Emphasize that the algorithm 'two-digit multiplication' involves three calculations: two multiplications and an addition.
- Work problems 1 and 2 together with the class. Encourage pupils to check their answers and explanations with a partner. Problems such as these should be given to the pupils frequently while they are still in the "thinking strategy" stage of developing mastery. (see page 207)
- Allow pupils some freedom in the way they record their way for finding the products 3 (a)-(h). The lesson which follows and others from the text can be used to develop a standard recording format.

Answers:

1. a. $\begin{array}{r} 26 \\ \times\ 5 \\ \hline 130 \end{array}$ and $\begin{array}{r} 26 \\ \times\ 10 \\ \hline 260 \end{array}$ b. $\begin{array}{r} 16 \\ \times\ 20 \\ \hline 320 \end{array}$ and $\begin{array}{r} 16 \\ \times\ 7 \\ \hline 112 \end{array}$

   c. $\begin{array}{r} 57 \\ \times\ 2 \\ \hline 114 \end{array}$ and $\begin{array}{r} 57 \\ \times\ 30 \\ \hline 1710 \end{array}$ d. $\begin{array}{r} 93 \\ \times\ 40 \\ \hline 3720 \end{array}$ and $\begin{array}{r} 93 \\ \times\ 8 \\ \hline 744 \end{array}$ (Pupils may prefe ordering the prc ducts differentl

2. Answers will vary. Some pupils may wish to explain the short-cut using a rectangle, others may choose to use the "add two smaller products" approach. Both should be discussed with the class.

3 a 1173 b. 1003 c. 2052 d. 1615

  e. 2576 f. 3132 g. 1725 h. 1452

  Allow some freedom in the way the pupils write out the algorithm. The next lesson will make another step toward recording of a common algorithm.

THE SUM OF TWO SMALLER PRODUCTS

1. Find the products.

A	38 x 1	38 x 2	38 x 3	38 x 4	38 x 5	38 x 6	38 x 7	38 x 8	38 x 9
B	38 x 10	38 x 20	38 x 30	38 x 40	38 x 50	38 x 60	38 x 70	38 x 80	38 x 90

2. 38 x 34 - - - - - A _____ B - - - - - A + B	3. 38 x 76 - - - - - _____ - - - - -	4. 38 x 85 - - - - - _____ - - - - -	5. 38 x 27 - - - - - _____ - - -
6. 38 x 78 - - - - - _____ - - - - -	7. 38 x 92 - - - - _____ - - - - -	8. 38 x 59 - - - - _____ - - - - -	9. 38 x 53 - - - - _____ - - - - -
10. 38 x 37 - - - - - _____ - - - - -	11. 38 x 82 - - - - _____ - - - -	12. 38 x 74 - - - - - _____ - - - - -	13. 38 x 29 - - - - - _____ - - - - -

<u>The Sum Of Two Smaller Products</u>

Mathematics teaching objectives:

. Develop skill in using a common multiplication algorithm.

Problem-solving skills pupils <u>might</u> use:

. Break a problem into manageable parts.

. Study the solution process.

Materials needed:

. None

Comments and suggestions:

. Have pupils work with a partner to obtain answers to A and B. Have them compare the answers in A with those in B and review the "annex a zero" as a way for multiplying by 10.

. Review the ideas from the previous lesson. This lesson is really a systematic way for recording two products and a sum.

. Work 2 and 3 with the class by referring to 1A and B. This enables pupils to use the algorithm easily even though they still may be having difficulty with their basic multiplication facts. Let them work the remaining exercises independently.

Answers:

1. A. 38, 76, 114, 152, 190, 228, 266, 304, 342

   B. 380, 760, 1140, 1520, 1900, 2280, 2660, 3040, 3420

2.	152 1140 1292	3.	228 2660 2888	4.	190 3040 3230	5.	266 760 1026
6.	304 2660 2964	7.	76 3420 3496	8.	342 1900 2242	9.	114 1900 2014
10.	266 1140 1406	11.	76 3040 3116	12.	152 2660 2812	13.	342 760 1102

<u>Comment</u>: Pupils need more practice than is given in this section before they master the multiplication algorithm. More lessons can be provided

(Continued on the next page...)

nswers: (cont.)

similar to this one and additional problems can be given from the textbook. As pupils work toward automatically performing two-digit multiplication, some teachers find recording the algorithm on grid paper to be helpful to pupils.

For example:

			3	9	
		x	4	7	
		2	7	3	
	1	5	6		
	1	8	3	3	

However this should not be done until after pupils have demonstrated some understanding of the process itself.

As one continues to develop the multiplication algorithm, pupils will need to extend it to cover three-digit multiplication. When this time comes, probably in grade 5, the procedure could be an extention of "the sum of two smaller products" to "the sum of three smaller products." Also, special care needs to be taken in situations such as

```
  398
x 206
```

. The zero in 206 leads to difficulties.

STORY PROBLEMS

Marta made up this story problem for the number sentence,

$$55 \times 12 = \square$$

Clayton and his parents are traveling by car to San Francisco. They go 55 miles every hour and they travel for 12 hours. How many miles is it to San Francisco?

1. Write story problems for these. Do not solve them.

   a. $\begin{array}{r} 37 \\ \times 28 \\ \hline \end{array}$

   b. $49 \times 16 =$

   c. $35¢ \times 24 =$

2. Leslie used special squared paper and drew this rectangle.

   a. Write a number sentence for finding the number of small squares in the rectangle.

   b. This rectangle could be used to solve a story problem. Use postage stamps in the problem.

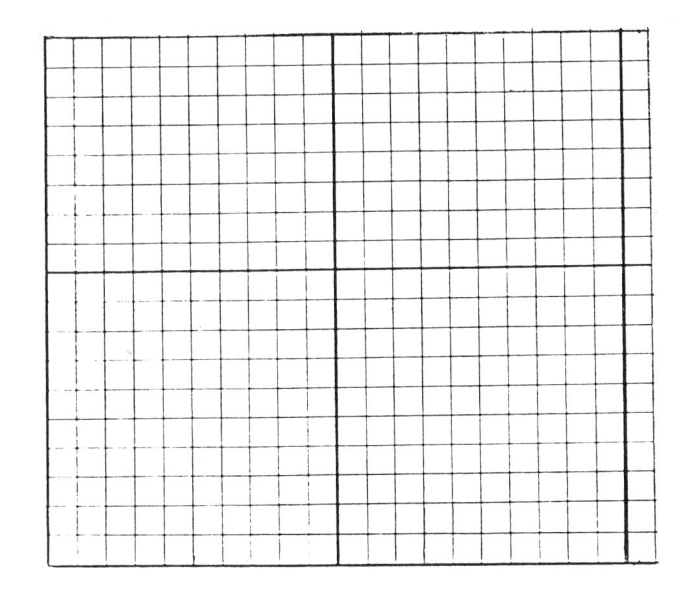

3. Write the number sentence that could be used to solve each of these problems. Do not solve the problems.

   a. Paper tablets cost Sue 49¢ each. She used 14 tablets last school year. How much did she spend on tablets?

   b. Erasers cost a quarter each. Mike bought 12 erasers last year. How much did they cost in all?

   c. Helen jogs 16 blocks <u>each</u> <u>day</u>. How many blocks would she jog in 3 weeks.

Mathematics teaching objectives:

. Solve story problems.

. Introduce pupils to a variety of settings in which multiplication can be used.

Problem-solving skills pupils might use:

. Use mathematical expressions for problem situations.

. Invent other problems which can be solved by a given number sentence.

Materials needed:

. None

Comments and suggestions:

. Read the introductory problem to the class. Point out the correspondence between the number sentence and the story problem. Ask pupils to invent other story problems for the number sentence.

. Let pupils work independently on 1 and 2. After 10 minutes, have pupils share their stories with a small group or with the total class Also review the area setting for multiplication.

. Point out that Exercise 3 calls for the number sentence only---no solutions. Exercise 4 asks for answers.

. The focus of this lesson is on multiplication settings The lesson should be followed by textbook story problems which include operations other than multiplication.

Answers:

1. Answers will vary.

2. a. 18 x 21 = ☐

   b. Answers will vary. Here are two very different "stories."

   . A page has places for 18 rows of postage stamps. Each row has 21 stamps. How many stamps are on a page?

   . A stamp costs 18¢. What would be the cost of 21 stamps?

(Answers continued on next page...)

4. Solve each story problem below.

   a. Nancy collects marbles. So far, she has collected 18 dozen. How many marbles does she have?

   b. Betsy helped put in a garden. She planted 12 rows of tomato plants. She put 23 plants in each row. How many tomato plants did she plant?

   c. Susan wants to read 35 pages a day each day during the month of August. How many pages would she be reading that month?

   d. Jim is saving quarters. He has saved 21 quarters so far. He wants to buy a book which costs $4.95. Has he saved enough quarters to buy the book?

Answers: (cont.)

3. a. 49¢ x 14 = □

   b. 25¢ x 12 = □ (requires careful reading)

   c. 16 x 21 = □ (requires careful reading)

4. a. 18 x 12 = 216 marbles

   b. 12 x 23 = 276 tomato plants

   c. 35 x 31 = 1085 pages (requires a search for facts)

   d. 21 x .25 = $5.25 He has enough money to buy the book

Grade 4

VII. GEOMETRY

VII. GEOMETRY

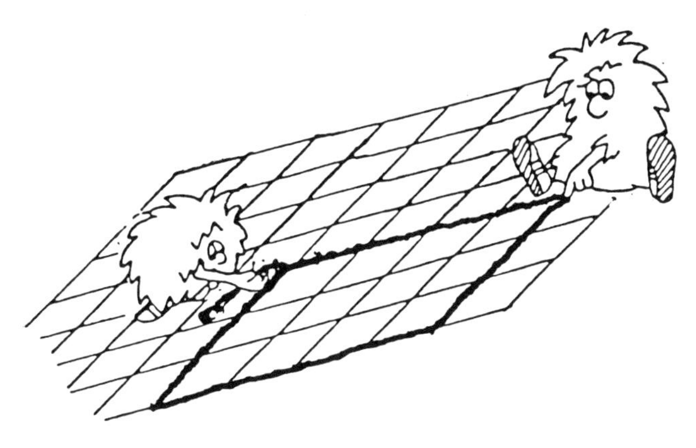

Mathematics is of little general value unless it can be applied to the solution of problems taken from the surrounding environment. Many of the problems in our environment combine ideas of geometry and number. This is very evident when we solve practical problems involving area and perimeter. The number of "inside unit squares" becomes the area of a shape and the number of unit segments around the shape becomes its perimeter.

By fourth grade, some pupils are more geometry-oriented while others are more number oriented. Including more geometry activities in the middle grades will help the geometry-minded pupils feel less at sea in a typically number dominated curriculum. It will also answer the frequent concern of educators that geometry is too small a part of the elementary curriculum.

This section includes activities involving two-dimensional shapes (triangle, square, rectangle, etc.), a lesson on three-dimensional shapes, and introductory lessons on perimeter and area. The lessons involve explorations using tangrams, two-dimensional cut-outs, and the geoboard. The geometry content is a follow-up of the drawing of rectangles on grid paper in the previous section, Multiplication And Division Concepts And Rectangles, and serves as additional readiness for the next section, Two-Digit Multiplication. There are many other topics that can and should be included in fourth-grade geometry. These can be provided by texts, math labs and other materials.

Using The Activities

Because curriculum guides seldom agree on how and when the topics of geometry should be taught in the middle grades, it is a good idea to coordinate your geometry lessons with fifth- and sixth-grade teachers. The problem solving sections could be shared with some lessons switched to different grade levels as appropriate for your curriculum guide. (The fifth-grade geometry includes symmetry, the exploration of 3-dimensional figures, and line segments and squares on the geoboard.) Fifth- and sixth-grade teachers will also be teaching area and perimeter from their regular materials and wil want to know what has been done in grade four.

The vocabulary in the activities includes triangle, square, rectangle, parallelogram, trapezoid, polyhedron, length, perimeter and area. Since pupils often confuse the words area and perimeter, you might want to point out the "rim" in peRIMeter. Usually pupils will visualize a jar rim and remember perimeter "goes around the outside." Shading the interior of a region can help pupils relate area to the inside rather than the boundary of a shape.

The geometry lessons should be used in the suggested order but not necessarily on successive days. However some discretion may be necessary depending upon "course of study" considerations. The first five lessons use the tangram as a "hands-on" way to acquaint pupils with two-dimensional shapes. Vocabulary for these shapes is emphasized in all the lessons with the primary focus on constructing from tangram pieces certain shapes as indicated:

"Tangram Shapes 1" - triangles, squares, rectangles
"Tangram Shapes 2" - triangles, rectangles, parallelograms
"Tangram Shapes 3" - rectangles, parallelograms, trapezoids
"Tangram Shapes 4"* - triangles
"Tangram Shapes 5"* - rectangles, parallelograms

The materials needed include a classroom set of geoboards, geoboard record paper, and tangram pieces. Directions are included for making geoboards (see page 261). Patterns for tangram pieces and dot paper for recording are included in the pupil materials (see pages 264 and 263). Actually having geoboards (1 for every 2 pupils) is best since more activity is involved and the use of the rubber bands leaves no record of mistakes. However the record paper can be used without the geoboards (see page 263).

* These lessons are more difficult than the first three.

GEOBOARD CONSTRUCTION

You will need:

- a 4' x 8' x $\frac{5}{8}$' sheet of plywood
- a hammer (or 1 hammer for each pupil, if pupils are doing the construction)
- at least 900 $\frac{3}{4}$" round-headed nails (brass escutcheon pins work well)
- 36 geoboard pattern sheets (see page 262)
- black spray paint
- sand paper

- Have your woodshop cut the 4' x 8' x $\frac{5}{8}$' piece of plywood into thirty-six 10 x 10 squares.
- Sand the sides and edges.
- Spray the board (or at least the top of the board) with black paint.
- Center the pattern sheet on the board. Tape it in place.

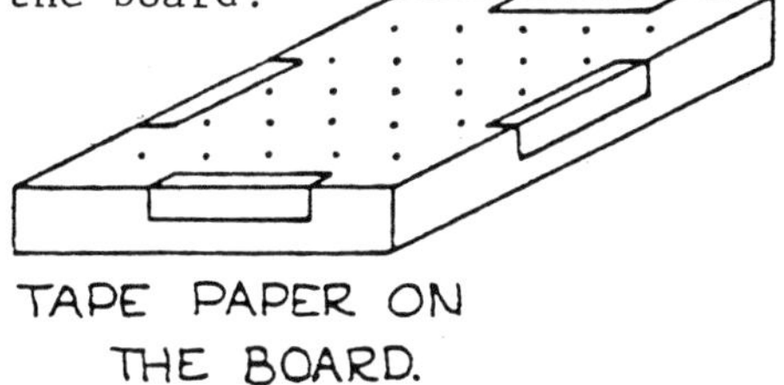
TAPE PAPER ON THE BOARD.

- Hammer the nails through the dots. Be sure the nails are pounded in far enough to be firm. They should all be the same height. (A large nut placed around the nail when hammering will result in uniform nail heights.)

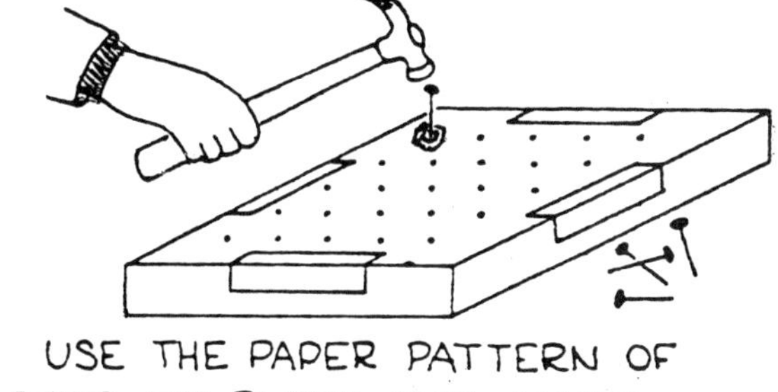
USE THE PAPER PATTERN OF DOTS TO PLACE THE NAILS.

- When all 25 nails are in, tear off the pattern sheet.

GEOBOARD PATTERN SHEET

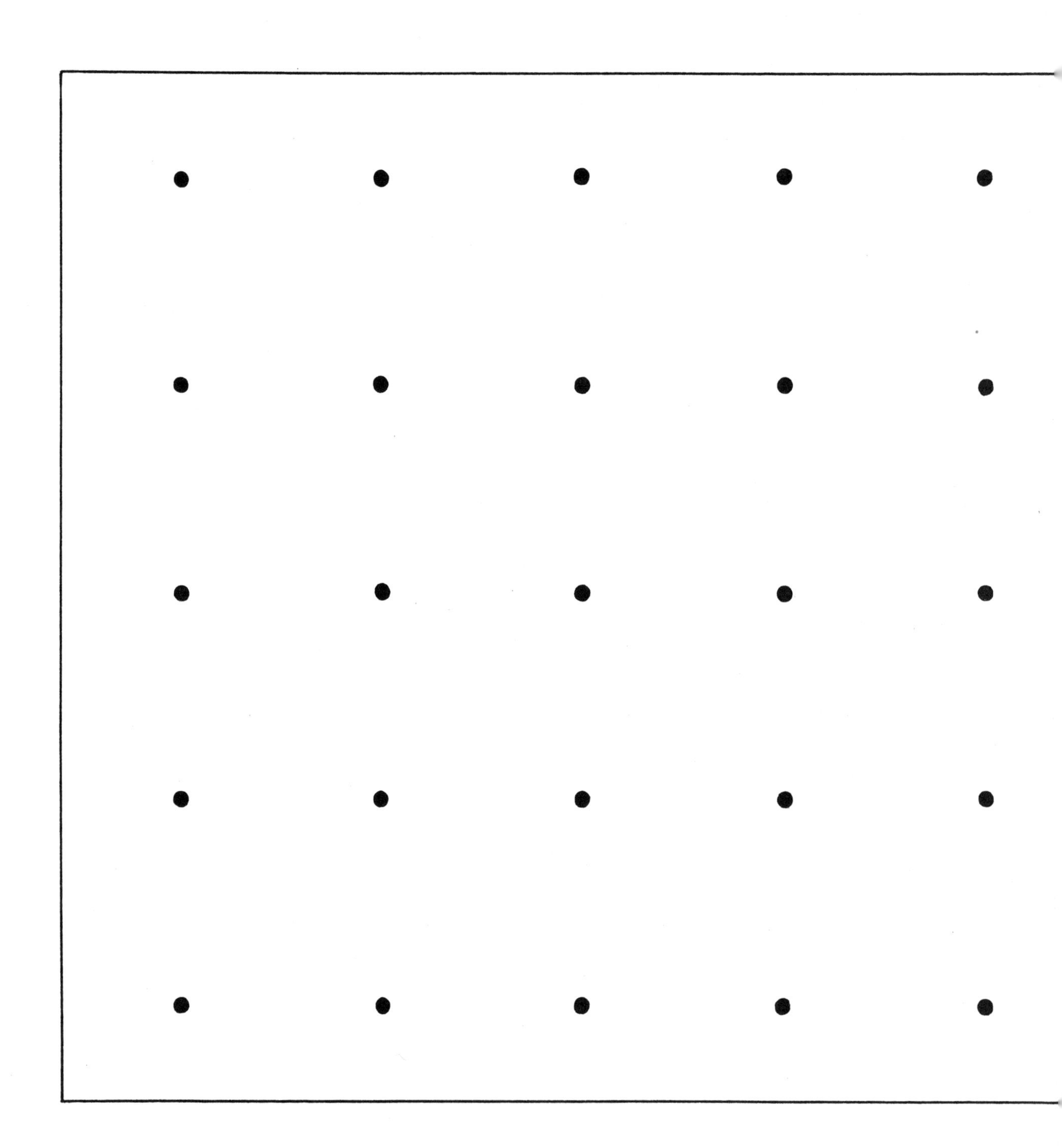

DOT PAPER MASTER

TANGRAM PATTERN

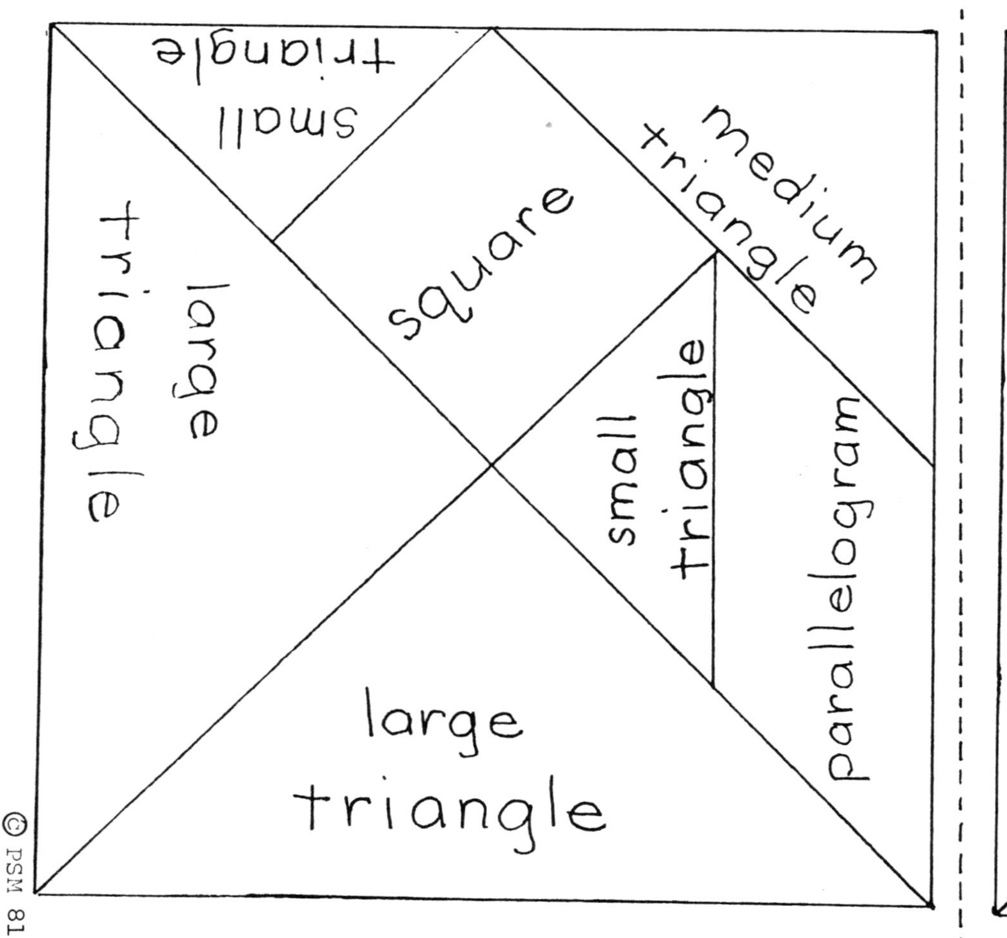

TANGRAM PATTERN

small triangle
square
medium triangle
large triangle
small triangle
parallelogram
large triangle

TANGRAM SHAPES - 1

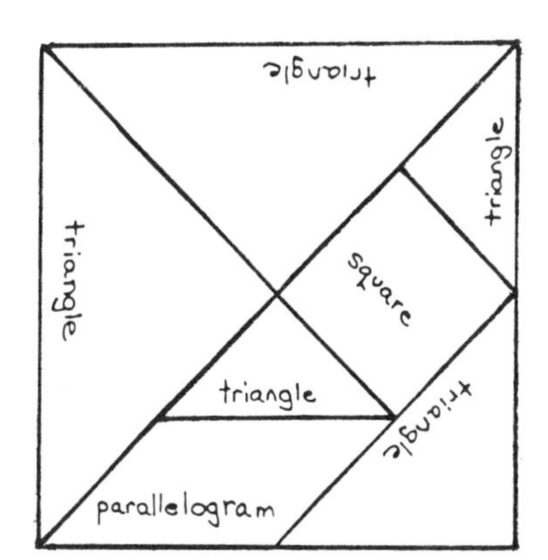

GET Tangram pattern
Scissors

DO 1. Use the tangram pattern your teacher gives you. Cut it apart.

Use the two small triangles. Make:

. a square . a larger triangle

Sketch and label each shape.

2. Use the two small triangles and the square. Make:

. a long rectangle . a larger triangle

Sketch and label each shape.

3. How many different shapes can you make using the two small triangles and the medium triangle?

Find out. Sketch each shape. Label those you can.

Tangram Shapes-1

Mathematics teaching objectives:

- Identify, construct, and draw squares, triangles, and rectangles.

Problem-solving skills pupils might use:

- Make and/or use drawings and physical models.
- Guess and check.
- Record solution possibilities.

Materials needed:

- Tangram patterns on page 264. (Reproduce pattern on cover stock or construction paper and cut apart. Each pupil needs one set of seven pieces.) The tangram pieces can be used on an overhead projector for discussing pupil solutions to the various problems.

Comments and suggestions:

- Pupils can cut out their own tangram puzzle pieces.
- Pupils should be familiar with the terms triangle, square and rectangle. You may want to review some of the basic properties of these shapes: triangles have 3 sides, etc.
- As pupils complete the problems, they can be encouraged to compare their solutions (sketches) with those of a classmate. Pupils can learn problem strategies by observing the way others manipulate the tangram pieces to get their answers.
- A bulletin board display of the various pupil responses to problem 3 will spark interest and discussion.

Answers:

1.

2.

3.

Rectangle Square Triangle

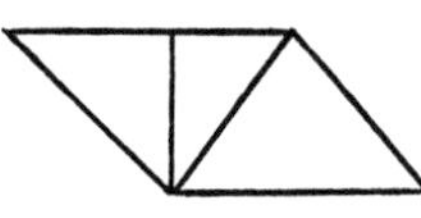
Parallelogram

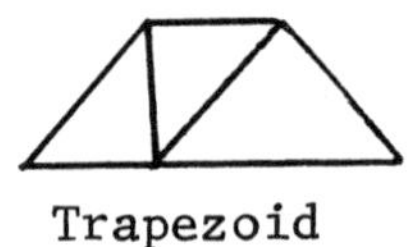
Trapezoid

There are other possibilities

TANGRAM SHAPES - 2

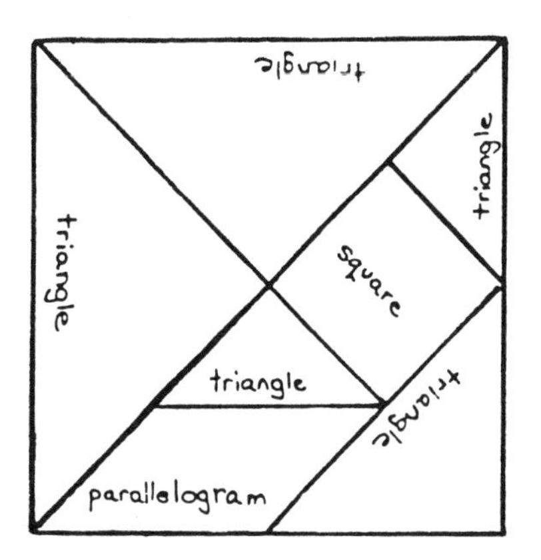

GET Tangram pattern
Scissors

DO 1. Use the tangram pattern your teacher gives you. Cut it apart.

Use the two small triangles and the parallelogram. Make:

. a long rectangle
. a larger triangle
. a larger parallelogram

Sketch and label each shape.

2. Use the two small triangles, the square and the parallelogram. Make:

. a long rectangle
. a large parallelogram
. a 6-sided shape

Sketch and label each shape.

3. Make many different shapes using all five triangles. Sketch each shape.

Tangram Shapes - 2

Mathematics teaching objectives:

- Identify, construct, and draw squares, triangles, rectangles, parallelograms, and 6-sided shapes.

Problem-solving skills pupils *might* use:

- Make and/or use drawings and physical models.
- Guess and check.
- Be aware of other solution possibilities.
- Record solution possibilities.

Materials needed:

- Tangram patterns on pupil page 264. The pieces can be used on an overhead projector for discussing and comparing answers.

Comments and suggestions:

- Pupils can complete the page individually or in pairs. Opportunities to discuss and compare answers will help pupils see other solutions.
- Again, a bulletin board display of responses to problem 3 will increase pupil interest.

Answers: (These are only sample answers. In most cases, there are other possibilities.)

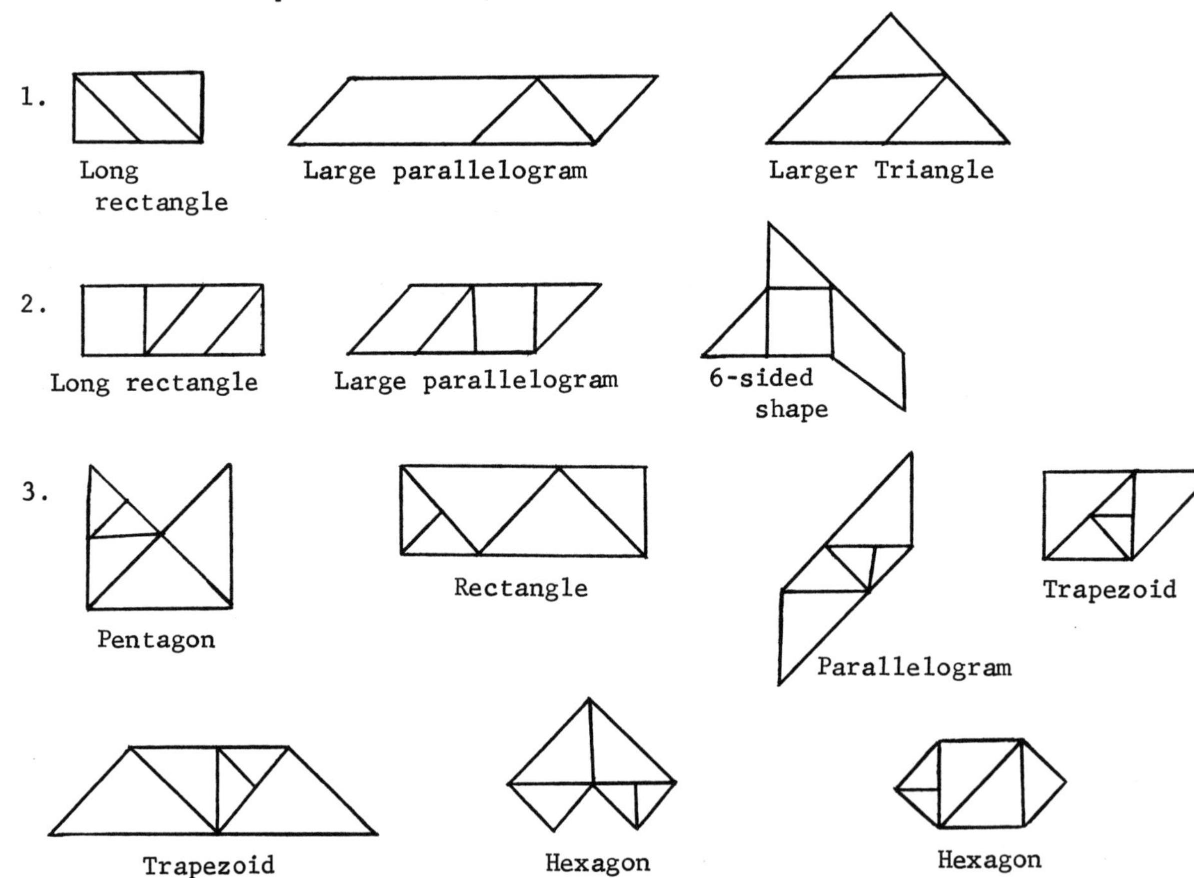

TANGRAM SHAPES - 3

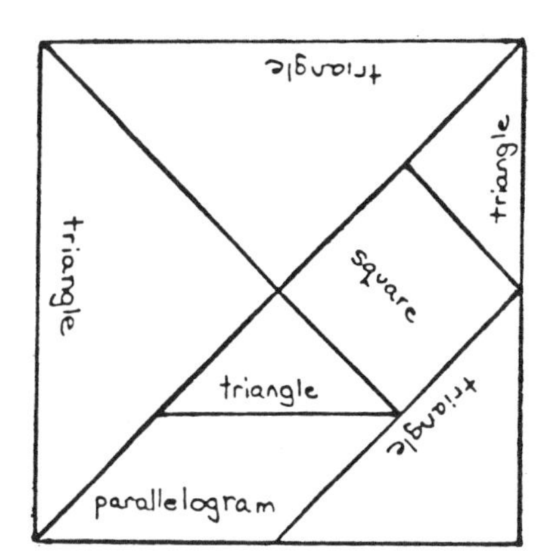

GET Tangram pieces
Scissors

DO 1. Get your envelope of tangram pieces. Use the two small triangles, the medium triangle, and the square.

Make
- a long rectangle.
- a parallelogram.
- a trapezoid (or)

Sketch and label each shape.

2. Use the 2 small triangles, the parallelogram, and the medium triangle.

Make
- a long rectangle.
- a parallelogram.
- a trapezoid.

Sketch and label each shape.

3. Use all the pieces except the 2 large triangles.

Make as many different shapes as you can.

Sketch and label each shape.

Tangram Shapes-3

Mathematics teaching objective:

. Identify, construct, and draw rectangles, parallelograms and trapezoids.

Problem-solving skills pupils might use:

. Visualize and record different shapes.

. Guess and check.

Materials needed:

. An envelope of a complete set of tangram pieces for each pupil

Comments and suggestions:

. Show pupils a variety of cardboard cut-outs of trapezoids. Also show them some four-sided shapes which are not trapezoids.

. Have pupils point out examples of such shapes in the classroom or in the school environment. Often newspapers and the yellow pages of a telephone book show trapezoids in advertisements. A rectangl drawn in perspective is often a trapezoid.

Answers:

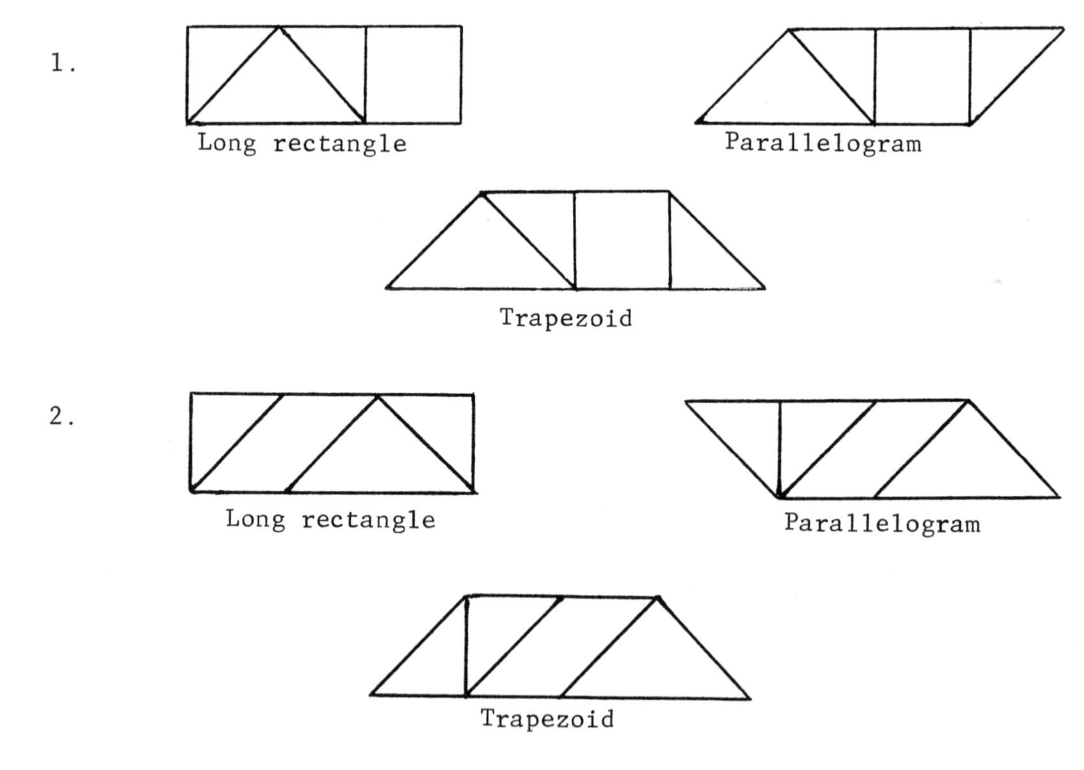

3. Answers will vary.

TANGRAM SHAPES - 4

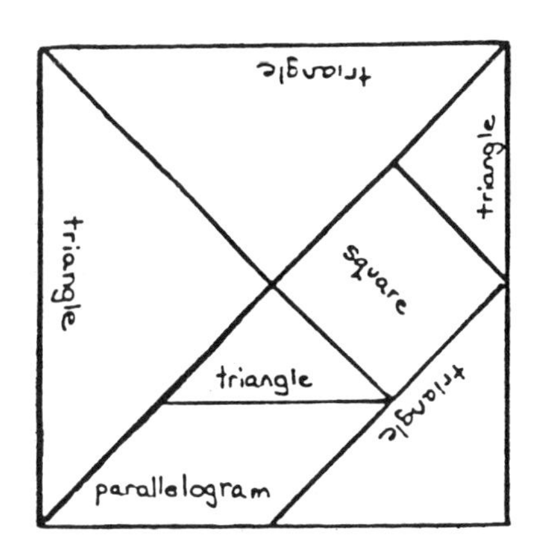

GET Tangram pieces
Scissors

DO 1. a. Get your envelope of tangram pieces. Use 2 pieces. Make a triangle. Sketch and label the shape.

b. Use 2 different pieces. Make a triangle. Sketch and label it.

2. a. Use the medium triangle and 2 other pieces. Make a triangle.

b. Make 2 other triangles that use 3 pieces. Sketch and label each.

3. a. Use a big triangle, a square, and 2 other pieces. Make a triangle. Sketch and label it.

b. Find a different way to make a triangle with 4 pieces. (Hint: One piece is a large triangle.)

4. Try to make a triangle with
   . 5 pieces.
   . 7 pieces.

   Sketch and label the triangles.

Tangram Shapes-4

Mathematics teaching objective:

. Identify, construct, and draw triangles.

Problem-solving skills pupils might use:

. Visualize and record different shapes.

. Guess and check.

. Search for other solutions.

Materials needed:

. An envelope of a complete set of tangram pieces for each pupil (A set can be made from the pattern on page 264.)

Comments and suggestions:

. Pupils will probably want to pursue these investigations independently (No one wants to share tangram pieces.) However, pupils should have opportunities to share and compare solutions.

. A bulletin board display of all the various, different solutions to each problem usually will motivate pupil interest and continued investigation.

Answers:

1. a. The two possibilities are the two sets of large and
   b. small triangles.

2. a.

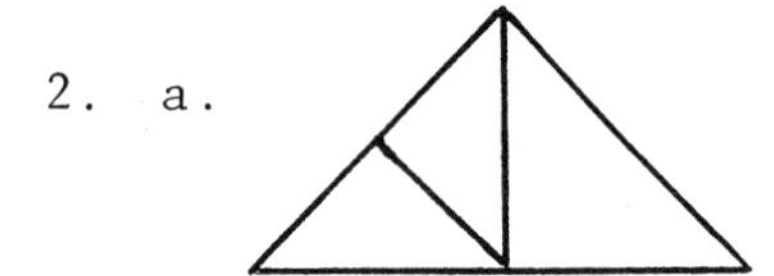

b.

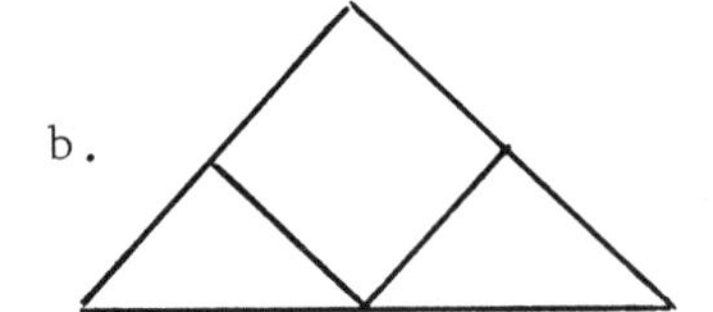

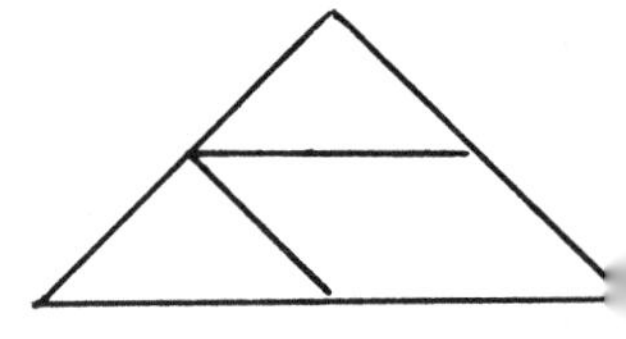

3. a.

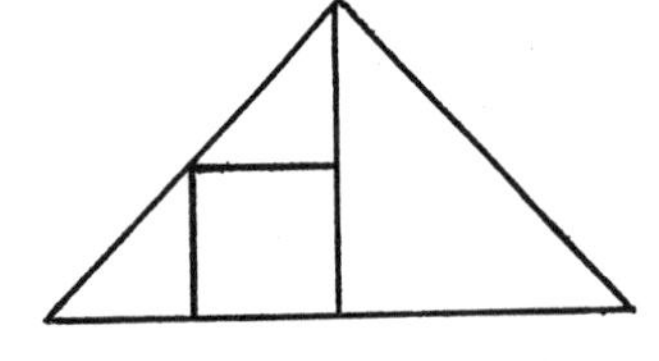

b.

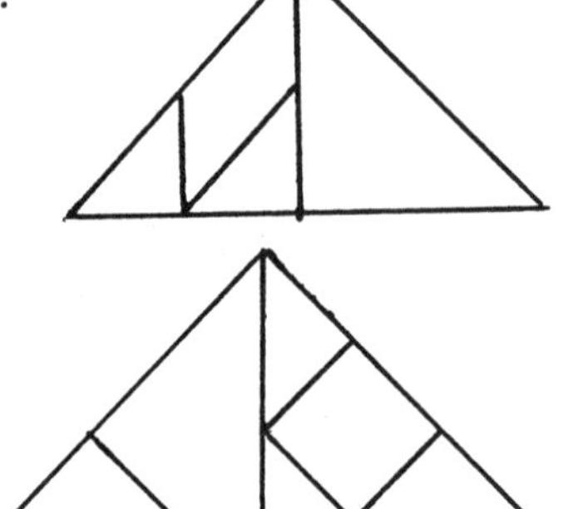

4.

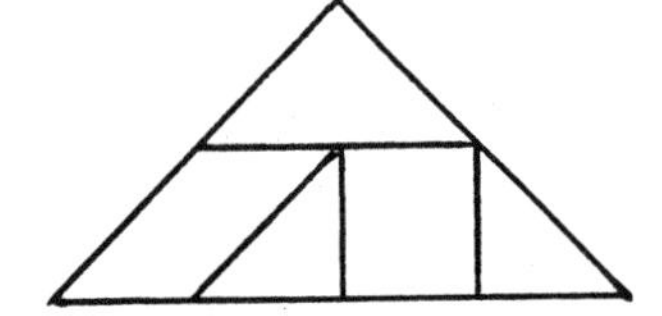

TANGRAM SHAPES - 5

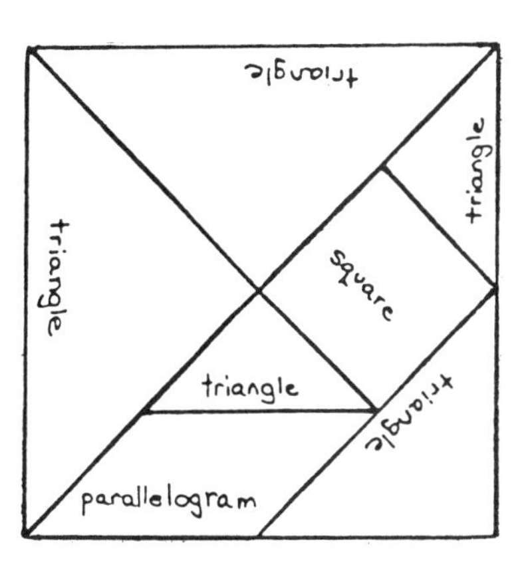

GET Tangram pieces
Scissors

DO

1. Get your envelope of tangram pieces. Try to make a rectangle using
   - . 3 pieces.
   - . 4 pieces.
   - . 5 pieces.
   - . 6 pieces.
   - . 7 pieces.

   Sketch and label each shape.

2. Find as many different ways as you can to make parallelograms.

   Sketch and label each parallelogram.

   Hint: You should be able to make parallelograms at least 10 different ways!

Mathematics teaching objective:

. Identify, construct, and draw rectangles and parallelograms.

Problem-solving skills pupils <u>might</u> use:

. Visualize and record different shapes.

. Guess and check.

. Search for other solutions.

Materials needed:

. An envelope of a complete set of tangram pieces for each pupil. (A set can be made from the pattern on page 264.)

Comments and suggestions:

. Multiple solutions are possible for most problems in exercise 1. Pupils should be encouraged to look for more than one right answer.

. Solutions to exercise 2 can be posted on a bulletin board. This will encourage pupils to continue to look for addition correct responses.

Answers:

1.

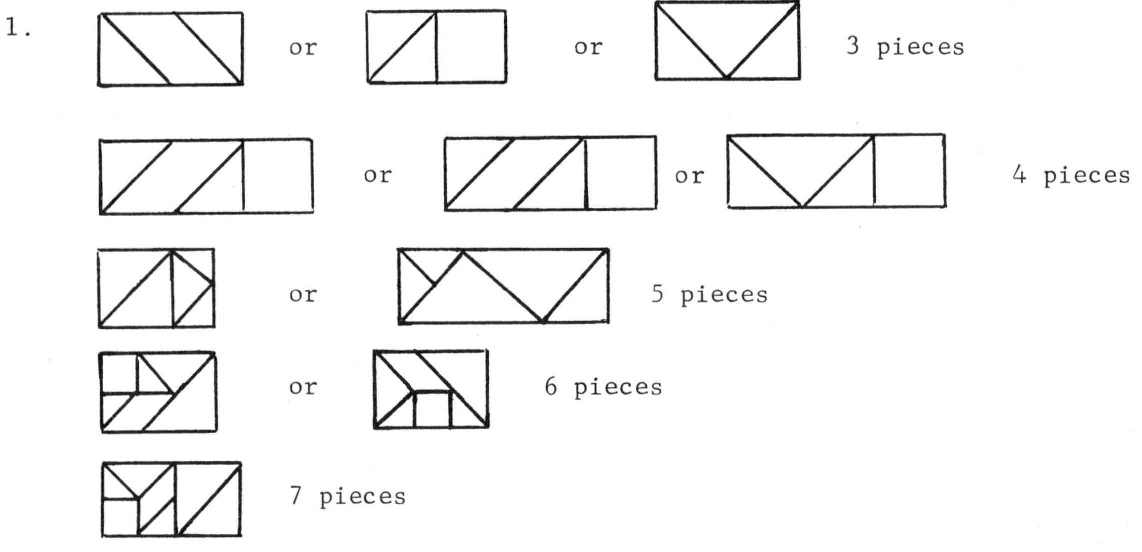

2. Some solutions are:

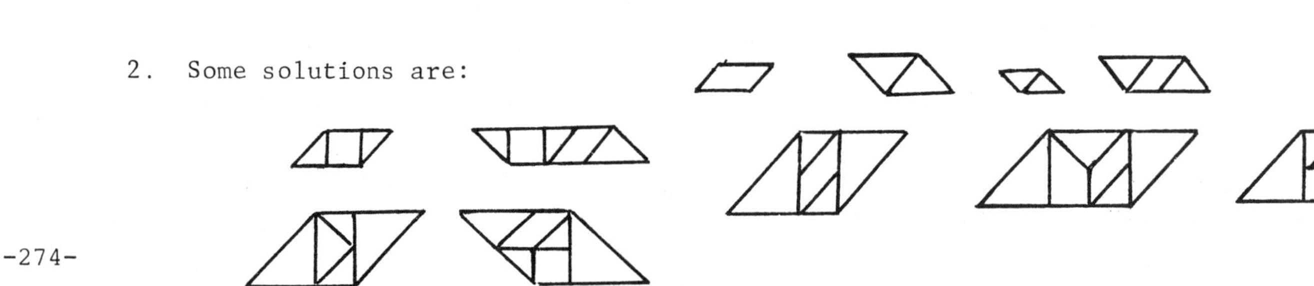

BUILDING POLYHEDRONS

You will need scissors, tape, and 4 "shape sheets."
Cut out the shapes on each sheet.
Use the shapes to solve the problems below.

1. Use 4 long rectangles and 2 squares.
   Make this polyhedron.

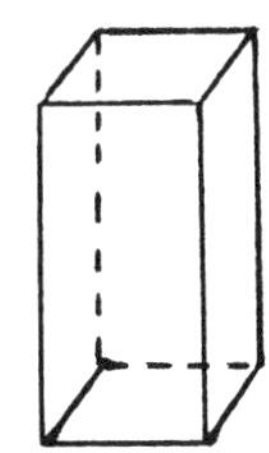

2. Use 1 square and 4 tall triangles.
   Make this polyhedron.

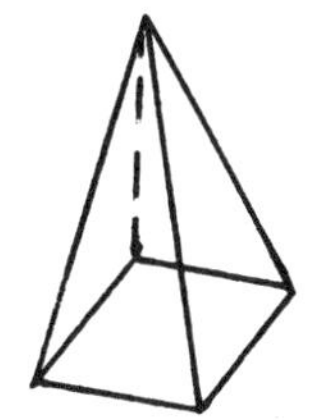

3. Use all squares.
   Make this polyhedron.

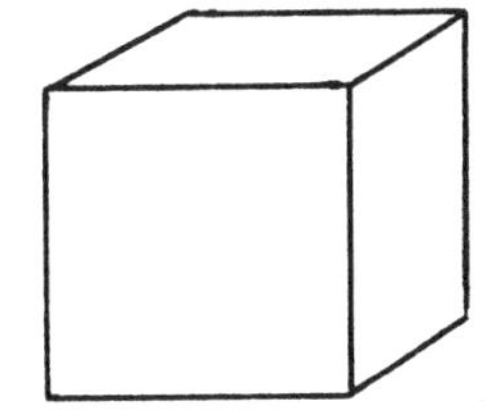

4. Use 1 small triangle and 3 tall triangles
   Make a polyhedron.
   Show your teacher.

5. Use 2 small triangles and 3 long rectangles.
   Make a polyhedron.

6. Use the remaining shapes.
   Make as many different polyhedrons as you can.

Building Polyhedrons

Mathematics teaching objectives:

. Develop 3-dimensional concepts.

. Construct polyhedrons by using two-dimensional shapes.

Problem-solving skills pupils might use:

. Make a model.

. Visualize an object from its drawing.

Materials needed:

. Each pupil will need -
. scissors
. tape (transparent or masking)
. 4 "shapes sheets" (see page 277 for pattern)

Comments and suggestions:

. Use the "shapes sheet" pattern on page 277. Reproduce about 120 copies (or 4 per pupil) on construction paper or oaktag.

. Have pupils work with a partner or in small groups. Pupils may need to share materials or need the help of another pair of hands.

. Work problems 1 and 2 as a class. Teach the new word polyhedron by showing examples in the classroom. Some examples are filing cabinets, a closed chalk box, pyramids of Egypt, ice cubes, or most houses. Some non-examples are a cone, a baseball, a football, an egg, a dough-nut, or a square nut. If possible, have a rectangular block and a pyramid with a square base available to show pupils. (These poly-hedrons are often included in commercial geometric solids sets.)

. Have pupils complete the remaining problems on their own. Check paperwork by circulating among the pupils as they work or by sharing results as a class near the end of the math period.

Answers:

1,2, & 3. Pictures are given as answers for the object to be constructed

4. 

5. 

6. Answers will vary.

Extension: Pupils who complete the activity ahead of their classmates might be asked to make drawings of their completed polyhedrons.

SHAPES SHEET

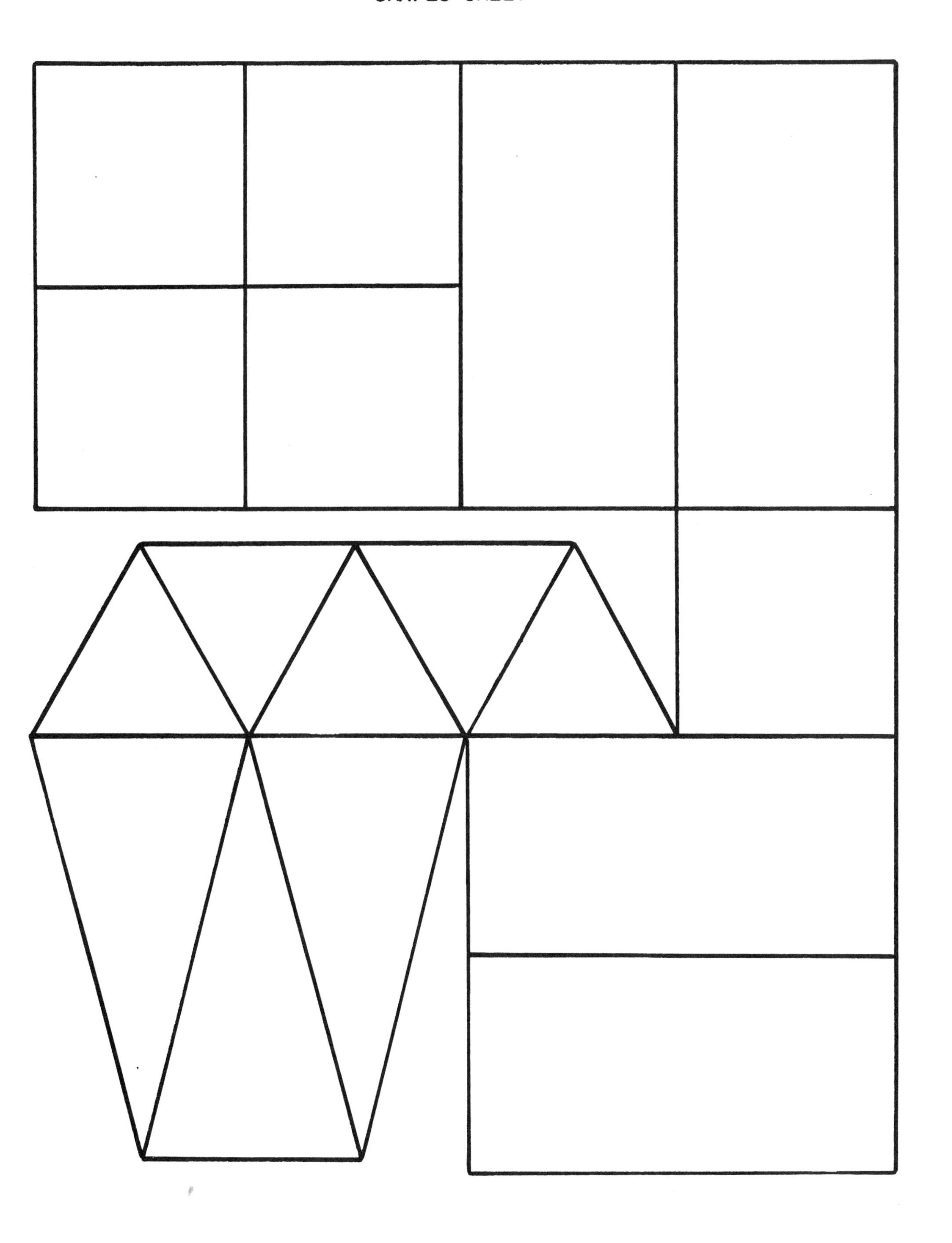

THE FENCE PROBLEM

1. Fuzz E. and Fuzz I. have fenced in 12 floor tiles.

   Find a different way to fence in 12 tiles.

   Record below.

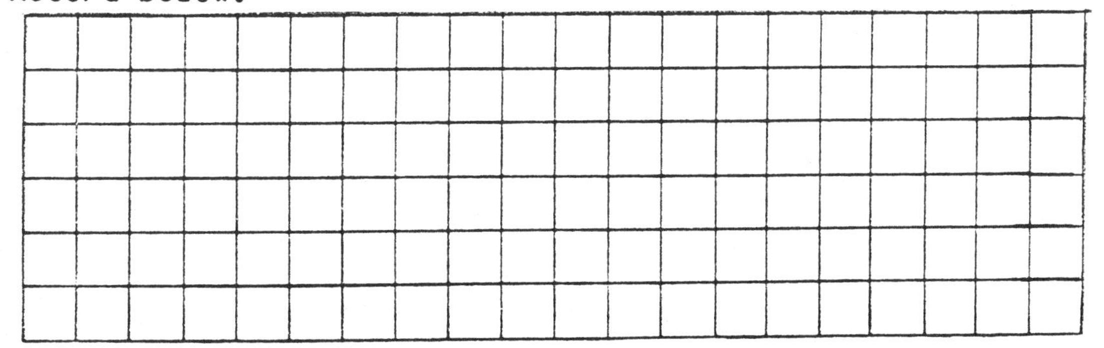

2. Find many ways to fence in 16 squares. Record each.
   Try to find 10 different ways.
   Hint: All the shapes do not need to be rectangles.

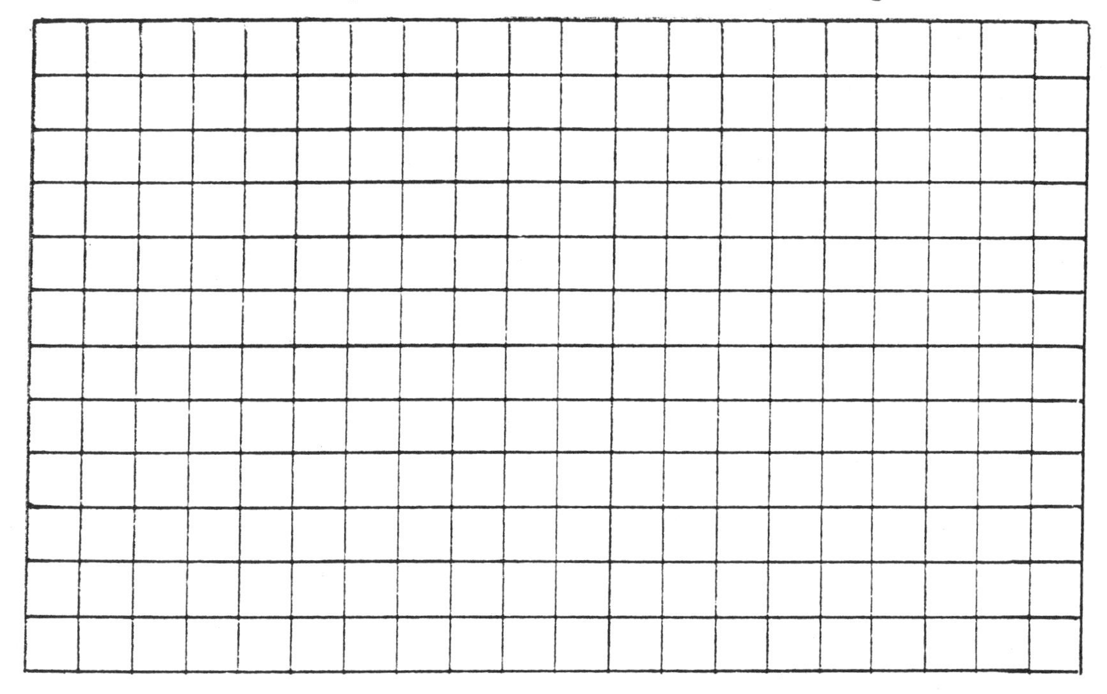

<u>Challenge</u>: Mark the fence shape that uses the least fencing with an X.

The Fence Problem

Mathematics teaching objectives:

. Visualize and record different arrangements of shapes.

. Recognize that a square has less perimeter than other rectangles with the same area.

Problem-solving skills pupils might use:

. Make and/or use drawings.

. Record solution possibilities.

. Search for and be aware of other possibilities.

. Organize data systematically.

Materials needed:

. A supply of grid paper (1 cm or one-half inch)

. Transparent grid paper for overhead projector (optional)

Comments and suggestions:

. The terms area and perimeter need not be mentioned at this time. Experiences with the idea before naming is often a good rule of thumb to follow.

. Begin the lesson by working the first problem. Encourage much pupil participation. Make certain some non-rectangular "fences" are included. Discuss whether a 3 by 4 fencing is the same as a 4 by 3 fencing. Let the pupils decide.

. Let pupils work the second problem on their own. Supply grid paper if needed. Reserve some time near the end of the period for a sharing of results. The discussion should include the shapes of the regions which require the least and the most "fencing." Some pupils may be able to describe how they found 10 different ways to fence in 16 squares.

. You might want pupils to find the amount of fence for each of the ways they have discovered in problems 1 and 2. This will help them recognize that shapes with the same area might have different perimeters.

Answers: 1. Many different answers possible
2. Many different answers possible.

Challenge: The 4 by 4 square uses the least fence.

A bulletin board display of the results would show the variety of answers possible.

GEOBOARD AREAS

GET 25-nail geoboard, rubber bands.

DO 1. Make this shape on your geoboard.

It has an area of one square unit.

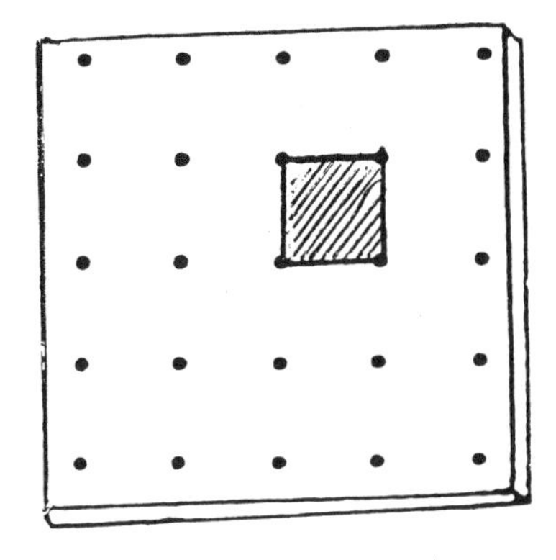

2. This shape has an area of 3 square units.

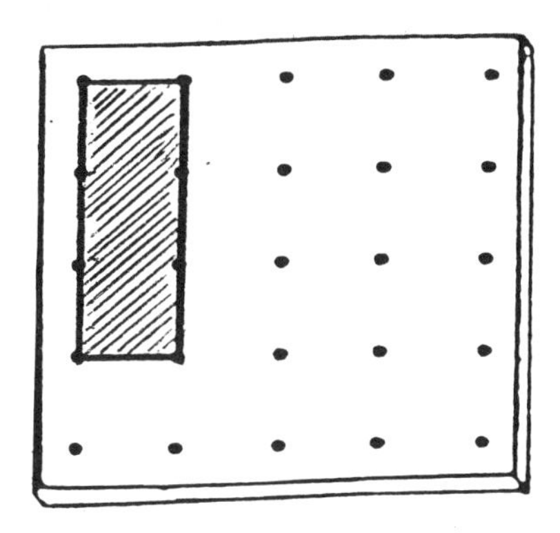

Make a different shape with an area of 3 square units.

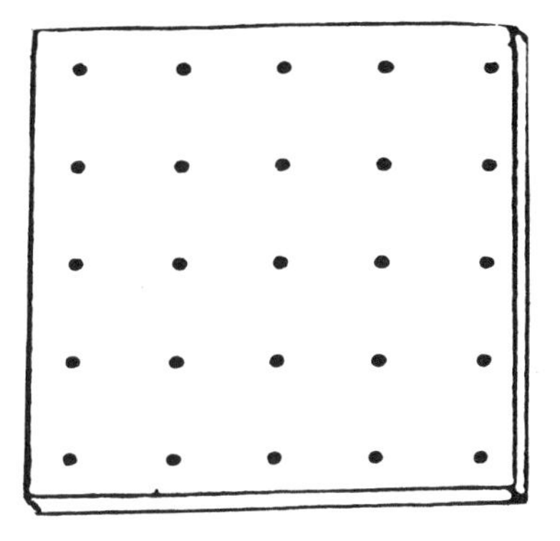

3. Each of these shapes has an area of _____ square units.

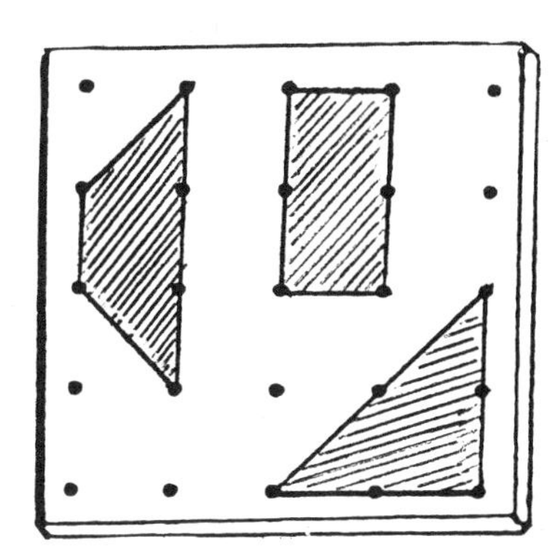

Geoboard Areas

Mathematics teaching objectives:

- Solve problems in which the term area is used.
- Make shapes with a given area.
- Find the area of shapes by counting unit squares and $\frac{1}{2}$ unit squares.

Problem-solving skills pupils might use:

- Make and use drawings and physical models.
- Record solution possibilities.
- Search for and be aware of other possibilities.
- Guess and check.

Materials needed:

- Classroom set of geoboards and rubber bands of various colors.
- A transparency of the 25-point geoboard pattern for use on overhead projector. (Optional)

Comments and suggestions:

- Work problems 1, 2 and 3 with the class, encouraging responses from as many pupils as possible. Emphasize the term area and the use of $\frac{1}{2}$ in determining area.
- Discussion in problem 2 should bring out that [shape] is the same shape as [shape] only tipped over.
- Let pupils work problem 4 on their own or in pairs. The activity should end with a sharing session in which pupils can discuss their results and the procedures they used.

Answers:

2. Permit shapes such as

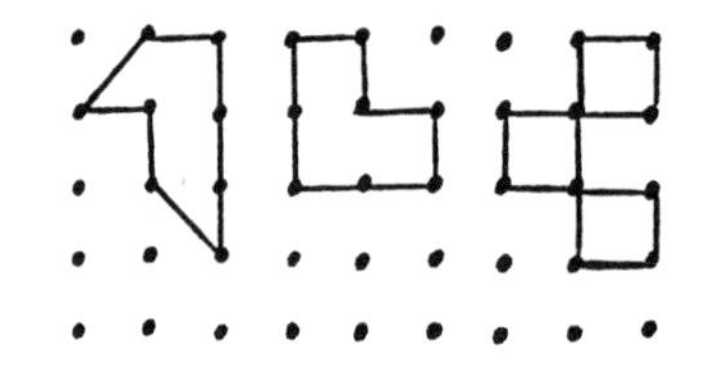

(Any closed figure which can be drawn without lifting a pencil)

3. All the shapes have an area of 2 square units.

4. There are many possible answers. After the activity is completed, pupils could classify the results. Here is one possibility:

   a. Has one or more slanting sides.

   b. All square corners.

   c. Lines cross.

Of course, some of these categories overlap.

4. How many different shapes with four square units can you make? Find out. Record each.

PERIMETERS - GETTING STARTED

ET 25-nail geoboard, rubber bands.

0

1. This rectangle has a perimeter of 6 units.

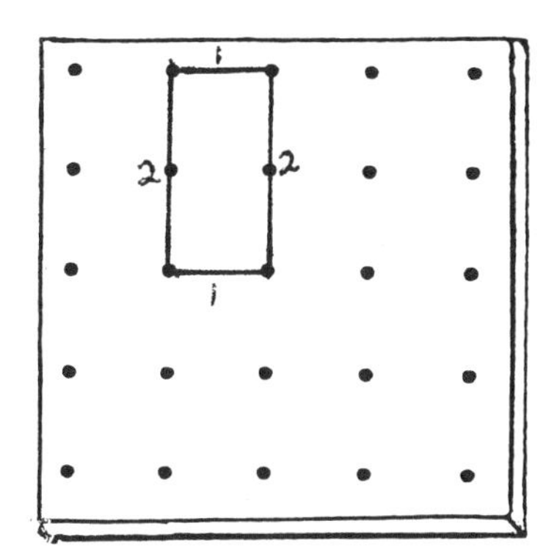

2. This rectangle has a perimeter of ____ units.

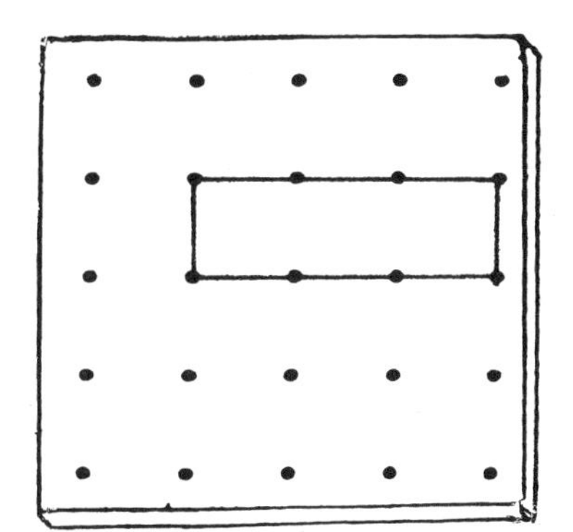

3. Make a <u>square</u> with a perimeter of 8 units. Record.

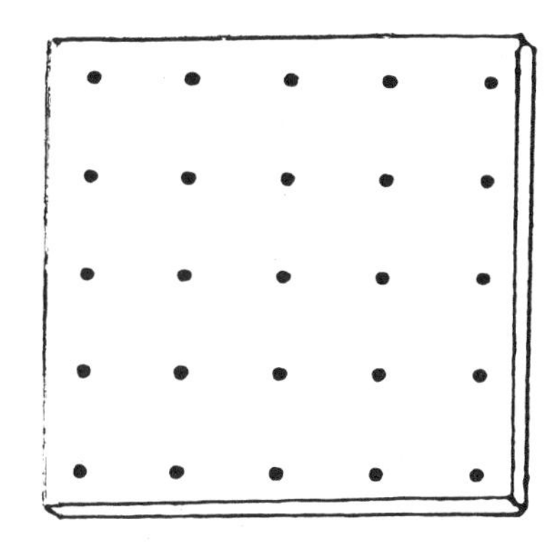

4. Tell the perimeter of each of these shapes.

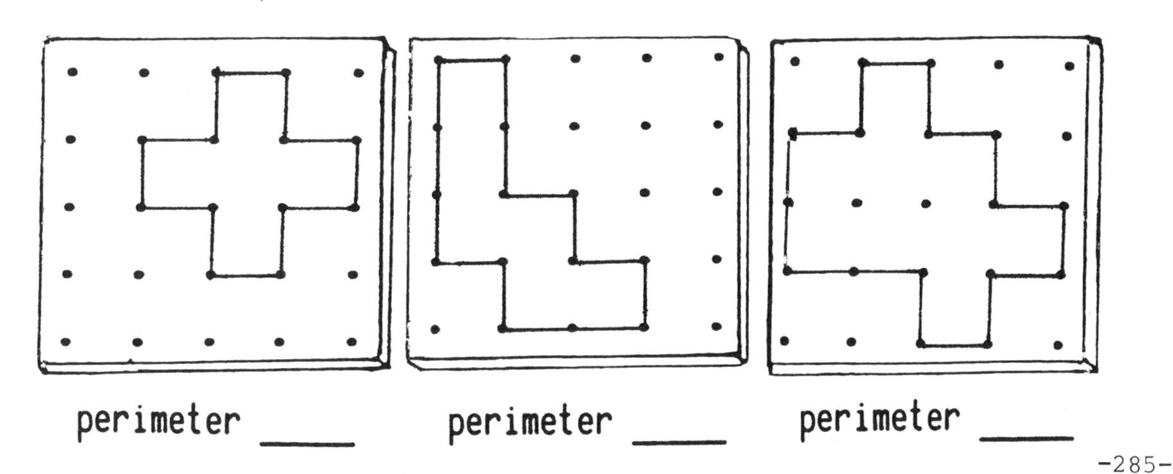

perimeter ____ perimeter ____ perimeter ____

Perimeters - Getting Started

Mathematics teaching objectives:

- Determine the perimeter of shapes by counting units segments.
- Make shapes with a given perimeter.
- Visualize and draw different shapes.

Problem-solving skills pupils *might* use:

- Make and use drawings or physical models.
- Search for and be aware of other possibilities.
- Record solution possibilities.
- Guess and check.

Materials needed:

- Classroom set of geoboards and rubber bands.
- Supply of geoboard record paper.
- Transparent geoboard for use on overhead projector. (Optional)

Comments and suggestions:

- If your pupils understand the vocabulary of the page, you might let them use their own resources in reading and following directions from the printed page.
- Finish the activity with a sharing session in which pupils discuss their results and any methods of solution they used.

Answers:

2. 8 units

3. 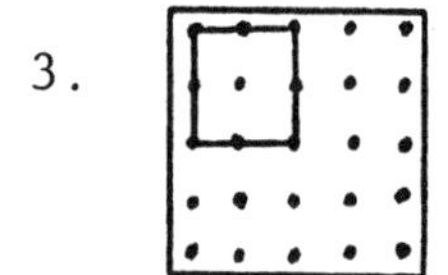

4. 12, 14, 16

5. How many different shapes can you make with a perimeter of 10 units. Do not use slanted lines.

   Find out. Record each.

Answers: (cont.)

5 Some possible square-corner shapes with a perimeter of 10.

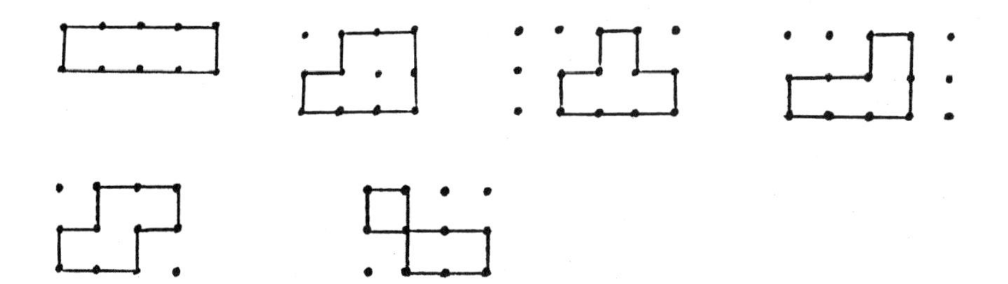

Review question: Find the area of each shape.

Have pupils shade in the space as they find the area.

Extension:

. Is it possible to make on a geoboard a square-corner shape with a perimeter that is an "odd" number? (No, but some pupils will experiment with the geoboards a long time before discovering this.

PERIMETER PATTERNS

GET 25-nail geoboard, rubber bands.

DO

1. Make this shape.
   It has a perimeter
   of _____ units.

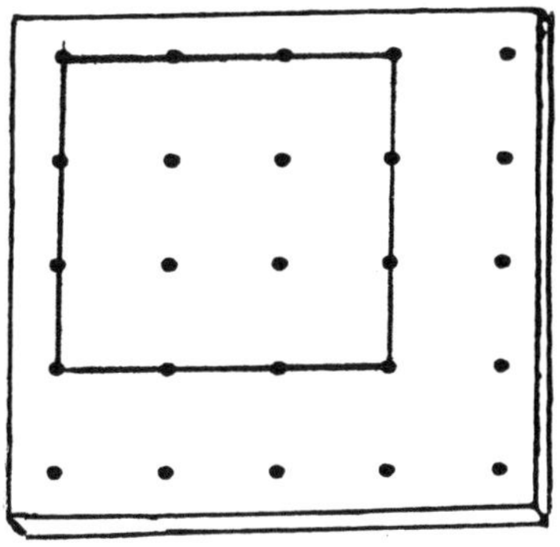

2. Change it to
   this shape.

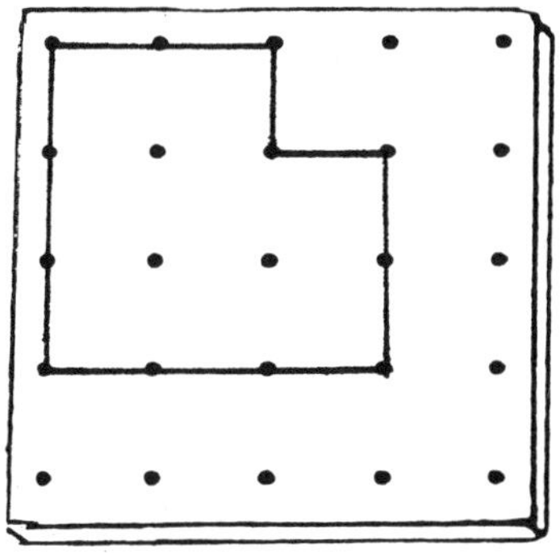

   What happens to
   the perimeter?

   ____
   ____
   ____

3. Change it to
   this shape.

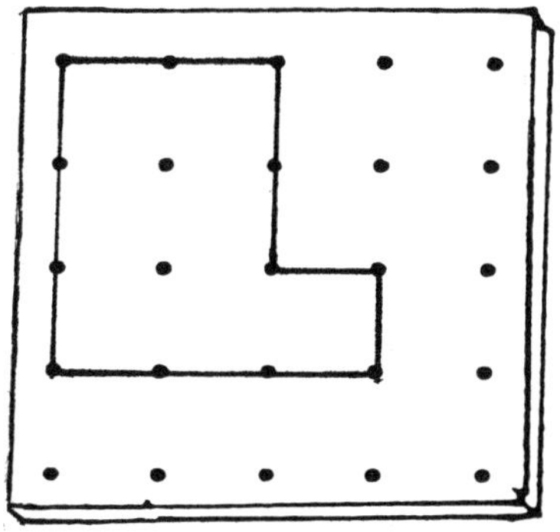

   Now what happens
   to the perimeter?

   ____
   ____
   ____

4. Make as many different shapes as you can with a perimeter of 14 units. (No slanted lines allowed.) Record each.

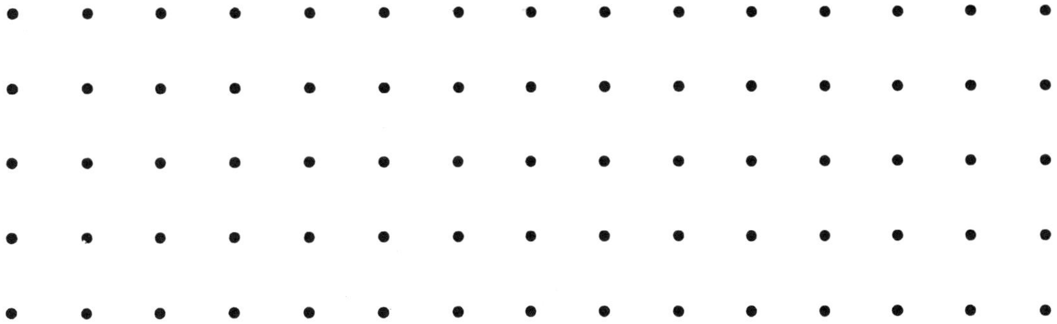

Perimeter Patterns

Mathematics teaching objectives:

. Solve perimeter and area problems.

. Recognize that square-corner shapes with the same perimeter need not have the same area.

Problem-solving skills pupils <u>might</u> use:

. Make and use drawings or physical models.

. Record solution possibilities.

. Search for and be aware of other possibilities.

Materials needed:

. Classroom set of geoboards and rubber bands
. Supply of geoboard paper
. Transparent geoboard for use on overhead projector (optional)

Comments and suggestions:

. Let pupils work the page on their own. Discuss and compare results.

. Finish the activity with a discussion of solutions.

. Follow these activities with related problems from the text.

Answers:

1. 12 units
2. Remains the same (12 units) but area is 8 square units.
3. Remains the same (12 units) but area is 7 square units.

Some possible shapes

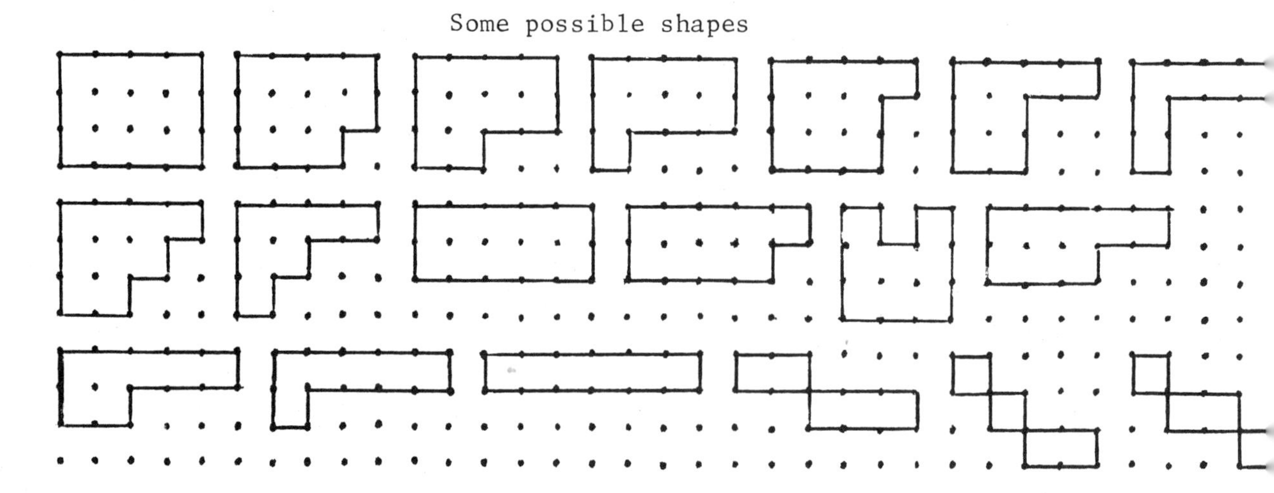

Review question:

What is the area of each of the shapes?
Emphasize that all the shapes have the same perimeter but the areas vary.
As they determine the areas, have them shade in the shapes.

Grade 4

VIII. RECTANGLES AND DIVISION

TEACHER COMMENTARY - GRADE 4

VIII. RECTANGLES AND DIVISION

Long division is usually introduced to fourth graders during the second emester. The algorithm should be more meaningful if pupils have seen ong division with a model.

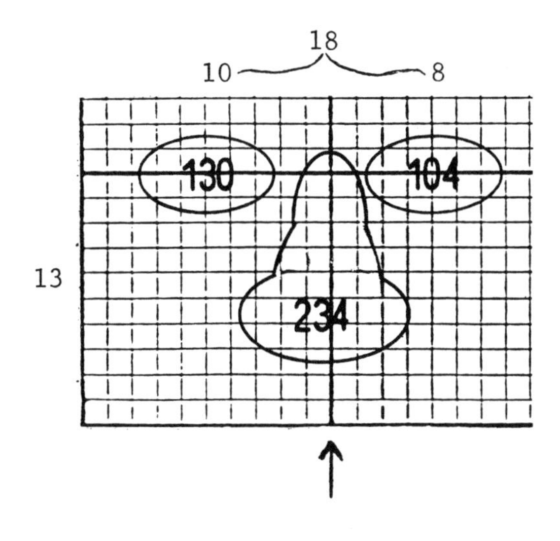


```
     18
13 ⟌234
    130
    104
    104
```

Notice in the drawing the number of units in the rectangles to the left nd to the right of the arrow and how these numbers correspond to the two ubtractions in the algorithm. The approach in this section is to teach upils this visualization of division and is based upon the model used in ection VI, Two-Digit Multiplication. Ideally, pupils should have worked hrough that section before starting this one. Also, it is assumed that upils already have some skill in using an algorithm for dividing numbers ess than 1,000 by a single digit. However, this skill is reviewed by sing the rectangle model. This latter model then serves as a vehicle for eveloping long division.

The instructional development in this section egins with a concrete phase--using flats, longs, nd units that pupils cut out from tagboard for onstructing rectangles with a given number of units and sing these pieces for constructing a given-sized rectangle with a missing imension. There are many problem-solving situations in this phase as well s many opportunities for drill and practice with place value.

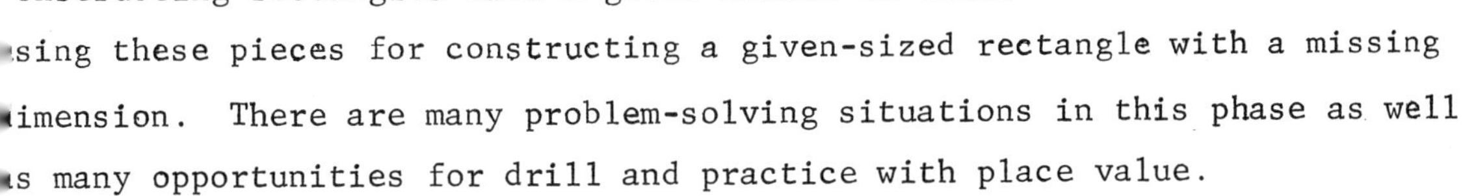

In the second instructional phase, pupils are directed to develop efficient procedures for finding the missing dimension of a rectangle, first using drawings and then developing the division algorithm pictured by the drawing. During this phase the appropriate associative, commutative and distributive properties are used implicitly in the development. Some of the details of the development of this phase are discussed in the commentary on the back of the pupil pages.

The final instructional phase involves drill and practice with the algorithms. The last few lessons in this section make a start. Other exercises will be needed from the class text or other sources. For additional comment see pages 207 and 208 of VI. Two-Digit Multiplication.

Story problems are scattered throughout. Emphasis is placed upon the use of mathematics symbols to describe problem situations and also upon inventing story problems to match given mathematical sentences. Pupils will need more practice than this with such translating and interpreting. Supplementary work can be found in most fourth-grade mathematics texts.

This section is designed to be used in sequence. Some supplementary work may be needed and care will need to be taken to select activities consistent with the presentations given here.

Many of the lessons in this section were adapted (with permission) from

Robert W. Wirtz, DRILL AND PRACTICE AT THE PROBLEM SOLVING LEVEL, Curriculum Development Associates, 1973.

This section is a revision of an earlier version. Many of the improvements incorporated in this revision were the results of suggestions from Anita Gray who used the entire section with her class at Willagellespie School in Eugene, Oregon.

Each pupil will need five sheets of tagboard (card stock) marked with a grid for making flats, longs, and units. See page 297 for a master for duplication purposes. They will also need a supply of special grid paper. See page 298 for a master.

The outline of the lessons for this section along with a few notes follows:

GRID FOR FLATS, LONGS, AND UNITS

SQUARED PAPER MASTER 3

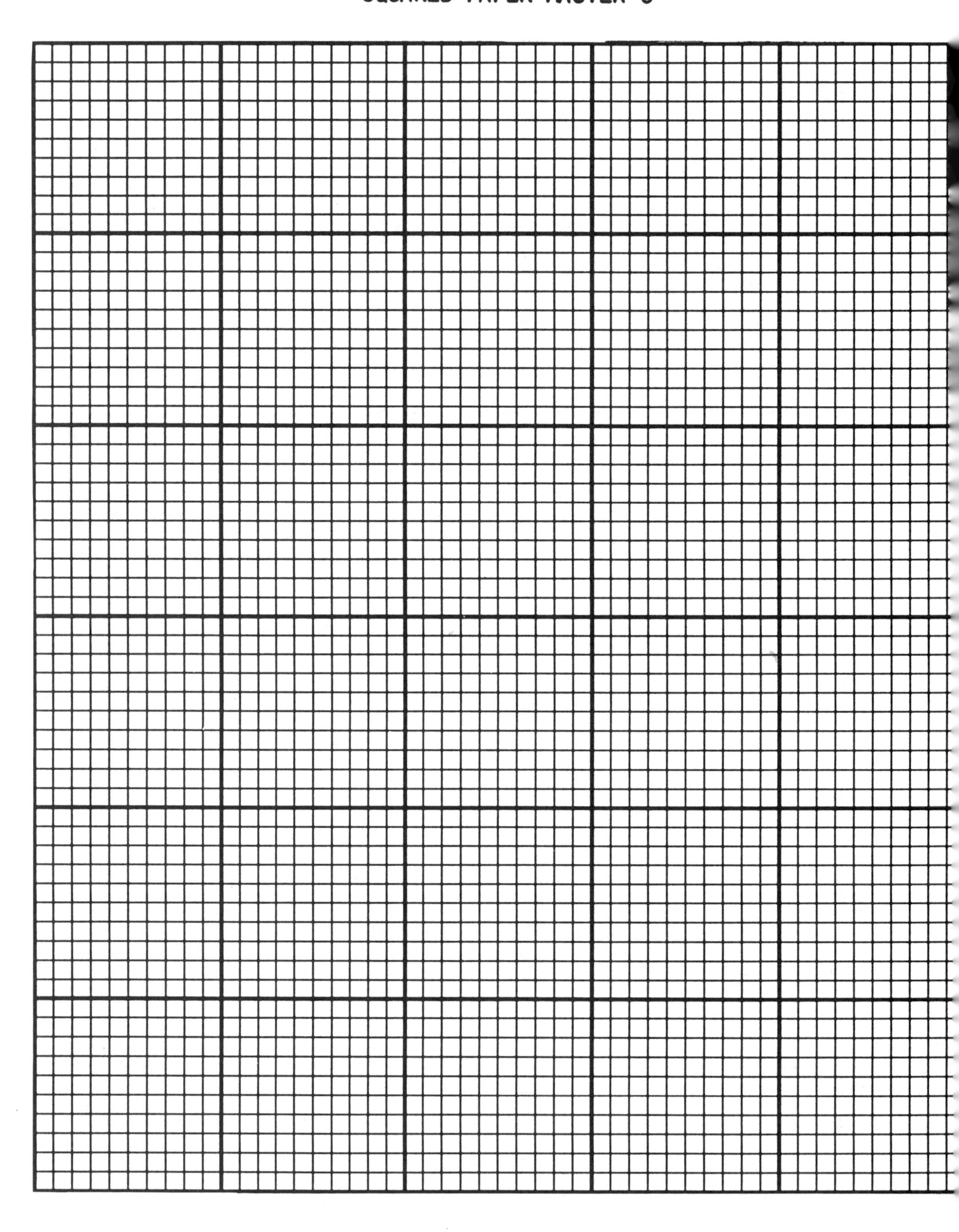

MAKING RECTANGLES - I

1. Take 5 sheets for making flats, longs, and units, a pair of scissors, and 1 large envelope.

Cut 4 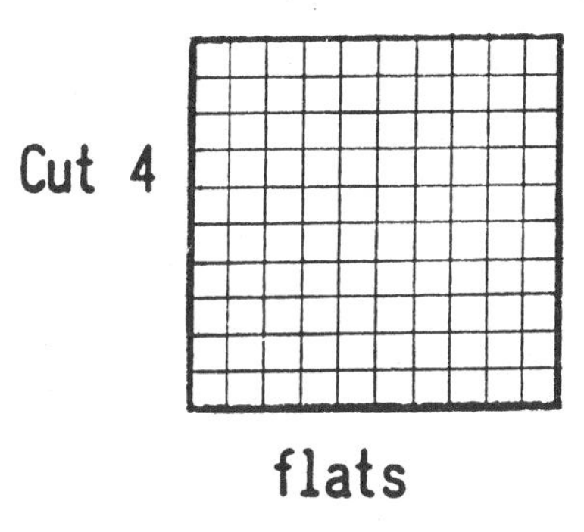

flats

and 20 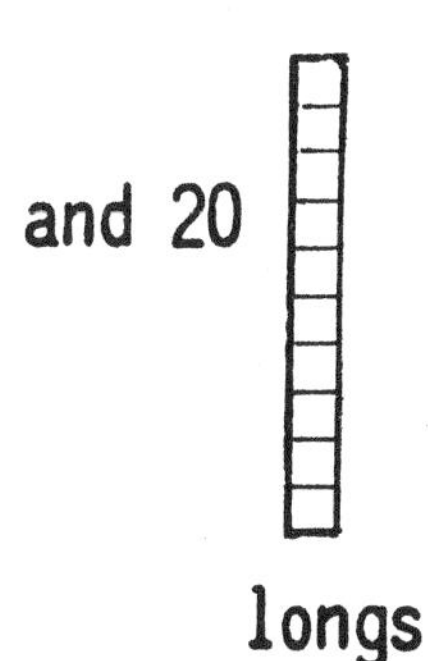

longs

Cut the rest of the paper into small square units.

We will call each of these pieces a <u>unit</u>.

2. Use the pieces. Make rectangles with these dimensions.

   a. 10 by 13 c. 10 by 14

   b. 12 by 10 d. 11 by 15

   Show your teacher.

3. Put all the pieces in a large envelope <u>except</u>

   1 flat
   9 longs
   9 units (small squares).

   Use enough pieces to make a rectangle that is 12 by 13.

   a. How many longs did you use? __________

   b. How many units (small squares) did you use? __________

Making Rectangles-I

Mathematics teaching objectives:

- . Use flats, longs, and units to make rectangles.
- . Provide readiness activities for understanding long division.
- . Visualize base ten place value concepts.
- . Visualize the distributive property (readiness).

Problem-solving skills pupils might use:

- . Make and use a model.
- . Guess and check.
- . Search for and record other solutions.

Materials needed:

- . 5 sheets (tagboard) of grid for flats, longs, units (see page 297)
- . Scissors
- . A 9" x 12" manilla envelope for each pupil

Comments and suggestions:

- . Have pupils cut out the flats, longs, and units as specified in the first activity. This is an important part of the lesson. It will take 15 to 20 minutes to complete this phase of the lesson.
- . Emphasize the vocabulary word "unit" as a shorter name for a small square. The word "dimension" should cause no difficulty since the term was used extensively in the Two-Digit Multiplication section.
- . Remind pupils that the flat is a special rectangle whose dimensions are equal. Such rectangles are called squares. Many pupils have difficulty with this idea. They think rectangles must have unequal dimensions!
- . Ask questions about the pieces with the total class, e.g., How many small squares or units in a flat? a long? How many small squares in 2 longs and 1 flat? etc. This review of place value will help in subsequent lessons.
- . Let pupils continue with activities 2, 3, 4, and 5 individually at first but later in pairs. It is not necessary for pupils to complete the last activity.
- . Move around the classroom. Pupils often put the rectangles together in interesting ways!

Answers:

3. 5 longs. 6 units.

(Answers continued on the next page...

4. Make 5 other rectangles. Make each different.
   Record the dimensions of each rectangle below.

______ by ______
______ by ______
______ by ______
______ by ______
______ by ______

5. Use as many pieces as you wish. Make still other rectangles.
   Record below.

______ by ______
______ by ______
______ by ______
______ by ______
______ by ______
______ by ______
______ by ______
______ by ______
______ by ______
______ by ______
______ by ______

When time is up, put all pieces in the envelope.

Answers: (cont.)

4. Answers will vary. Some possibilities are:

11 by 12	11 by 16
11 by 13	11 by 17
11 by 14	11 by 18
11 by 15	12 by 14

5. Answers will vary.
   Often pupils want to combine their efforts to see how big a rectangle they can make!

MAKING RECTANGLES-II

1. Take 1 flat, 3 longs, and 2 units. Use all the pieces.

   a. Make a rectangle. Give its dimensions.

      _____ by _____

   b. Tell the total number of small square units it contains: _____
      (Hint: There are more than 100 small square units.)

2. Make a rectangle using

	Total number of small square units
a. 1 flat, 4 longs, and 3 units. Dimensions are _____ by _____	_____
b. 1 flat, 6 longs, and 8 units. Dimensions are _____ by _____	_____
c. 1 flat, 5 longs, and 6 units. Dimensions are _____ by _____	_____
d. 2 flats, 8 longs, and 6 units. Dimensions are _____ by _____	_____
e. 1 flat, 8 longs, and 15 units. Dimensions are _____ by _____	_____

Making Rectangles-II

Mathematics teaching objectives:

- . Use flats, longs, and units to build rectangles.
- . Review place value ideas.
- . Provide readiness for factoring numbers.
- . Provide readiness for the distributive property.

Problem-solving skills pupils might use.

- . Make and use a model.
- . Guess and check.
- . Search for other solutions.

Materials needed:

- . Envelope of flats, longs, and units from "Making Rectangles-I"

Comments and suggestions:

- . Conduct a warm-up activity with the flats, longs, and units, e.g., you or a pupil hold up 4 flats, 6 longs, and 2 units. Ask how many units altogether. Continue with the warm-up for several minutes.
- . Work 1 and 2(a) with the class. Let them continue with the remaining activities independently. Have pupils compare their answers. Problem 2(d) and 3(f) each have two correct answers. Emphasize that more than one correct answer for a problem also happens in mathematics.
- . As you move around the room, try to determine how many pupils see the similarity between problems in parts 2 and 3. This similarity should be made explicit before going on with the next lesson.

Answers:

1. a. 12 by 11
   b. 132

2. a. 11 by 13. 143 units
   b. 12 by 14 168 units
   c. 12 by 13 156 units
   d. 13 by 22 or 26 by 11 286 units
   e. 15 by 13 195 units

Notice the number of units in 2(e) cannot be obtained as in 2(a)-(d) by merely recording in succession the number of flats, the number of longs, and the number of units.

3. Use flats, longs, and units. Make rectangles having the total number of small square units listed below. Record the dimensions on the chart.

Total Number of Units	Dimension	Dimension
a. 143		
b. 140		
c. 156		
d. 144		
e. 168		
f. 264		
g. 196		

CHALLENGE

Find the rectangle that uses 2 flats, some longs, and some units and which needs the fewest total pieces.

Give its dimensions: _______ by ______

Tell the total number of small square units in the rectangle. _____

Compare your results with those of your classmates.

Answers: (cont.)

3. a. 11 by 13
   b. 14 by 10
   c. 12 by 13
   d. 12 by 12
   e. 12 by 14
   f. 22 by 12 or 24 by 11
   g. 14 by 14

Challenge: 11 by 21 231 units

Pupils who have spent time on the challenge should be given a fe moments prior to the next lesson to talk about their answers. Allowing some class time for the challenge will encourage more pupils to try them.

FLATS, LONGS, AND PLACE VALUE

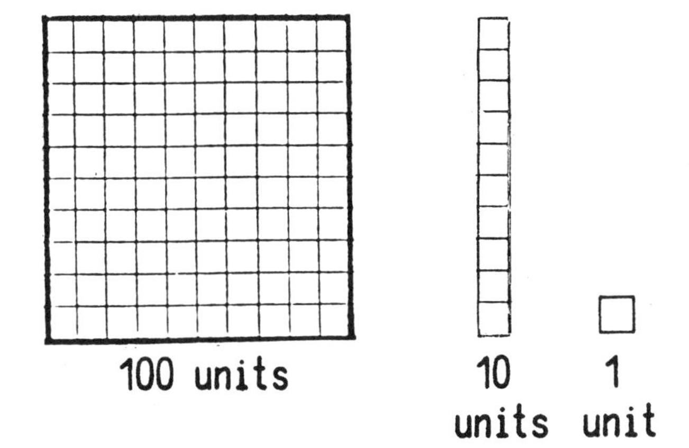

1. You have 1 flat, 2 longs, and 2 units. How many units do you have altogether? ________

2. You have 2 flats, 12 longs, and 15 units. How many units do you have altogether? ________

3. You have 14 flats, 5 longs, and 6 units. How many units do you have altogether? ________

4. Answer these:

	Flats	Longs	Units	Units Altogether
a.	1	5	0	
b.	3	4	2	
c.	0	16	0	
d.	2	0	18	
e.	0	36	5	
f.	3	17	0	
g.	0	21	16	
h.	3	48	0	
i.	2	35	13	
j.	12	0	0	
k.	14	5	6	
ℓ.	14	14	0	

Flats, Longs, And Place Value

Mathematics teaching objectives:

. Review place value ideas (making exchanges in base 10).

. Compute mentally (adding multiples of 10).

. Provide readiness for the distributive property.

Problem-solving skills pupils *might* use:

. Make use of a model.

. Guess and check.

Materials needed:

. Envelope of flats, longs, and units from "Making Rectangles-I"

Comments and suggestions:

. Work problems 1-3 with the class. Notice that in problem 2, exchanges are involved in recording the number of flats and longs. In problem 3, an exchange is involved in recording the number of flats. A concrete demonstration of the exchange can be vividly shown with Dienes blocks. This demonstration would be helpful for some pupils.

. Let pupils proceed on their own with problem 4. Permit the use of the flats, longs, and unit pieces if pupils find them helpful. Problem is more difficult.

. Permit pupils to compare answers and help each other.

. In part 6, remind pupils they will need to exchange longs for flats and units for longs before they can make some of the rectangles. It is not necessary that all the problems be completed before going on with the next lesson.

. Design other lessons like this and use periodically for practice and review.

Answers:

1.	122	2.	335	3.	1456
4. a.	150	e.	365	i.	563
b.	342	f.	470	j.	1200
c.	160	g.	226	k.	1456
d.	218	h.	780	l.	1540

5. Try these harder ones:

	Flats	Longs	Units	Units Altogether
a.	26	34	3	
b.	47	52	5	
c.	32	75	21	
d.	0	132	57	
e.	23	476	321	

6. Use flats, longs, and units. Make rectangles having the total number of units listed below. Record the dimensions on the chart.

	Total Number of Units	Dimension	Dimension
a.	180		
b.	120		
c.	165		
d.	231		
e.	195		
f.	182		
g.	288		
h.	208		
i.	256		
j.	324		

Answers: (cont.)

5. a. 2943
   b. 5225
   c. 3971
   d. 1377
   e. 7381

6. a. 18 by 10*
   b. 12 by 10
   c. 15 by 11
   d. 21 by 11
   e. 13 by 15
   f. 13 by 14
   g. 16 by 18
   h. 13 by 16
   i. 16 by 16
   j. 17 by 12

   * Permit answers such as 9 by 20. However, strictly speaking, the problem did imply the use of one or more flats.

This is an enrichment activity suggested by a teacher who piloted this section

ENRICHMENT ACTIVITY

To give pupils further practice -

1. Have them make a new chart:

Total Number Small Squares	Dimension	Dimension
a.		
b.		
c		

2. Then, have them trade papers with another pupil.

3. Now each pupil makes a rectangle of his/her own and then records the total number of small squares on the paper---leaving the dimension columns blank.

   Do 10 rectangles this way, recording only the number of small squares.

4. Now have pupils return the paper to its original owner and try to find the missing dimensions!

   (Kids loved it and really gave each other challenging problems!)

PICTURE THIS

1. Below are some pictures of rectangles Kim made with flats, longs, and units.

   Make these rectangles using your flats, long, and units.
   Tell . the dimensions of each rectangle.
   . the total number of units each rectangle contains.

a.

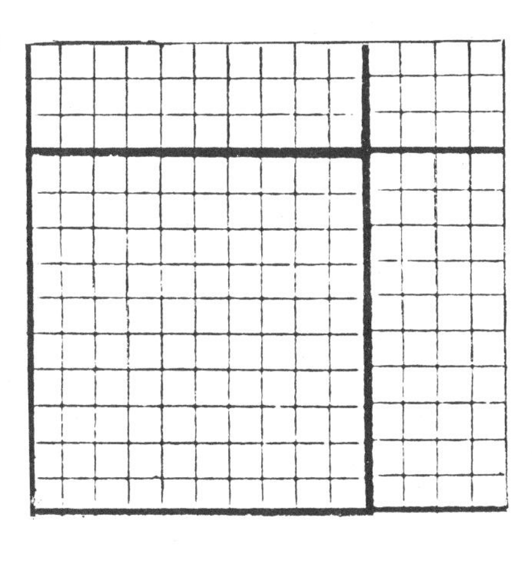

_____ by _____

Total number of of units _____

b.

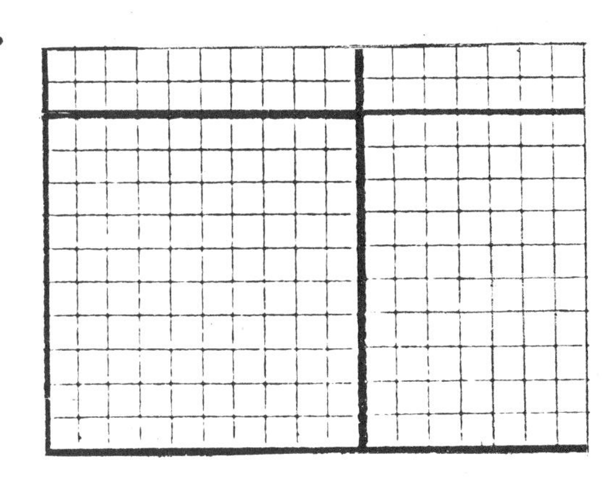

_____ by _____

Total number of of units _____

c.

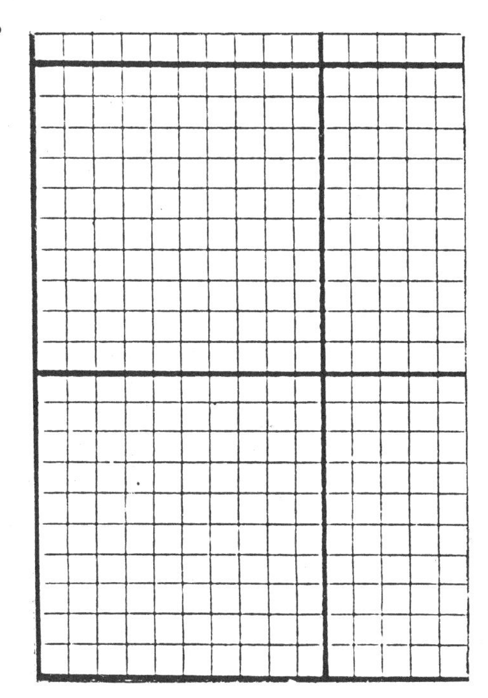

_____ by _____

Total number of units _____

SM 81

Picture This

Mathematics teaching objectives:

- Provide readiness background for an understanding of the division algorithm.
- Practice making models from drawings.
- Solve a division problem using a drawing.

Problem-solving skills pupils might use:

- Make and use drawings and models.
- Make generalizations based upon examples.
- Solve problems using a drawing.

Materials needed:

- Envelope of flats, longs, and units from "Making Rectangles-I"
- Special squared paper

Comments and suggestions:

- Place 1(a), (b) and (c) on an overlay or on a laminated chart. Work through 1(a) with the class and let them work the other parts independently.
- Work parts 2 and 3 with the class. The main purpose of this is to help pupils record in a special way the rectangles they make with their flats, longs, and units. This special way of recording will be used later to develop the division algorithm.
- Let them work parts 4 and 5 independently. Every pupil should try working the story problem. It will be used as the starting point for the next lesson.

Answers:

1. a. 13 by 14 (or 14 by 13) 182 units

   b. 12 by 17 (or 17 by 12) 204 units

   c. 21 by 15 (or 15 by 21) 315 units

   Remind pupils the dimensions of a rectangle can be read either way.

(Answers continued on the next page....)

Picture This (cont.)

2. Kim made 4 other rectangles and drew these pictures of them on a sheet of special squared paper:

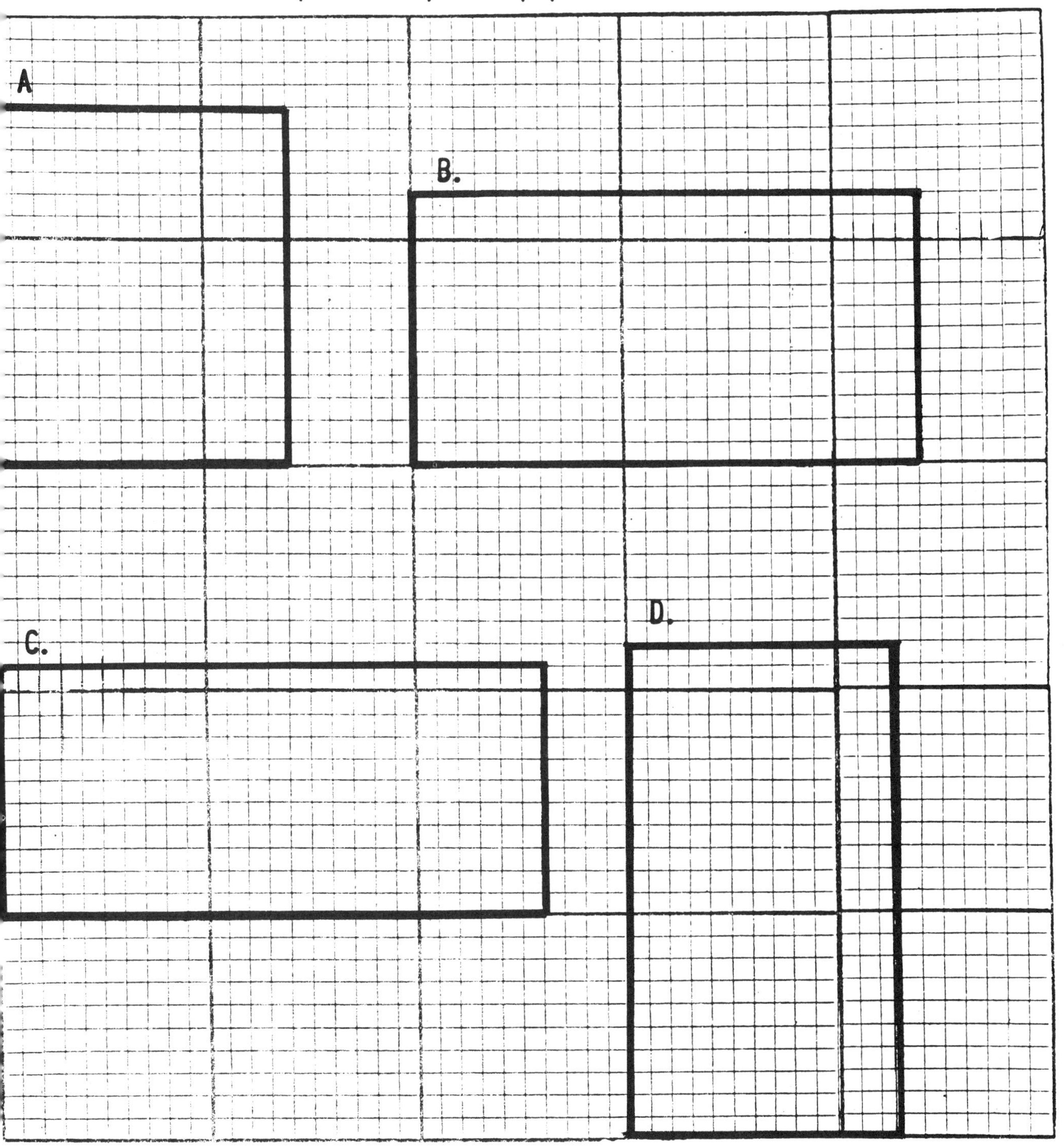

Use the pictures Kim drew to answer these questions:

Answers: (cont.)

2. a. 16 by 14
   b. D
   c. B
   d. C and D
   e. line
   f. The lower left corner of each rectangle is placed in the corner formed by two heavy black lines on the special graph paper.

3. a. A drawing of a 18 by 23 rectangle
   b. A drawing of a 24 by 12 rectangle
   c. A drawing of a 24 by 11 or a 12 by 22 rectangle*

   Check to see if pupil used Kim's way to record the rectangles they made.

4. a. A drawing of a 13 by 21 rectangle
   b. A drawing of a 15 by 11 rectangle
   c. A drawing of a 21 by 10 or a 7 by 30 rectangle*

5. 22 cases. Pupils might recognize that the rectangle made for 3(b) suggests the answer to the problem.

*Pupils should be reminded that often there is more than one answer to a problem.

a. The dimensions of rectangle A are ____ by ____ .

b. Rectangle ____ measures 22 by 13.

c. Rectangle ____ was made with 2 flats, 8 longs, and 8 units.

d. Rectangles ____ and ____ each contain the same total number of units.

e. Each rectangle "sits" on a heavy black ________ .

f. Tell what you notice about where Kim placed the lower left corner of each rectangle.

3. Use a sheet of special squared paper. Use Kim's way.

   a. Draw a rectangle with dimensions 18 by 23.

   b. Draw a rectangle made with 2 flats, 8 longs, and 8 units.

   c. Draw a rectangle that contains 264 units.

4. Draw these rectangles.

   a. a rectangle whose dimensions are 13 by 21.

   b. a rectangle made with 1 flat, 6 longs, and 5 units.

   c. a rectangle that contains 210 total units.

5. Solve this problem any way you can. You may find special squared paper or the flats, longs, and units to be helpful.

   Mr. Smith's class is in charge of ordering pop for the school picnic. They need 288 cans of pop. The pop comes in cases which hold 24 cans. How many cases of pop should the class order?

SOME DIVISION PROBLEMS

1. Use squared paper or flats, longs, and units. Solve each problem below.

   a. One dimension of a rectangle is 24. There are 288 units in the rectangle. What is the other dimension? ________

   b. Twenty-four pupils from Miss Cone's room collected 288 empty bottles. They decided to divide up the bottles evenly and return them to the grocery store for the deposit fee. How many bottles would each pupil get to return? ________

   c. Mr. Smith's class is in charge of ordering pop for the school picnic. They need 288 cans of pop. The pop comes in cases which each hold 24 cans. How many cases of pop should the class order? ________

2. Answer these questions about the three division problems you just solved. Discuss your answers with the class.

   a. What do you notice about the answers? ____________________

   b. In what other ways are the problems alike?

   c. Which problem is a <u>missing-dimension</u> problem? ________

   d. Which problem is a <u>divide-evenly</u> problem? ________

   e. Which problem can be done by doing many subtractions? ______

Some Division Problems

Mathematics teaching objectives:

- Use a drawing to solve division story problems.
- Invent division story problems.
- Write number sentences for story problems.
- Practice division by single-digit divisor.
- Find the missing dimension of a rectangle using a drawing.

Problem-solving skills pupils *might* use:

- Make and use a drawing.
- Find likenesses and differences.
- Describe situations using mathematical expressions.
- Work backwards.

Materials needed:

- Special squared paper

Comments and suggestions:

- Spend two days on this lesson. The first day should include 1-4.
- Place 1 and 2 on an overlay and work them together as a class. The same division number sentence, $288 \div 24 = \square$ can be used to find the answer to 1(a), (b) and (c). Each problem is a different interpretation of division and this fact should be the outcome of the discussions for 2(a)-(c). The three division types could be referred to as the "missing dimension," "divide evenly" (or partition), and "repeated subtraction" interpretations. An extensive treatment of these types with the class is not appropriate at this time.
- Start the class on problem 3 by working part (a) in class. Let them work parts (b)-(e) and the review in part 4 on their own. More review of this type may be needed. If so, refer to the textbook.
- Begin the second day by having pupils compare their rectangles with classmates. Work 5(a) and (b) with the class. The given dimension for these problems has 2 rather than 1 digit as in 3(a)-(e). Let pupils complete the rest of the assignment independently.
- Have interested pupils read some of their invented story problems in class.

(Answers are on the next page...)

Some Division Problems (cont.)

3. Use special squared paper. Make the rectangles listed below. Record the missing dimensions on the chart.

	Total Number of Units	Dimension	Dimension
a.	84	6	
b.	84		7
c.	56	4	
d.	90	6	
e.	91		7

4. Work these: Some have remainders.

a. $9\overline{)117}$

b. $8\overline{)136}$

c. $105 \div 7 = \square$

d. $114 \div 6 = \square$

e. $8\overline{)145}$

f. $8\overline{)192}$

g. $53 \div 4 = \square$

h. $283 \div 10 = \square$

5. Use special squared paper. Make the rectangles listed below. Record the missing dimension on the chart.

	Total Number of Units	Dimension	Dimension
a.	180	10	
b.	198	11	
c.	228		19
d.	252	18	
e.	240		16

Some Division Problems

Answers:

1. a. 12
   b. 12
   c. 12

2. a. All answers are the same.
   b. The problems can all be solved by division. All the numbers given in each problem are the same.
   c. 2 a
   d. 2 b
   e. 2 c

3. a. 14
   b. 12
   c. 14
   d. 15
   e. 13

   Check to see if the pupils have drawn their rectangles correctly or have pupils check each other.

4. a. 13
   b. 17
   c. 15
   d. 19
   e. 18 remainder 1
   f. 24
   g. 13 remainder 1
   h. 28 remainder 3

5. a. 18
   b. 18
   c. 12
   d. 14
   e. 15

   Check pupils drawings.

6. 14 tiles long

7. a. $96 ÷ 4 = □
   b. 76 ÷ 4 = □
   c. $1.80 x 13 = □
   d. 360 ÷ 18 = □

8. Answers will vary.

6. Make a drawing to solve this problem.

   Dick used 252 square tiles to cover a rectangular table top. The table was 18 tiles wide. How many tiles long was the table?

7. Write a division or multiplication sentence which can be used to solve these.

   a. Susan's family paid $96 for 4 used bikes. Each bike cost the same amount. How much did each bike cost?

   b. The school bus seats 76 pupils in rows of 4 across. How many rows of seats in the bus?

   c. A dozen cookies cost $1.80. How much will 13 dozen cost?

   d. There are 360 gum drops in a candy jar. Eighteen gum drops are being placed in paper sacks. How many sacks of candy can be made?

8. Make up some division story problems. Solve them using special squared paper.

A DRAWING SHOWING DIVISION

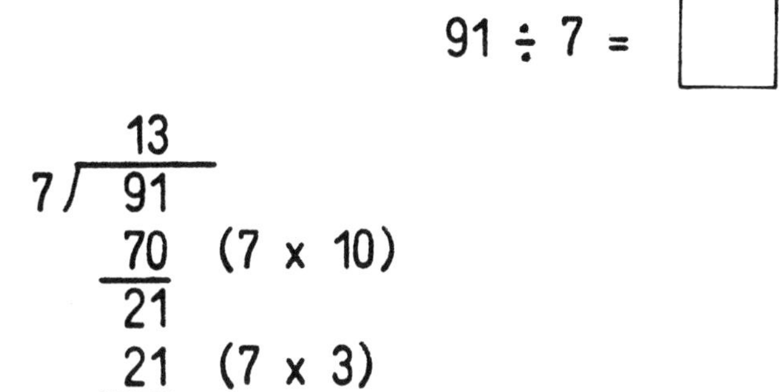

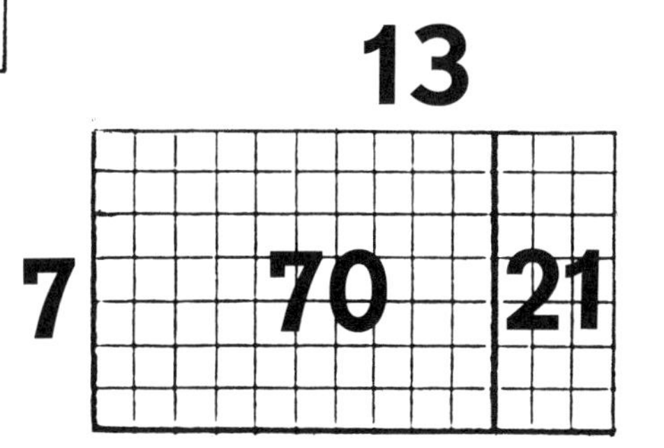

1. Study the division problem above and its drawing. Make a drawing for these. Fill in the numbers.

a.
```
     16
9 / 144
     90  (9 x 10)
     54
     54  (9 x 6)
```

b.
```
     19
8 / 152
     80  (8 x 10
     72
     72  (8 x 9)
```

c.
```
     23
7 / 161
    140  (7 x 20)
     21
     21  (7 x 3)
```

2. Study the division problem and its drawing.

```
    12
8 / 98
    80
    18
    16
     2 remainder
```

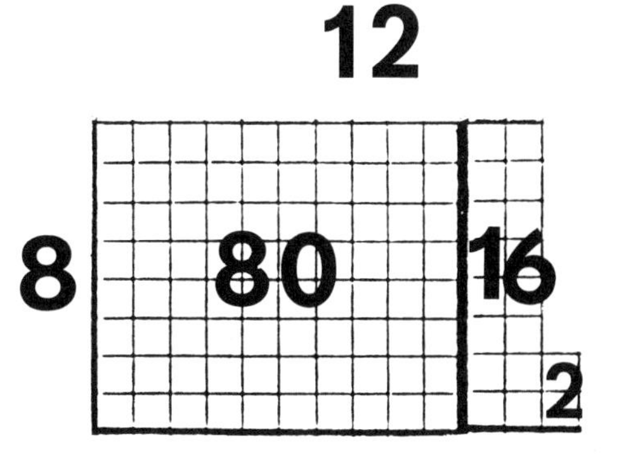

A Drawing Showing Division

Mathematics teaching objectives:

. Use a drawing to explain the 1-digit divisor algorithm.

. Practice division by a single-digit divisor with remainders.

. Invent division story problems.

. Visualize the distributive property.

Problem-solving skills pupils might use:

. Make and use a drawing.

. Study the solution process.

. Make explanations.

. Work backwards.

Materials needed:

. Special squared paper

Comments and suggestions:

. Review the missing dimension problems from part 3 of the previous lesson. This lesson includes a more detailed study of the process used. It should now be obvious to the pupils that missing dimension problems can be thought of as a division problem.

. Have pupils study the introductory problem and its solution. Write on the chalkboard (7 x 10) + (7 x 3) = 91. Have pupils explain how the drawing shows this.

. Elicit from the pupils a way for making a similar drawing for 1(a). Let them complete 1(b) and 1(c) independently and compare their drawings with a classmate.

. Circulate around the classroom as pupils complete the lesson independently or with a partner. They should not have difficulty with the remainder concept. However, some may not like to attach the remainder to the rectangle. This is O.K.!

Answers:

1. a., b. and c. Drawings

2. a.

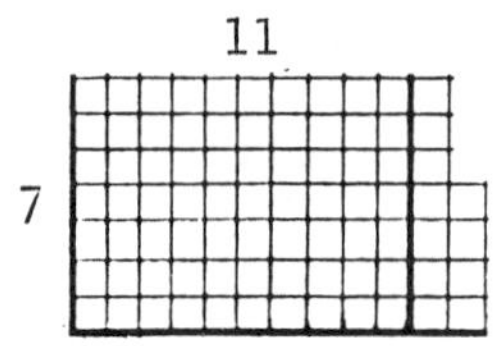

11

7

The remainder of four can be placed anywhere the pupils like.

b. and c.

Drawings similar to the one for 2(a)

2. (continued)

   Make a drawing for these. Fill in the numbers.

   a.
$$\begin{array}{r} 11 \\ 7\overline{)81} \\ \underline{70} \\ 11 \\ \underline{7} \\ 4 \end{array}$$
   remainder

   b.
$$\begin{array}{r} 14 \\ 6\overline{)89} \\ \underline{60} \\ 29 \\ \underline{24} \\ 5 \end{array}$$

   c.
$$\begin{array}{r} 23 \\ 5\overline{)117} \\ \underline{100} \\ 17 \\ \underline{15} \\ 2 \end{array}$$

3. Suppose you were asked to make drawings for these. Which ones would be "perfect" rectangles? Do not make the drawings. Give reasons for your answer.

   a. $3\overline{)49}$

   b. $6\overline{)84}$

   c. $8\overline{)92}$

   d. $7\overline{)75}$

   e. $9\overline{)105}$

   f. $7\overline{)91}$

   g. $4\overline{)68}$

   h. $5\overline{)79}$

   i. $7\overline{)105}$

4. Make up 4 division story problems.
   The answers to two of them should have remainders.

Answers: (cont.)

3. b, f, g, and i are "perfect" rectangles. All these "come out even." The others all have a remainder.

4. Answers will vary. Often pupils like to read the problems invented by other class members.

FOUND - SOME MISSING DIMENSIONS

1. Fill in the blanks with the dimensions for each rectangle.

a.

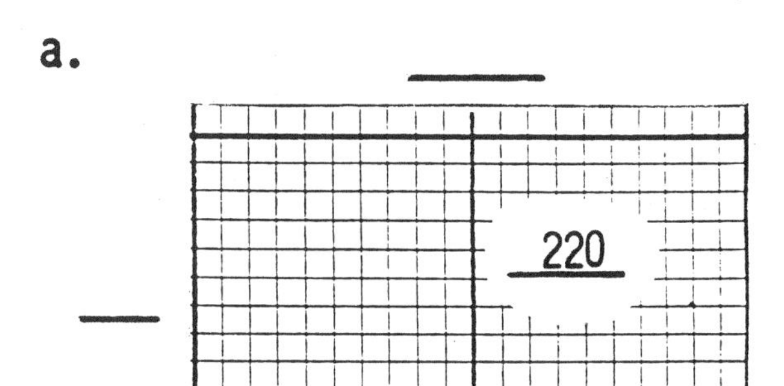

b.

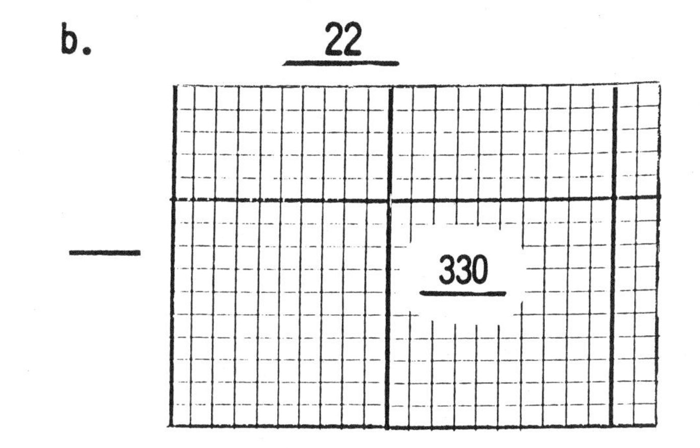

c.

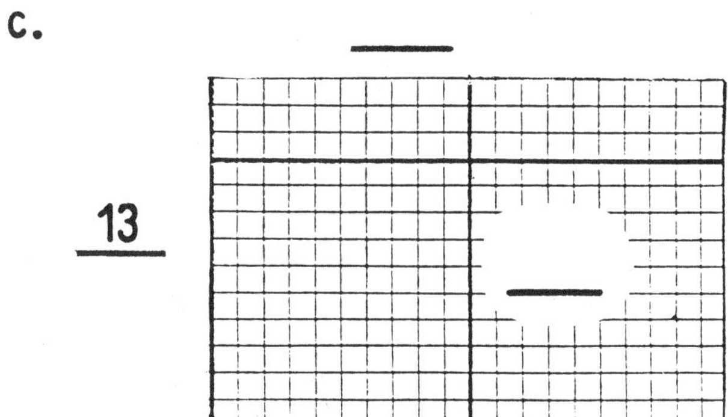

2. The printer for this page failed to ink her press correctly. Some of the rectangles did not print completely. Try to fill in the blanks for each rectangle.

a.

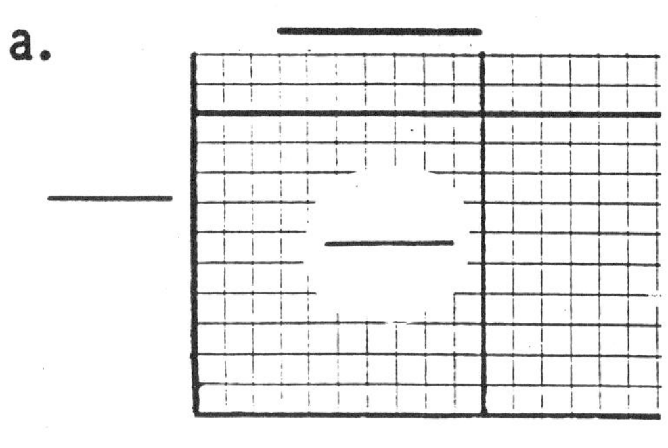

b.

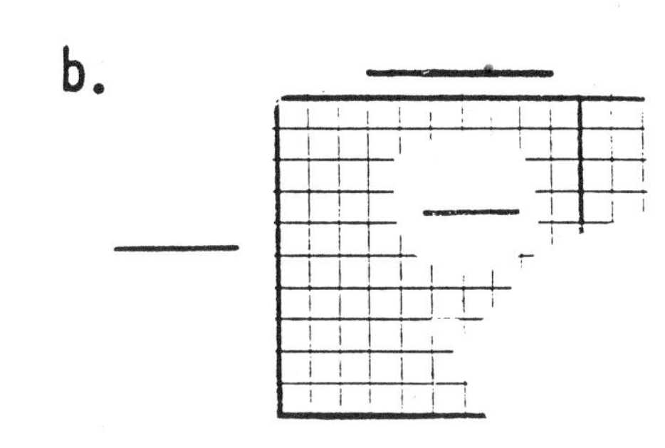

c.

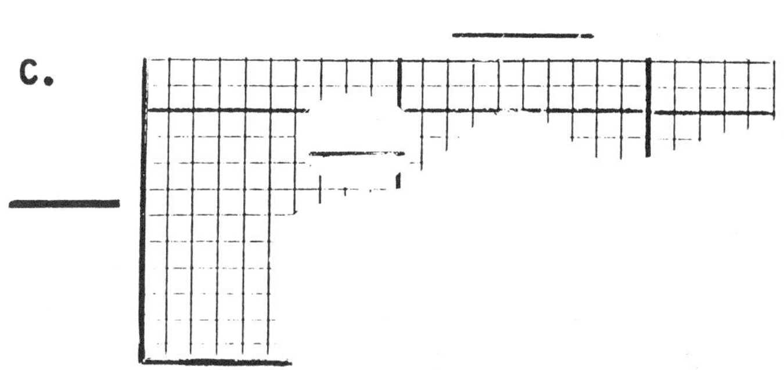

Found - Some Missing Dimensions

Mathematics teaching objectives:

. Write division numbers and story problems from drawings.

Problem-solving skills pupils might use:

. Make and use a drawing.

. Use mathematical expressions to describe drawings.

. Invent problems suggested by drawings.

Materials needed:

. Special squared paper

Comments and suggestions:

. Have pupils proceed on their own after a brief introduction. The purpose of the lesson is to extend the drawing method for dividing by a one-digit number to dividing by a two-digit number.

. After pupils have completed the lesson, have them discuss how they found the number of units in 2(b) and (c). These exercises emphasize the relationship between multiplication and division.

. Ask pupils to read some of their missing dimension problems, 3(a)-(d) with the class.

Answers:

1. a. 11 by 20
   b 22 by 15
   c. 13 by 20 260 units

2. a. 12 by 16 192 units (12 x 16 = 192)
   b. 10 by 12 120 units (10 x 12 = 120)
   c. 12 by 25 300 units (12 x 25 = 300)

3. Stories will vary.

Make up division story problems to match these drawings.
Make each story as different from the others as you can.

a.

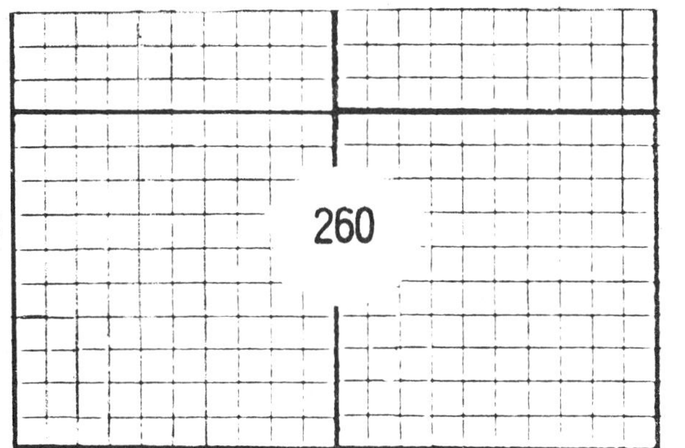

b.

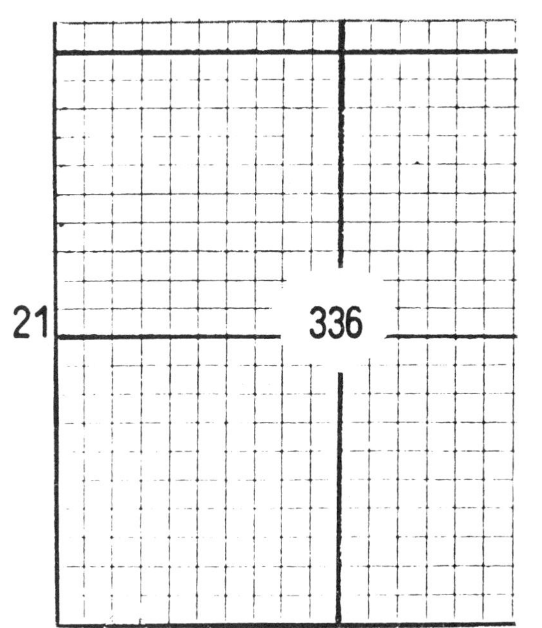

c.

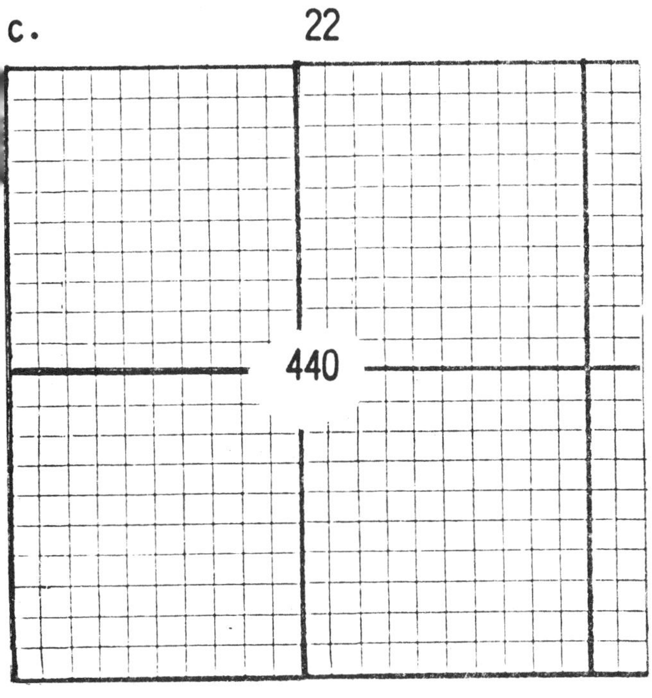

d.

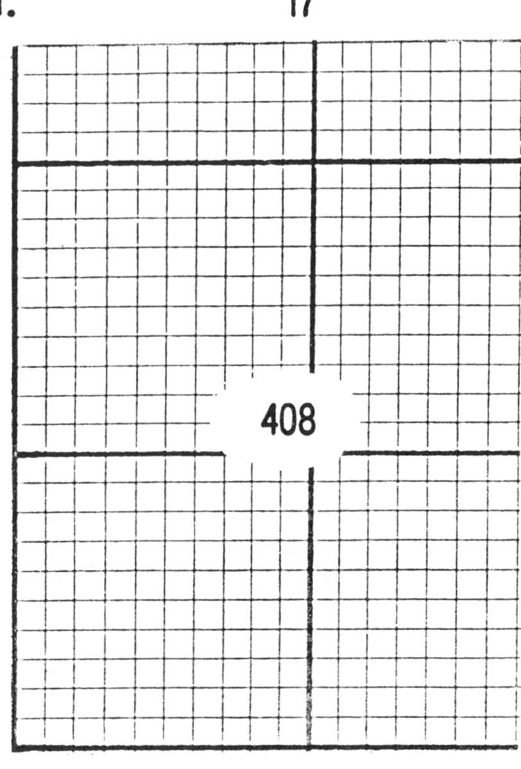

RECTANGLES AND DIVISION - A

Draw these rectangles on special squared paper. Fill in the blanks.

a.

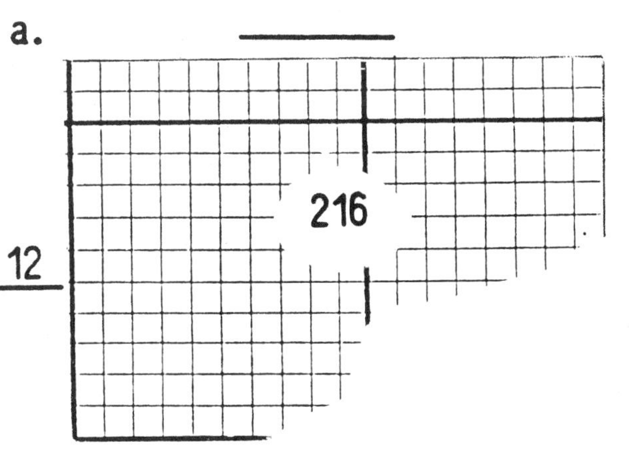

b.

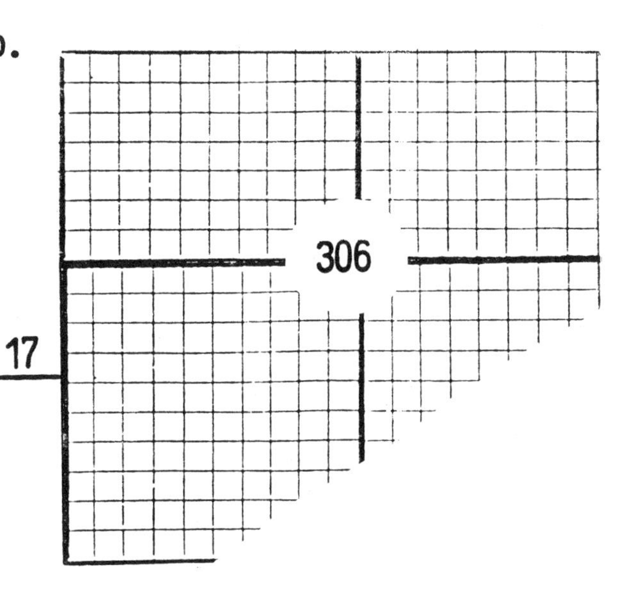

c.

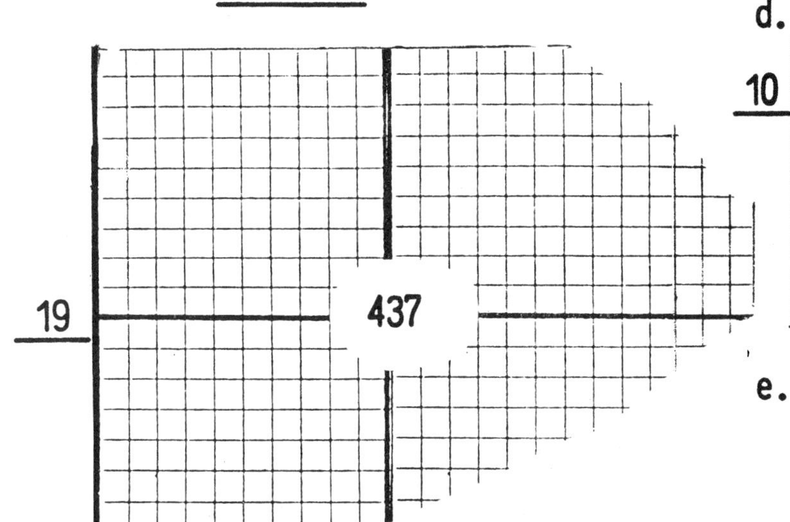

d.

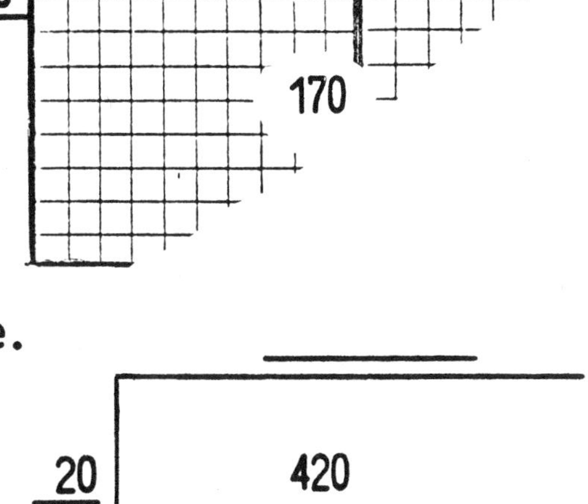

e.

20 | 420

f.

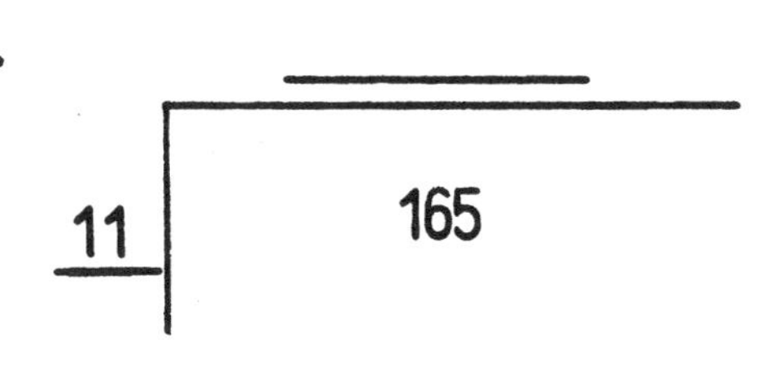

g.

18 | 216

h. $14 \overline{)224}$

i. $14 \overline{)294}$

Rectangles And Division-A

Mathematics teaching objectives:

- . Solve long division problems using drawings.
- . Search for a short-cut for solving division problems.
- . Write division number problems from drawings.

Problem-solving skills a pupil *might* use:

- . Make and use a drawing.
- . Study the solution process.
- . Solve a problem by using a different procedure.
- . Identify patterns suggested by drawings.

Materials needed:

- . Special squared paper

Comments and suggestions:

- . Give out the lesson and circulate around the room. See what pupils can do on their own with only an occasional suggestion. After awhile have pupils work in groups of 2 or 3.

Note: Do not assign the lesson as homework. The object of the lesson is for pupils to discover something about the division algorithm. If pupils take it home, adults may inadvertently work against this objective.

Answers:

1.
   - a. 12 by 18 - 216 units
   - b. 17 by 18 - 306 units
   - c. 19 by 23 - 437 units
   - d. 10 by 17 - 170 units
   - e. 20 by 21 - 420 units
   - f. 11 by 15 - 165 units
   - g. 18 by 12 - 216 units
   - h. 14 by 16 - 224 units
   - i. 14 by 21 - 294 units

2.
   - a. $15\overline{)375}$ or $375 \div 15 = \square$
   - b. $13\overline{)286}$ or $286 \div 13 = \square$
   - c. $30\overline{)360}$ or $360 \div 30 = \square$
   - d. $22\overline{)330}$ or $330 \div 22 = \square$

3. Answers will vary. Read some of the story problems in class.

2. Write a division number problem to match each rectangle below.

a.

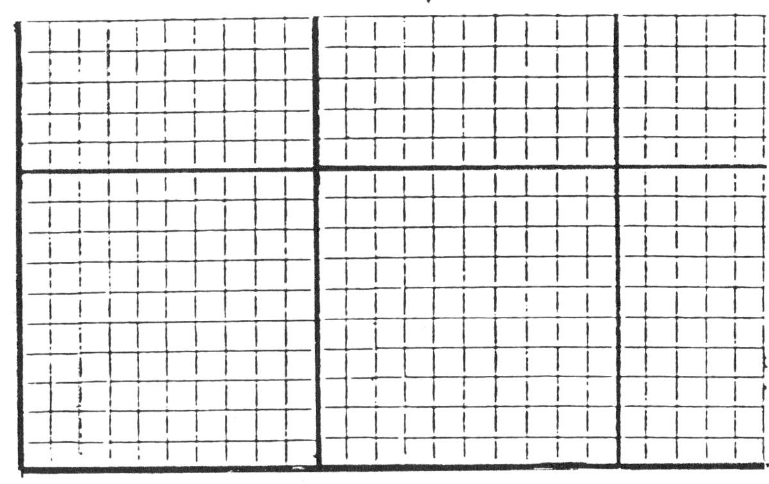

b.

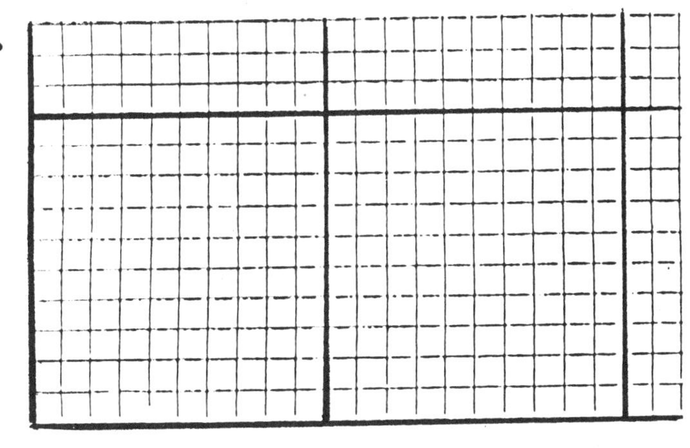

c.

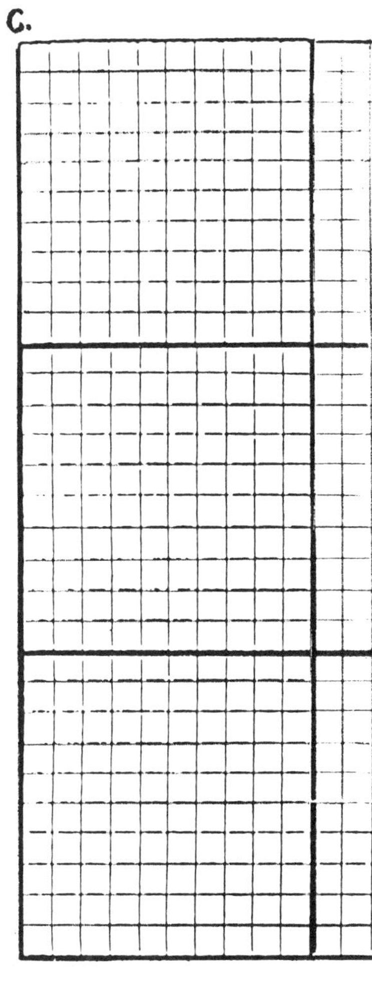

d.

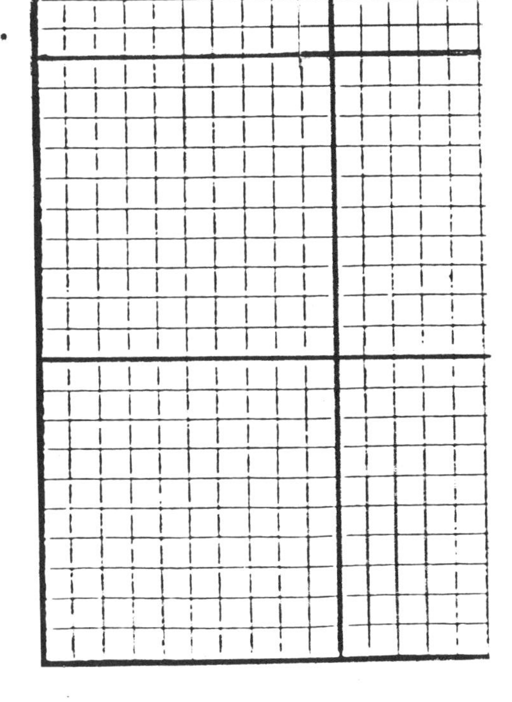

3. Write a story problem for 2a and 2b.

RECTANGLES AND DIVISION - B

1. Solve these division problems. Use the special squared paper.

a. $16 \overline{)224}$

b. $19 \overline{)285}$

c. $21 \overline{)252}$

d. $17 \overline{)289}$

e. $17 \overline{)221}$

f. $13 \overline{)312}$

2. Mental arithmetic. See if you can get all these answers in a minute!

a. $20 \times 15 = \square$

b. $23 \times 20 = \square$

c. $43 \times 10 = \square$

d. $30 \times 25 = \square$

e. $40 \times 6 = \square$

f. $25 \times 40 = \square$

g. $30 \times 23 = \square$

h. $16 \times 20 = \square$

i. $18 \times 30 = \square$

j. $40 \times 20 = \square$

Rectangles And Division-B

Mathematics teaching objectives:

. Solve long division problems using drawings.

. Search for a short-cut for solving division problems.

. Write division number problems for story problems.

Problem-solving skills pupils might use:

. Study the solution process.

. Use mathematical expressions for problem situations.

. Make and use a drawing.

. Solve a problem using a different procedure.

Materials needed:

. Special squared paper

Comments and suggestions:

. Do not insist that pupils use the special squared paper if they seem to be making progress developing their own algorithms. The purpose of this lesson is to create a need for finding a more efficient method and to provide a background for understanding the usual division algorithm in the next lesson.

. Move about the room providing only enough help to keep pupils at task. The focus of any assistance should still be on getting the answer by using drawings.

. After about 20 minutes of drawing rectangles for part 1, have pupils do the mental arithmetic, 2(a)-(j).

Answers:

1. a. 14
   b. 15
   c. 12
   d. 17
   e. 13
   f. 24

Study the pupils' papers to see how they obtained their answers. This information could be helpful in planning future lessons.

2. a. 300
   b. 460
   c. 430
   d. 750
   e. 240
   f. 1000
   g. 690
   h. 320
   i. 540
   j. 800

Pupils need much practice with exercises such as these if they are to develop skill with the division algorithm or estimatin in general. There may be exercises like this in the class textbook. If not, it would be advisable to write some for the class.

3. Write multiplication and division sentences which can be used to solve these story problems. Do not solve the problems. The numbers are too big!

   a. Miguel's stamp book has room for 11,520 stamps. Each page holds 120 stamps. How many pages does the book have?

   b. Sue has a paper route. She delivers 246 papers each day of the week. How many papers does she deliver in a year?

   c. The football stadium holds 19,671 people. There are 83 rows of seats. Each row has the same number of seats. How many seats are in each row?

   d. Rosa's family spends $4114.20 a year on house payments. How much are their monthly house payments?

   e. It would take 10,146 bottle caps to cover a long lunchroom table. The table is 267 bottlecaps long. How many bottlecaps wide is it?

Answers: (cont.)

3. a. $11,520 \div 120 = \square$ or $120\overline{)11,520}$

b. $246 \times 365 = \square$ or

$$\begin{array}{r} 246 \\ \times\ 365 \\ \hline \end{array}$$

c. $19,671 \div 83 = \square$ or $83\overline{)19,671}$

d. $\$4114.20 \div 12 = \square$ or $12\overline{)4114.20}$

e. $10,146 \div 267 = \square$ or $267\overline{)10,146}$

A SHORTER METHOD FOR FINDING THE MISSING DIMENSION

Problem: The total number of units in a rectangle is 221. One dimension is 17. What is the other dimension?

1. <u>Shorter Method</u>

```
      3 }
     10 } 13
17 ) 221
     170 ←(17 x 10)
      51
      51 ←(17 x 3)
```

<u>Drawing Method</u>

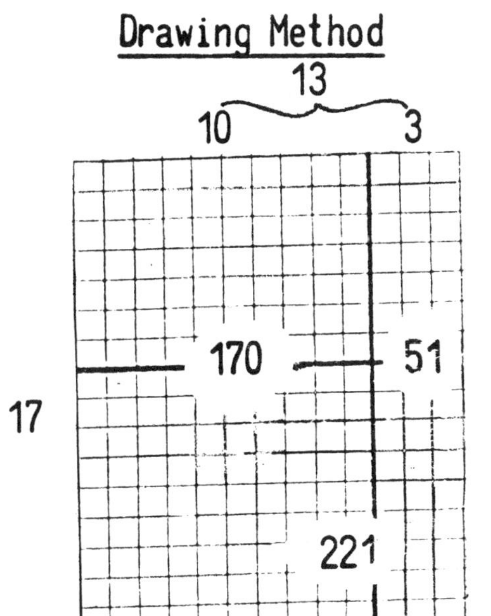

a. Notice where these numbers are in both methods.

17 13 10 3 221 170 51

b. What is the other dimension? ____

2.

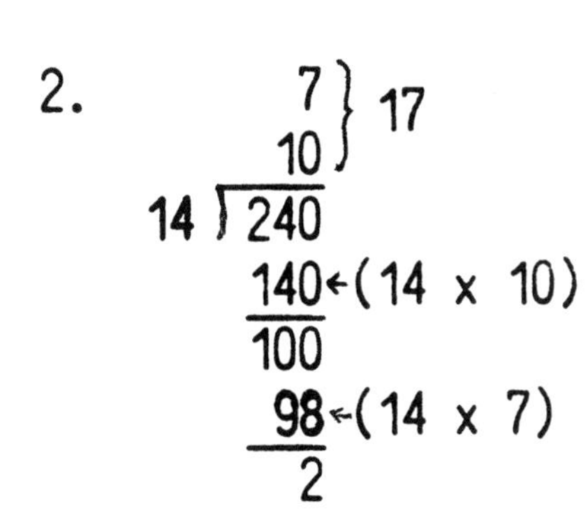

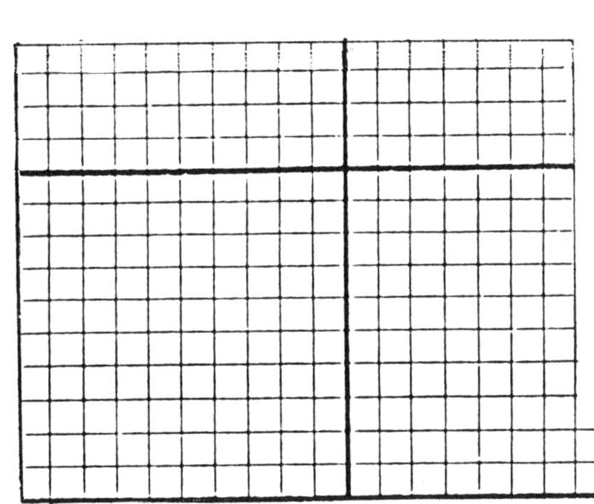

Put these numbers on the drawing as in 1-a.

14 17 10 7

238 140 98

2

3.

```
      4 }
     10 } 14
15 ) 210
     150
      60
      60
```

Make a drawing to show the problem. Fill in each of the numbers used in the problem.

A Shorter Method For Finding The Missing Dimension

Mathematics teaching objectives:

- . Teach the division algorithm with understanding.
- . Practice using the division algorithm.
- . Write story problems.

Problem-solving skills pupils <u>might</u> use:

- . Study the solution process.
- . Make and use drawings.
- . Identify patterns suggested by drawings.
- . Use mathematical expressions for problem situations.

Materials needed:

- . Special squared paper

Comments and suggestions:

- . Prepare an overlay of page 339. Work through parts 1 and 2 along with the class. They will have some difficulty placing the numbers in the appropriate places. Notice the dimensions of the rectangle in the drawings are assigned so they correspond easily with the numbers in the algorithm. Up until this time, no set procedure was used in assigning the divisor as the length or width. Pupils should sense that this restricted assignment is a matter of convenience rather than necessity.
- . In problem 1 some pupils think of (17 x 10) as 17 tens but (17 x 3) as 3 seventeens. Encourage such flexibility with these pupils.
- . Notice part 2 shows one way to picture a remainder.
- . Have pupils work parts 3 through 6 independently or in groups of 2 or 3. Circulate around the room offering assistance where pupils fail to understand. Pupils may need more practice.

Answers:

1. b. 13

2.

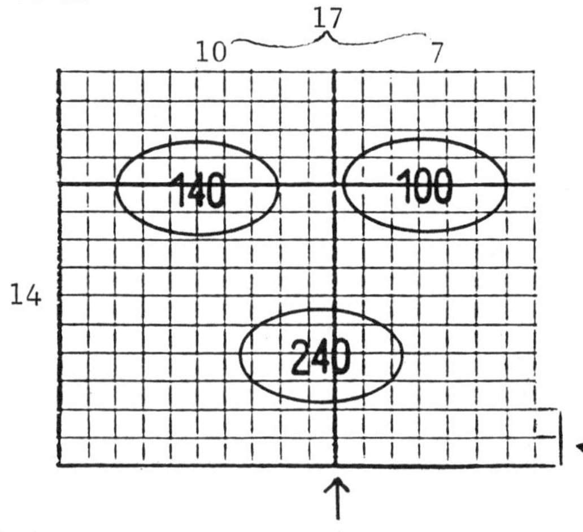

14 is the width or height of the rectangle.

17 is the other dimension.

140 - the number of units to the left heavy line marked with the arrow.

100 - the number of units to the right that line, including the 2 units not a part of that rectangle.

240 - the number of units in the rectangle plus the 2 other units.

3. A drawing similar to the one shown in part 1 of the pupil page.

4.

$$\begin{array}{r} 14 \\ 16 \overline{)227} \\ \underline{160} \\ 67 \\ \underline{64} \\ 3 \end{array}$$

Make a drawing. Fill in the numbers.

5. Find the answer to these division exercises.
   Use the shorter method. Some may have a remainder.

   a. $19 \overline{)228}$

   b. $204 \div 17$

   c. $23 \overline{)302}$

   d. $385 \div 35$

   e. $21 \overline{)315}$

   f. $305 \div 29$

6. Write a story problem to match problems 5a and 5b.

Answers: (cont.)

4. A drawing similar to the answer for part 2. (See page 340.)

5. a. 12 d. 11

b. 12 e. 15

c. 13 r 3 f. 10 r 15

6. Answers will vary. (Ask for volunteers to share their problem with the class.)

PROBLEMS TO SOLVE

1. Use the "shorter method." Solve these problems. Some have remainders.

a. $15\overline{)195}$

e. $13\overline{)208}$

b. $17\overline{)204}$

f. $21\overline{)253}$

c. $14\overline{)182}$

g. $25\overline{)280}$

d. $18\overline{)198}$

h. $16\overline{)288}$

2. See if you can get all these answers in a minute. Do as many as you can mentally.

a. 20 x 17 = ☐

f. 37 x 20 = ☐

b. 30 x 44 = ☐

g. 87 x 10 = ☐

c. 28 x 30 = ☐

h. 24 x 30 = ☐

d. 10 x 98 = ☐

i. 19 x 40 = ☐

e. 52 x 20 = ☐

j. 23 x 50 = ☐

Problems To Solve

Mathematics teaching objectives:

- . Practice using the division algorithm.
- . Write story problems.

Problem-solving skills pupils *might* use:

- . Study the solution process.
- . Invent problems for mathematical expressions.

Materials needed:

- . None

Comments and suggestions:

- . Work 1(a) and 1(b) with the class before having them do the others independently.
- . After about 20 minutes on part 1, have the class do the mental arithmetic in 2(a) through 2(j). This skill is needed for proficiency with the division algorithm.
- . Ask for volunteers to share the story problems with the class. The format of 3(a) through 3(c) almost forces pupils to write different types of division problems, namely "missing dimension, "divide evenly," and "repeated subtraction" (see commentary for "Some Division Problems," page 318).

Answers:

1. a. 13 e. 16

   b. 12 f. 12 r 1

   c. 13 g. 11 r 5

   d. 11 h. 18

roblems To Solve (cont.)

. Write a story problem to match each number problem below.
Answer each problem.

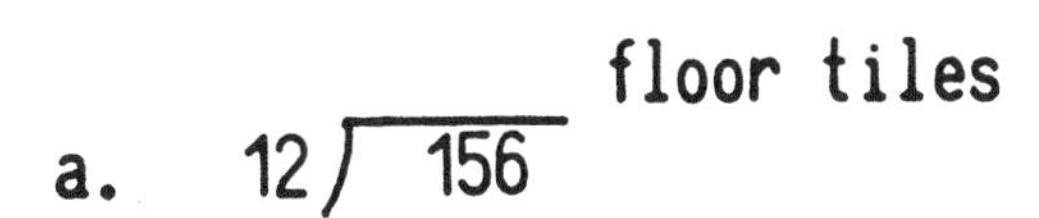

floor tiles

a. 12 ⟌ 156

cases of juice

b. 24 ⟌ 312

students in each room

c. 28 ⟌ 336

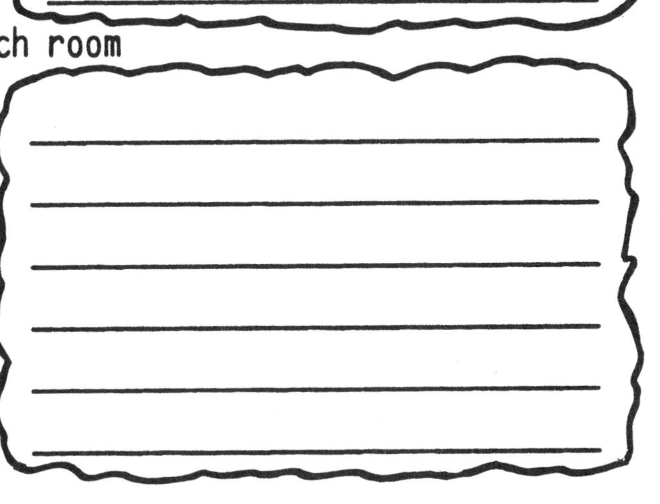

d. Write a story problem to match this number problem.

23 ⟌ 414

LARGER RECTANGLES WITH MISSING DIMENSIONS

Problem: The total number of units in a rectangle is 575. One dimension is 25. What is the other dimension?

1. Shorter Method

```
     3 } 23
    20 }
25 ) 575
    500
     75
     75
```

Drawing Method

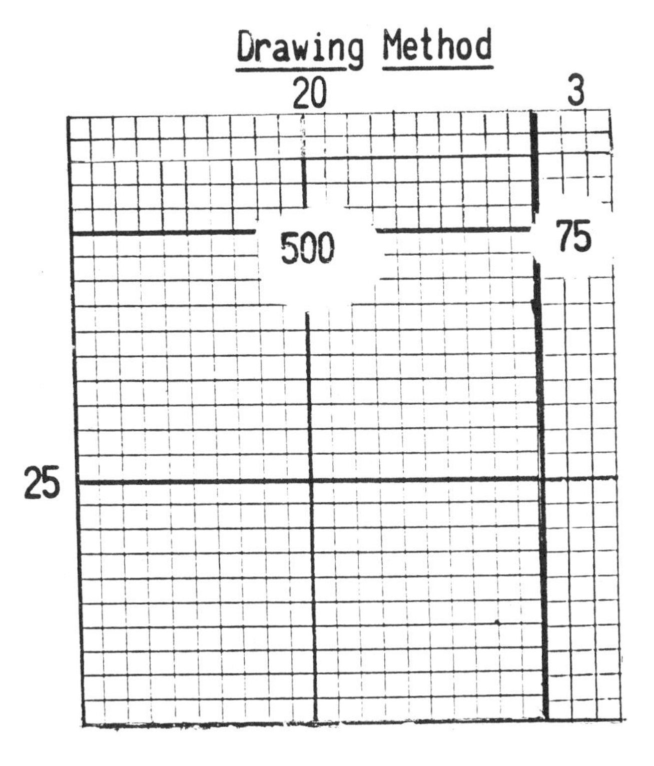

a. Where does 575 belong?

b. What is the "other" dimension?

c. Notice where the numbers are in each method.
25, 500, 20, 3, 75, 23

2.

```
     3 } 23
    20 }
22 ) 520
    440
     80
     66
     14
```

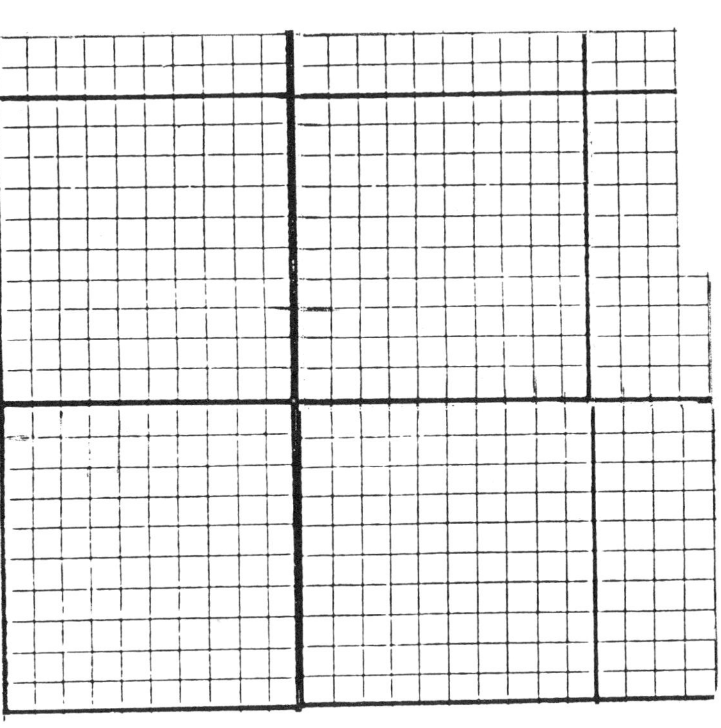

Place these numbers on the drawing as in 1c.

440 23 22 20

3 14 80 66

520

Larger Rectangles With Missing Dimensions

Mathematics teaching objectives:

- Teach the division algorithm with understanding (quotients greater than 19).
- Practice using the division algorithm.
- Write number division problems for drawings.

Problem-solving skills pupils *might* use:

- Study the solution process.
- Make and use a drawing.
- Identify patterns suggested by drawings.
- Invent problems for mathematical expressions.

Materials needed:

- None

Comments and suggestions:

- Prepare an overlay of page 347. Work through parts 1 and 2 along with the class.
- Elicit from the class the division algorithm to match the drawing in 3(a).
- Have pupils complete the rest of the lesson during supervised study time.
- Ask for volunteers to share their story problems for part 5. Pupils should know that many different story problems can be matched with a "pure" number problem.

Answers:

1. a. Have class decide where 575 should be placed so as to suggest all the units shown in the drawing.

   b. 23

(answers continued on the next page...)

Larger Rectangles With Missing Dimensions (cont.)

3. Write the problems which match these drawings.

a.

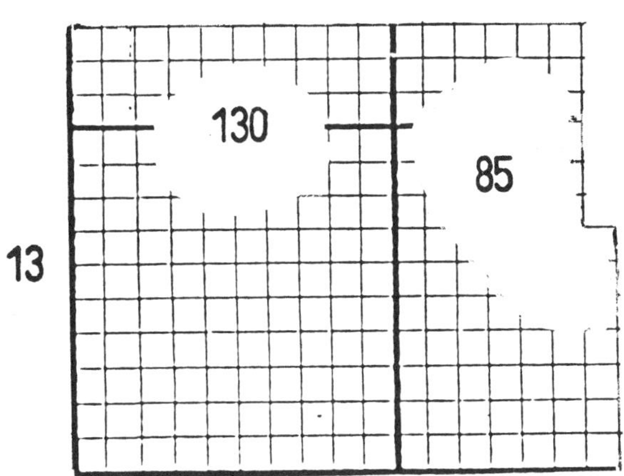

b.

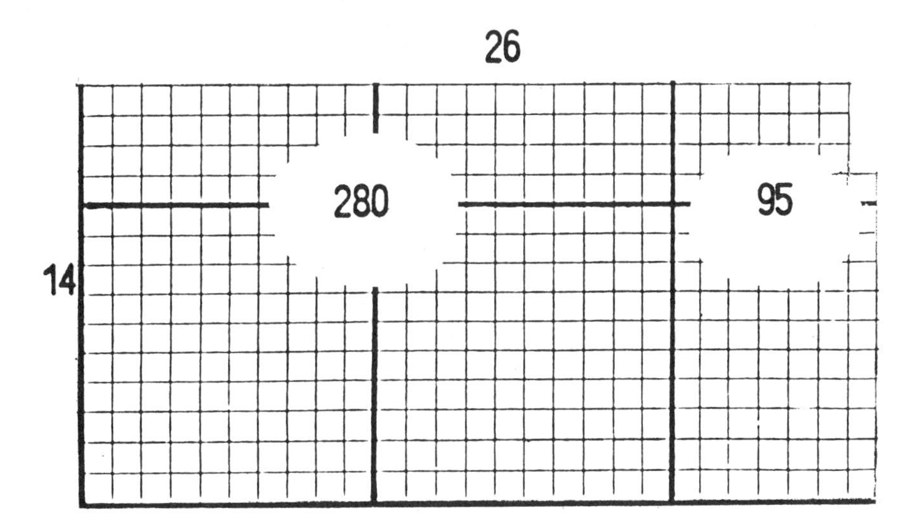

c.

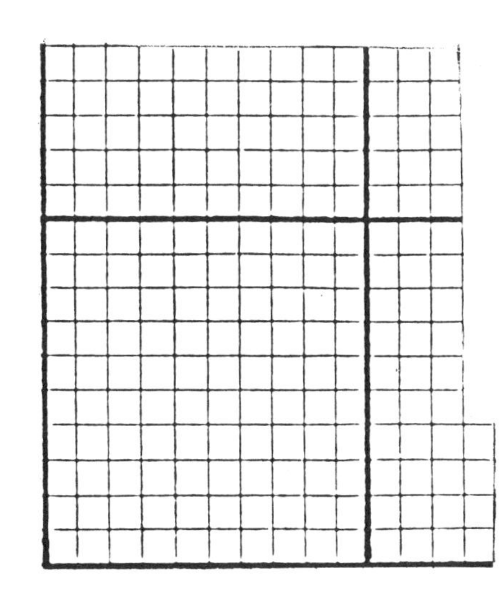

First label the drawing with the correct numbers as above.

Answers: (cont.)

2.

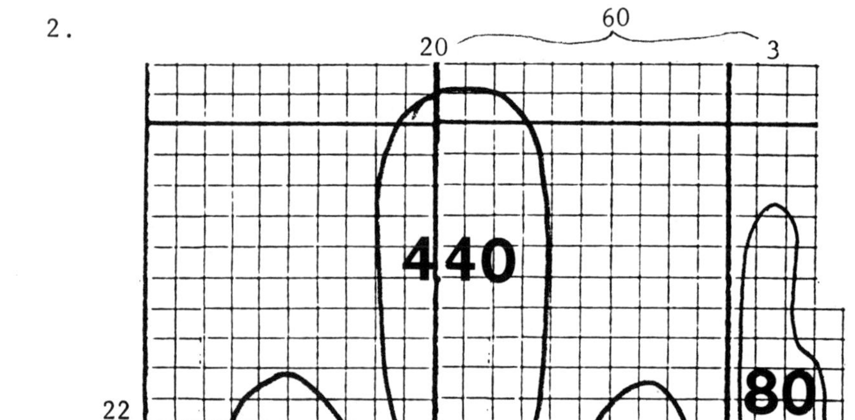

The 66 is the number of units in the 3 by 22 rectangle to the right of the arrow.

The remainder of 14 is what needs to be cut off to make a rectangle.

3. a.

```
      16
13 / 215
     130
      85
      78
       6
```

b.

```
      26
14 / 375
     280
      95
      84
      11
```

c.

```
      13
15 / 199
     150
      49
      45
       4
```

4. a. 23

b. 26

c. 27 r 16

d. 27

5. Answers will vary.

4. Find the answers to these division exercises.
   Use the shorter method.

   a. $621 \div 27$

   b. $676 \div 26$

   c. $21 \overline{)583}$

   d. $36 \overline{)972}$

5. Write a story problem to match 3a, b, and c.

SUBTRACT TWO PRODUCTS TO GET A QUOTIENT

B	37 x 1	37 x 2	37 x 3	37 x 4	37 x 5	37 x 6	37 x 7	37 x 8	37 x 9
A	37 x 10	37 x 20	37 x 30	37 x 40	37 x 50	37 x 60	37 x 70	37 x 80	37 x 90

-a. 37 ⟌ 851 A ____ - - - B ____	b. 37 ⟌ 1739 ____ - - - ____	c. 37 ⟌ 1961 ____ - - - ____	d. 37 ⟌ 2479 ____ - - - ____
3-a. 37 ⟌ 1454 ____ - - - ____	b. 37 ⟌ 2072 ____ - - - ____	c. 37 ⟌ 3589 ____ - - - ____	d. 37 ⟌ 3200 ____ - - - ____
4-a. 37 ⟌ 1687 ____ - - - ____	b. 37 ⟌ 2183 ____ - - - ____	c. 37 ⟌ 3091 ____ - - - ____	d. 37 ⟌ 3552 ____ - - - ____

Subtract Two Products To Get A Quotient

Mathematics teaching objectives:

. Develop skill in using the long division algorithm.

Problem-solving skills pupils <u>might</u> use:

. Break a problem into manageable parts.

. Study the solution process.

Materials needed:

. None

Comments and suggestions:

. Have pupils work with a partner to obtain answers to A and B. Have them compare the answers in A with those in B and review the "annex a zero" as a way for multiplying by 10.

. Work 2 and 3 with the class by referring to 1A and B. This enables pupils to work through the algorithm quickly even though they still may be having difficulties with the multiplication facts. Let them work the remaining exercises independently.

Answers:

1. A. 37, 74, 111, 148, 185, 222, 259, 296, 333

   B. 370, 740, 1110, 1480, 1850, 2220, 2590, 2960, 3330

Note: Remind pupils that a problem such as 37 x 40 can be done two different ways. It can be done by multiplying 37 by 10 and then by 4 or, as was done here, by multiplying first by 4 and then by 10. This is a specific application of the associative property of multiplication. Eventually, pupils should develop this flexibility in thinking about multiplication.

2. a.
```
       23
37 | 851
     740
     111
     111
```
b.
```
       47
37 | 1739
     1480
      259
      259
```
c.
```
       53
37 | 1961
     1850
      111
      111
```
d.
```
       67
37 | 2479
     2220
      259
      259
```

(Answers continued on the next page.....)

nswers: (cont.)

```
. a.     39  r 11     b.      56        c.      97        d.      86 r 18
     37 1454              37 2072           37 3589            37 3200
        1110                 1850              3330               2960
         344                  222               259                240
         333                  222               259                222
          11                                                        18
```

```
. a.     45 r 22      b.      59        c.      83 r 20   d.      96
     37 1687              37 2183           37 3091            37 3552
        1480                 1850              2960               3330
         207                  333               131                222
         185                  333               111                222
          22                                     20
```

omment:

. Pupils need more practice than is given in this section before they master the division algorithm. More lessons can be provided similar to this one and additional problems can be given from the textbook. As pupils work toward automatically performing the division algorithm, the use of grid paper may be helpful.

For example:

				4	5
3	8	1	7	2	5
		1	5	2	
			2	0	5
			1	9	0
				1	5

However, this should not be done until after pupils have demonstrated some understanding of the process itself.

. As one continues to develop the division algorithm, pupils will need to extend it to cover quotients with three digits. When this time comes, probably in grade 5, the procedure could be an extension of the lesson, "Subtract Two Products To Get A Quotient" to "Subtract Three Products To Get A Quotient."

STORY PROBLEMS

1. Write the number sentence for these problems. Solve the problem.

   a. Marty collects used bottlecaps. He has 837 bottlecaps in his collection. He displays them in jars which each hold 31 bottlecaps. How many jars does he need for the collection?

   b. Carl earned $106 picking beans. He wants to buy a bike which costs $139. How much more money must he save to buy the bike?

   c. Tom pasted 960 trading stamps in a stamp book. He exactly filled 12 pages. How many stamps were pasted on each page?

   d. Lisa spends 180 minutes a week practicing for her drum lessons. How many minutes a year does she practice?

   e. Susie used 414 square tiles to cover a table top. The table was 18 tiles wide. How many tiles long was the table?

2. Work these problems. Do your work on another sheet.

a. $17 \overline{)198}$	c. $31 \overline{)675}$	e. $38 \overline{)952}$
b. $312 \div 27$	d. $1122 \div 49$	f. $3578 \div 53$

Story Problems

Mathematics teaching objectives:

. Solve a variety of story problems.

. Write number sentences for story problems.

Problem-solving skills pupils might use:

. Invent problems for mathematics expressions.

. Use mathematical expressions for problem situations.

Materials needed:

. None

Comments and suggestions:

. Have pupils determine which of the five problems could be solved by dividing.

. Have them work the rest of the lesson during supervised study time.

. For more practice, assign them mixed story problems from the textbook.

Answers:

1. a. $837 \div 31 = \square$ or $31\overline{)837}$ answer = 27 jars

   b. $139 - 106 = \square$ or $106 + \square = 139$ answer = \$33

   c. $960 \div 12 = \square$ or $12\overline{)960}$ answer = 80 stamps

   d. $180 \times 52 = \square$ answer = 9360 minutes

   e. $414 \div 18 = \square$ or $18\overline{)414}$ answer = 23 tiles

2. a. 11 r 11 c. 21 r 14 e. 25 r 2

   b. 11 r 15 d. 22 r 45 f. 67 r 27

3. a. 24 cases 6 bottles \$3.60

   b. 19 jelly beans, 6 jelly beans left over. Pupils probably will not agree on what should be done with the extra beans!

   c. 13 baseball cards left over.

4. Answers will vary. Have volunteers share their problems with the class.

3. Solve these:

   a. A team of three girl scouts collected 582 pop bottles from their friends and neighbors. When they turned them in to the beverage company, they received $1.50 for every full case. A case contains 24 bottles. How many full cases did they turn in? How many bottles did they have left over for the next time? How much money did the girls get for their bottles?

   b. A bag containing 500 jelly beans was to be shared equally by the 26 persons at a class party. How many jelly beans should each person get? What should be done with the extra jelly beans?

   c. A man has 517 baseballs to pack in boxes which hold 24 baseballs each. How many baseballs will be left over when he has filled as many boxes as he can?

4. Write story problems for 2a and 2b. Make the stories as different as you can.

Grade 4

IX. CHALLENGES

IX. CHALLENGES

The activities in the *Getting Started* section were very directed
d pupils were encouraged to use (although not completely restricted to)
e problem-solving skill at a time. The challenge problems in this section
ave the choice of the problem-solving method up to the pupil. The intention
to allow for and encourage individual differences, creativity, and cooper-
ion.

Let's look at how one challenge problem, "Triple Sums" (page 367) can
used in the classroom. As you read the example, notice how the teacher
es not structure or direct the methods pupils use, but that the teacher does
ve these important functions:

. to help pupils *understand* the problem.
. to *listen* if pupils want to discuss their strategies.
. to *praise* and *encourage* pupils in their attempts, successful or not.
. to *facilitate* discussion of the problem and sharing of the strategies.
. to *give* hints or ask questions, if necessary.
. to *summarize* or *emphasize* methods of solution after pupils have
  solved the problem.

As we look in on Ms. Whiz's classroom, the page "Triple Sums" has just
een distributed. It is near the end of the math period - about 10 minutes
efore recess. Pupils are used to seeing a different challenge each week and
now they will be given several days to work on the problem.

s. W: Here is the challenge problem for the week. I'll let you look at the puzzle, give you time to read the directions and get started. After three or four minutes, we'll discuss the problem to be sure we all understand it. (Waits) Who can explain how to complete the puzzle? Susan.

usan: The puzzle has one blank box. I think 9 goes in the box because 6 plus 3 equals 9.

s. W: Lee, you look puzzled. Why might Susan put the answer to 6 plus 3 in the blank square?

ee: Oh! I get it. The squares all have answers to addition problems made with numbers they touch.

s. W: You and Susan explained the puzzle very well. Work on the next two puzzles. See if you can solve them before recess.

ale: (Hand raised) Ms. Whiz, I can do the second puzzle but I don't understand how to do any of the last three.

s. W: It wouldn't be called a challenge if you knew right away, would it? For tomorrow, try to solve one of the last three puzzles. If you get one of them, try to remember how you did it. This might help some of the rest of us. (Class is dismissed.)

The next day at the beginning of the period.

Ms. W: How many of you were able to do at least one of the last three puzzles on the challenge page I gave you yesterday? (Several pupils raise their hands.) Scott?

Scott: I got the first one!

Ms. W: Today we will spend a few minutes talking about one of the puzzles. Scott, what was your solution?

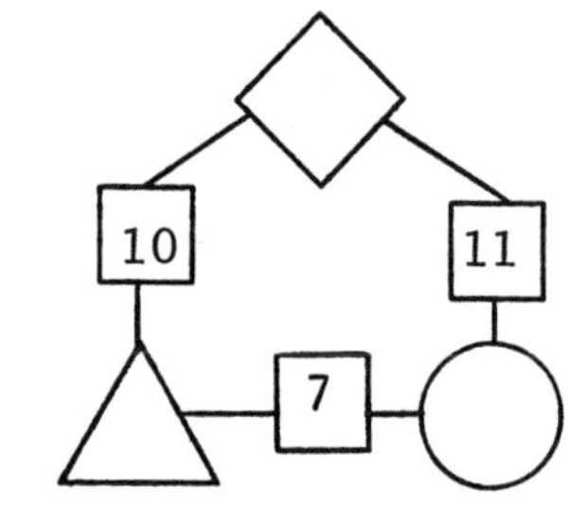

Scott: Seven goes in the diamond box, 3 in the triangle, and 4 in the circle. (The class agree Scott had solved the puzzle.)

Ms. W: Scott, what strategy did you use?

Scott: Strategy? What do you mean?

Ms. W: Oh! I'm sorry - guess I haven't used that word before. I'll ask the question a different way. What did you do to get your answers?

Scott: I just guessed and checked a lot. I don't remember any of the wrong guesses.

Ms. W: You did get the answers. You should feel good about that! Several of you said you solved this puzzle. Who remembers the strategy they used? Lee.

Lee: I tried to keep track of what I tried. I tried 3 in the diamond. It didn't work. Then I tried 3 in the circle. It didn't work either. When I tried 3 for the triangle, it worked! I used a guess and check strategy and also had some luck. It didn't work on the other puzzles.

Ms. W: Good. I'm pleased you kept track of your guesses. You also used a system. How did you do it, Susan?

Susan: Well, I knew that the "diamond" number and "triangle" must add up to 10. First I tried 5 + 5, then 4 + 6, 3 + 7, then 2 + 8. None of them worked. Then I switched them around - tried 6 + 4, then finally 7 + 3 and it worked!

Ms. W: I don't understand. Isn't 4 + 6 and 6 + 4 the same thing?

Susan: No. (showing signs of impatience) The first time the 4 was the "diamond" number. The next time it was the "triangle" number. That's different!

Ms. W: Oh! I think I see what you did. Do any of the rest of you understand (Merlin raises his hand.) What system did Susan use? Merlin, you can use the chalkboard if you care to.

Merlin: It is hard for me to explain but I'll try to show it on the board. (He places this systematic list of sums for 10 on the chalkboard.)

$5 + 5 = 10$
$4 + 6 = 10$
$3 + 7 = 10$
$2 + 8 = 10$

$6 + 4 = 10$
$7 + 3 = 10$

s. W: If some of you would like to talk about this puzzle some more, you might do so later with either Susan or Merlin. Also, if any of you have the solutions for all of the last three puzzles, try to invent others like them. Make the numbers in the squares "bigger." You might also try to make a puzzle that will not work!

s. Whiz terminates this discussion at this point and introduces the class) the geometry activities which she and the other fourth-grade teachers had lanned for the week. She was planning later in the week to continue with ne discussion of the challenge.

The above approach to challenge problems also gives opportunities for racticing the following problem-solving skills:

. State the problem in your own words.

. Clarify the problem through careful reading and by asking questions.

. Share data and the results with other interested persons.

. Listen to persons who have relevant knowledge and experiences to share.

. Study the solution process.

. Invent new problems by varying an old one.

THE TEACHER MUST BE AN ACTIVE, ENTHUSIASTIC SUPPORTER OF PROBLEM SOLVING

sing The Activities

Twenty varied challenge problems are provided. Some teachers give them s a "challenge of the week" or as a Friday activity. On the day the challenge s given out, time should be spent on getting acquainted with the problem. On ollowing days, a few minutes can be devoted to pupil progress reports. If here is little sign of progress, you can provide some direction by asking a ey question or suggesting a different strategy. At appropriate times, the ctivity can be summarized by a class discussion of strategies used and some roblem extensions.

Some of the challenges can be used as total class activities. However, main purpose of a challenge is for pupils to do some individual thinking.

One Plan For Using The Challenges (over a period of 1 or 2 weeks).

First day -

. Give out the challenge. (Possibly near the end of the period)

. Let pupils read written directions and possibly discuss with a classmate.

. Clarify any vocabulary which seems to be causing difficulty. Ask a few probing questions to see if they have enough understanding to get started.

. Remind them that during the next math class, time will be used to look at the problem again.

Second day -

. Have pupils share their ideas.

. Identify the problem-solving skills suggested by these ideas.

. Conduct a brainstorming session if pupils do not seem to know how to get started.

. Suggest alternative strategies they might try.

. Give an extension to those pupils who have completed the challenge.

On a subsequent day -

. Allow some class time for individuals (or small groups) to work on the challenge. Observe and encourage pupils in their attempts.

. Try a strategy along with the pupils (if pupils seem to have given up)

Last day -

. Conduct a session where pupils can present the unsuccessful as well as the successful strategies they used.

. Possibly practice a problem-solving skill that is giving pupils difficulty; e.g., recording attempts, making a systematic list, or checking solutions.

Key problem-solving strategies that pupils have used in solving the problems are given in the comments for each problem. Your pupils might have additional ways of solving the problems.

A challenge problem for the teacher: Keep the quick problem solver from telling answers to classmates. The extension in the commentary for each challenge should help solve this problem.

TRIPLE SUMS

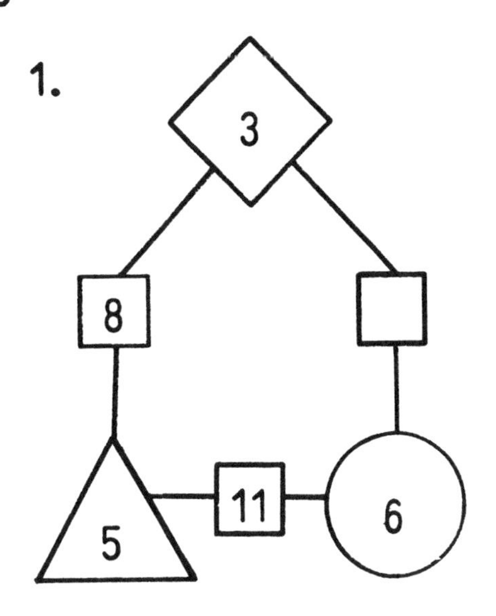

Dale found this puzzle and filled in all of the squares but one.

Complete the puzzle for Dale.

Discuss how you decided what number to use.

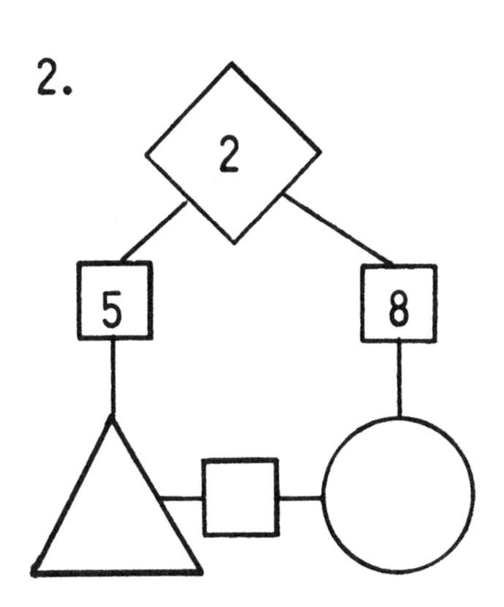

Here is a new puzzle.
Dale did part of the puzzle.

Complete the puzzle for Dale.

Now complete these:

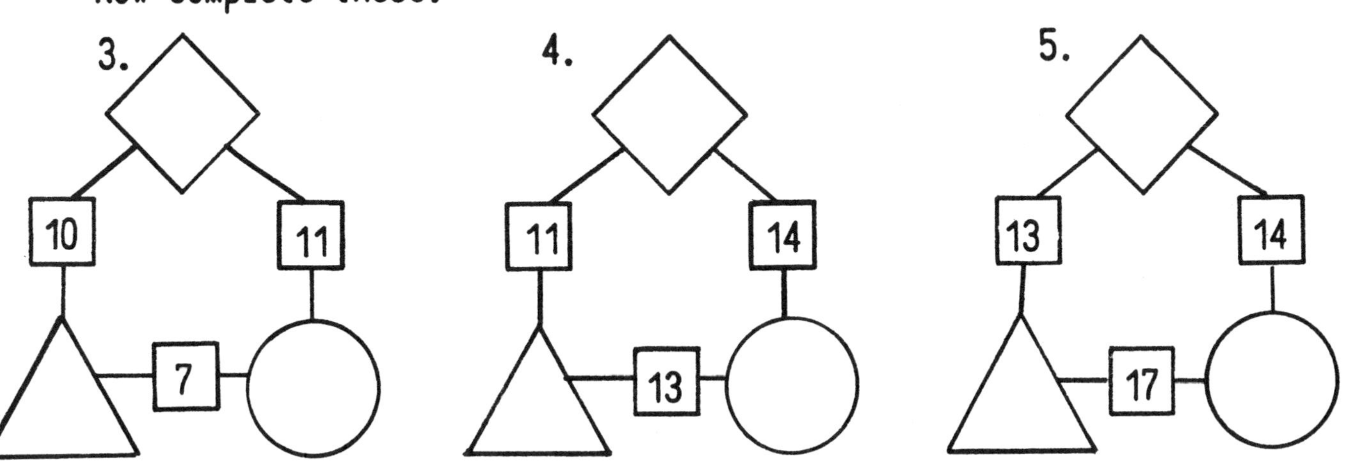

What strategies did you use to complete the puzzles?

Triple Sums

Problem-solving skills pupils might use:

- Guess and check.
- Work backwards.
- Make a systematic list.
- Recognize limits and eliminate possibilities.

Comments and suggestions:

- See the dialogue given in the overview for this section (pages 363- and review plan, page 366).
- One plan pupils usually discover is to focus attention on one of the numbers, usually the smallest. For example: The diamond and circle numbers must add up to 7; such sums might be 6 and 1 or 1 and 6, 2 and 5 or 5 and 2, 4 and 3 or 3 and 4; each time check by trying to complete the puzzle.

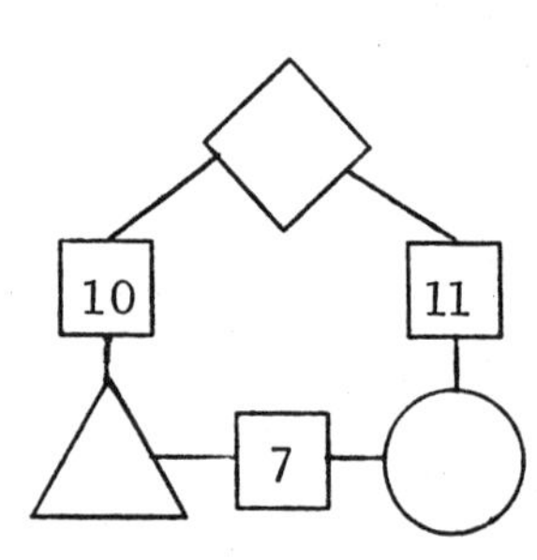

Answers:

1. Missing sum, 9
2. Triangle number, 3; circle number, 6; missing sum, 9.
3. Diamond number, 7; triangle number, 3; circle number, 4.
4. Diamond number, 6; triangle number, 5; circle number, 8
5. Diamond number, 5; triangle number, 8; circle number, 9

Extensions:

1. Make a triple sum puzzle with each sum greater than 25. Be certain it can be worked. Give to a classmate to solve.
2. Make a triple sum puzzle which you think does not have a solution.

PIRATE PATTY'S TREASURE

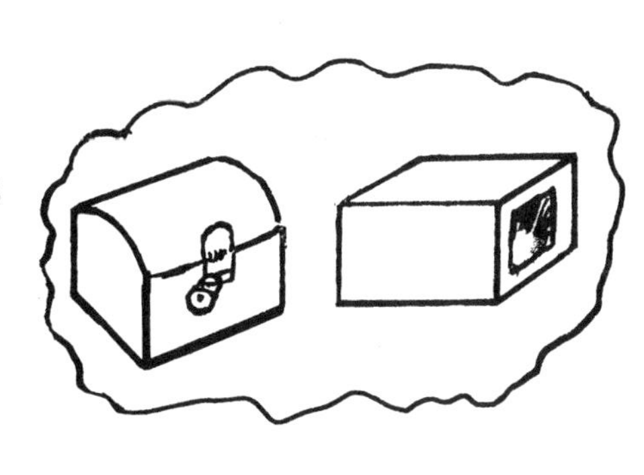

1. Pirate Patty protects her treasure chests by placing large cement blocks around the chest. (On __1__ treasure chest ___ blocks.)

Block	Block	Block
Block	Treasure Chest	Block
Block	Block	Block

2. She always places new treasure chests end-to-end.

	Treasure Chests		

__2__ treasure chests

___ blocks

3. Treasure Chests

__3__ treasure chests

___ blocks

4. __4__ treasure chests

___ blocks

5. __5__ treasure chests

___ blocks

6. How many blocks for:
   a. 10 treasure chests? ____
   b. 15 treasure chests? ____
   c. 100 treasure chests? ____

Pirate Patty's Treasure

Problem-solving skills pupils might use:

. Make and use a drawing.

. Make a systematic list.

. Look for patterns.

. Make predictions.

Comments and suggestions:

. Pupils could solve all the parts except 6(c) by making drawings.

. A strategy to get 6(c) is given in the answers.

. Eventually time should be taken for pupils to discuss and evaluate the strategies they have used.

. You may need to remind the pupils that they may get clues by study their drawings. (All block "houses" are 3 blocks wide. The lengt of the house is two blocks wider than the number of treasure chest

Answers:

1. 8 2. 10 3. 12 4. 14 5. 1

6. a. 26

b. 36

c. 206 (One hundred blocks above the treasure; one hundred blocks below the treasure; and three blocks on each end; 100 + 100 + 3 + 3 = 206.)

FOUR MARKERS

The example shows how to use 4 markers to get $25 + 5 + 5 + 1 = 36$.

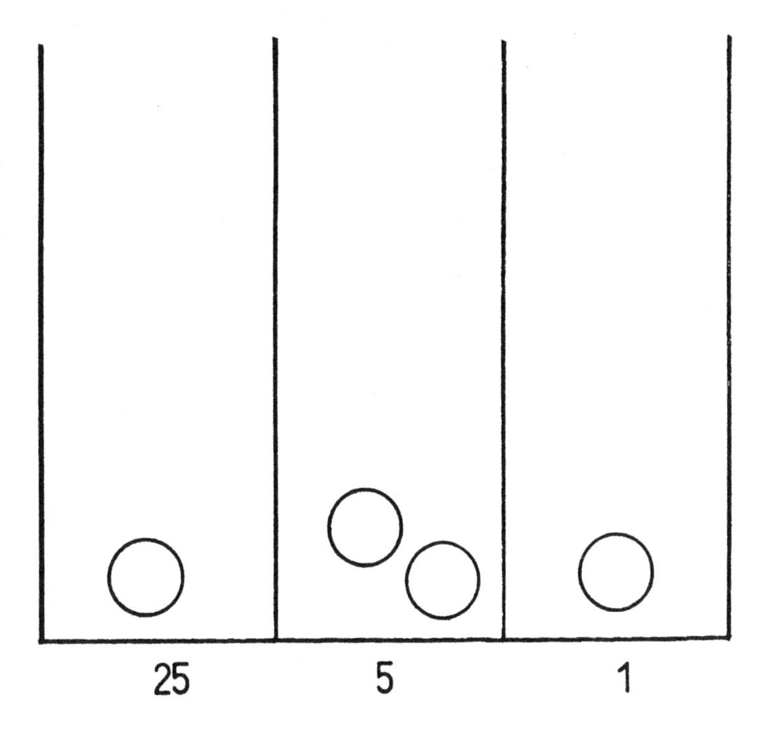

1. How can you use 4 markers to get 100?

   How about 12?

2. Record all the different totals you can get. Remember, you can only use 4 markers.

3. Add another "pocket" as pictured below. Still use 4 markers. Find at least twenty different totals you can get.

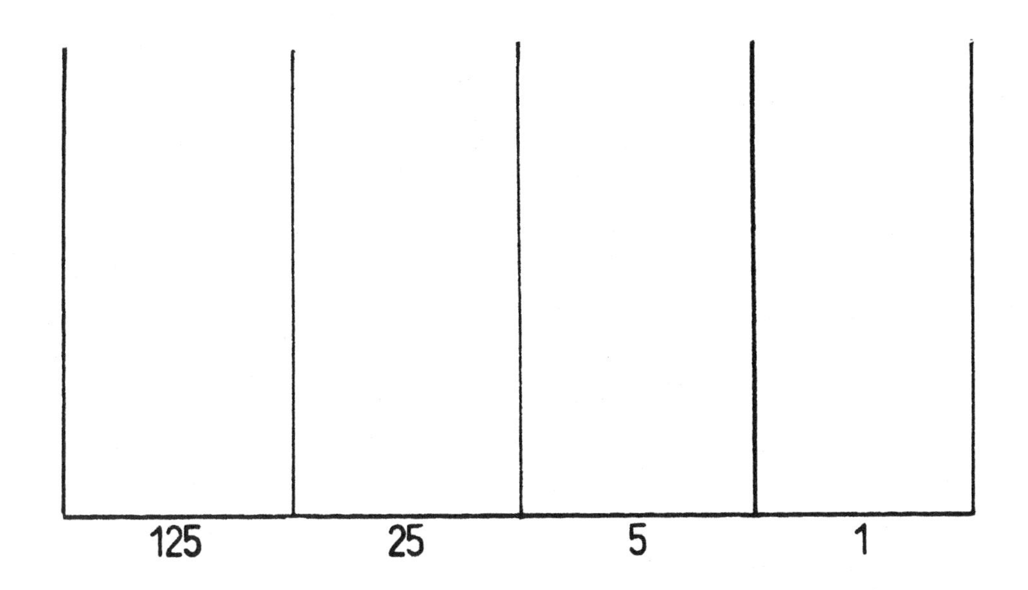

Four Markers

Problem-solving skills pupils *might* use:

- . Record solution possibilities.
- . Make a systematic list.
- . Invent new problems by varying an old one.

Comments and suggestions:

- . Review "One Plan For Using The Challenges," page 366.
- . Some pupils place the markers in the trays or columns without any apparent plan and merely record as many totals as they can.
- . Others will place the markers in the trays according to a plan and carefully record each placement they make.
- . During the culminating session, the systematic lists used should be placed on the overhead or chalkboard. Encourage pupils to look for patterns or common properties all the listed totals have. (See the answers below.)
- . This activity provides an opportunity to review place value.

Answers:

1. 4 markers in "25 column" to get 100.
   2 markers in "5 column" and 2 markers in "1 column" to get 12.

2. 15 different totals*

25	5	1	Totals
4	0	0	100
3	1	0	80
3	0	1	76
2	2	0	60
2	1	1	56
2	0	2	52
1	3	0	40
1	2	1	36
1	1	2	32
1	0	3	28
0	4	0	20
0	3	1	16
0	2	2	12
0	1	3	8
0	0	4	4

3. 35 different totals are possible. These are:
   500, 400, 380, 376, 300
   280, 276, 260, 256, 252
   200, 180, 176, 160, 156
   152, 140, 136, 132, 128.
   Also those in the table to the left.

Notice: Pupils' lists for problem 2 are not generally as systematic. Present and discuss this table with the class. Direct pupils to observe the patterns in all four columns.

Notice all the totals in problems 2 and 3 are divisible by 4. Possibly some of the pupils will discover this

Extension:

- . Rename the columns in problem 3 to 1, 10, 100, and 1000. Rework the challenge. Look for a common property of all the listed totals.

MAGIC SHAPES-1

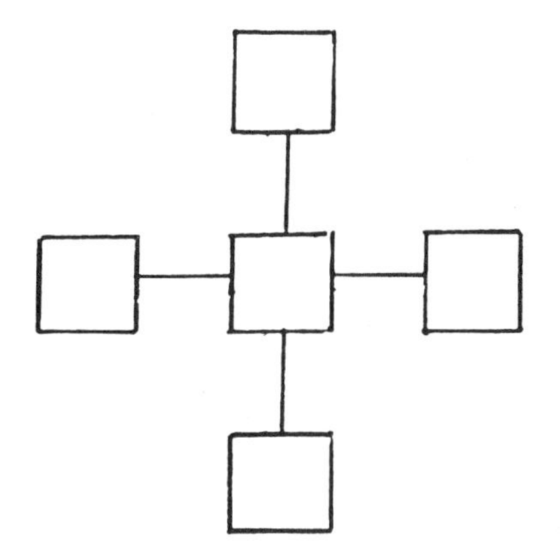

1. Use the digits 1, 2, 3, 4, 5.
   Place them in the boxes so the sum of the three numbers in each direction is the same.

   What is the magic sum? ______

2. Find two more solutions with a different magic sum.

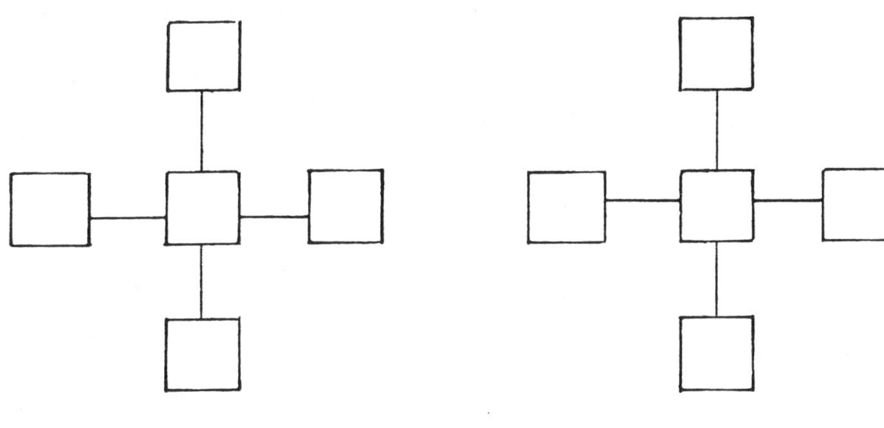

Magic Sum __________ Magic Sum __________

3. What do you notice about the middle numbers of the three solutions. ____________________

4. Use the digits 6, 7, 8, 9, 10.
   Place them in the boxes so the sum of the three numbers in each direction is the same. Find three solutions.

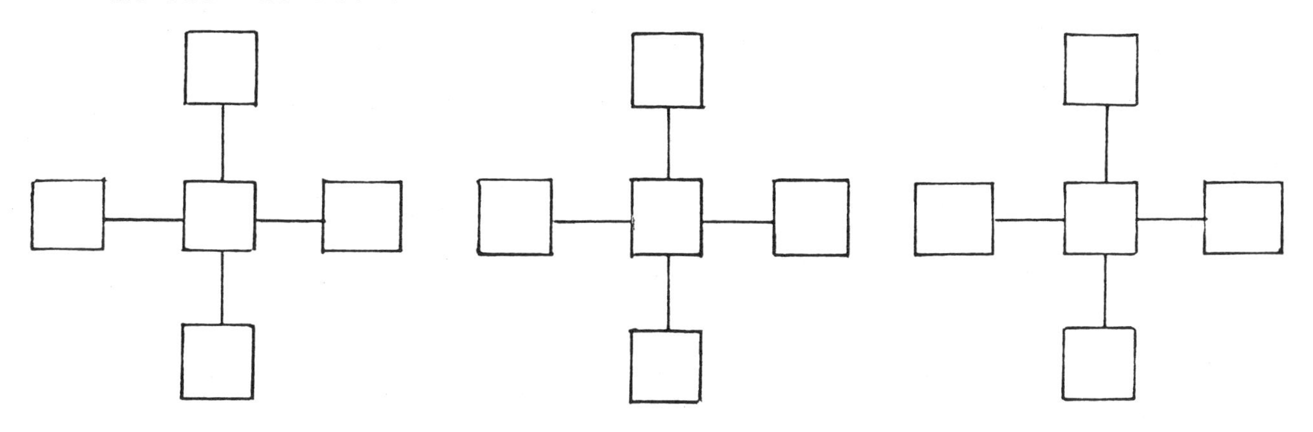

Magic Sum __________ Magic Sum __________ Magic Sum __________

Magic Shapes-1

Problem-solving skills pupils might use:

- Guess and check.
- Search for other solutions.
- Make explanations based upon data.

Comments and suggestions:

- At first most pupils use guess and check, but as they work they will discover that the middle number is the key to success and that the sum of the outer numbers in each direction must be the same.
- Some pupils will find a system for working these puzzles. See the answers for one such system. The culminating work on the puzzles should include a presentation of the pupils strategies.

Answers:

1,2.

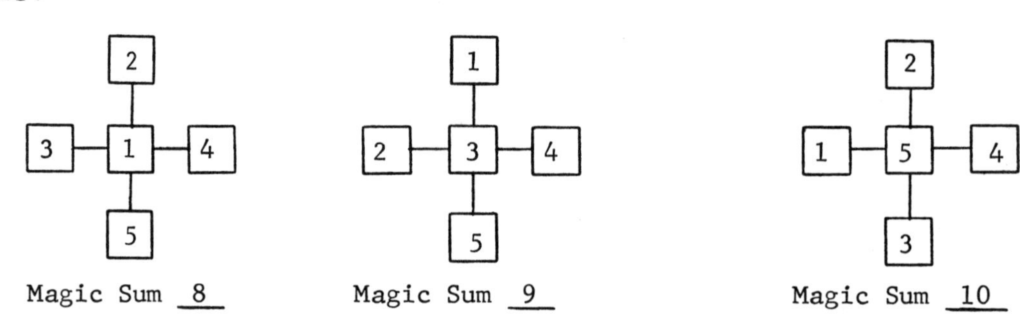

3. When the digits are in order, the center number can be a middle number for the puzzle. The first and last digits can also be the middle number.

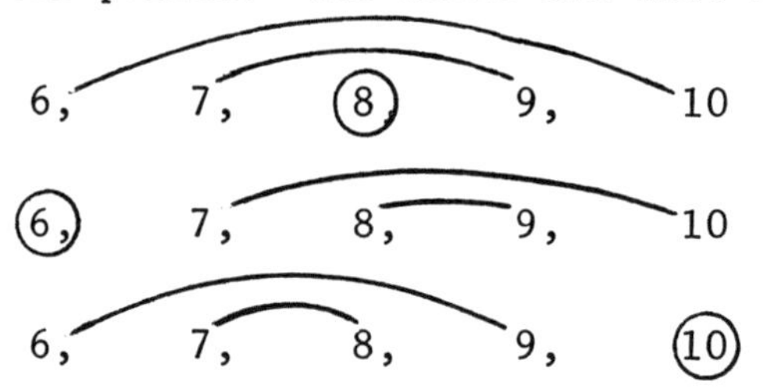

Circled number is the middle number for the puzzle

4.

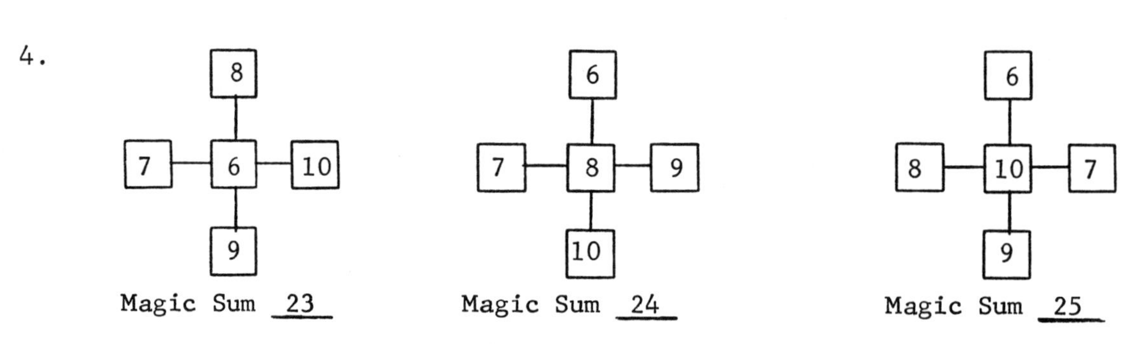

Extension:

Try to find other numbers which will work for the magic shape used in this challenge problem. Is it necessary that the five given numbers be consecutive?

MAGIC SHAPES-2

1. Use the digits 1, 2, 3, 4, 5 6, 7. Place them in the circles so the magic sum of the three numbers in each direction is the same. Find three solutions, each with a different magic sum.

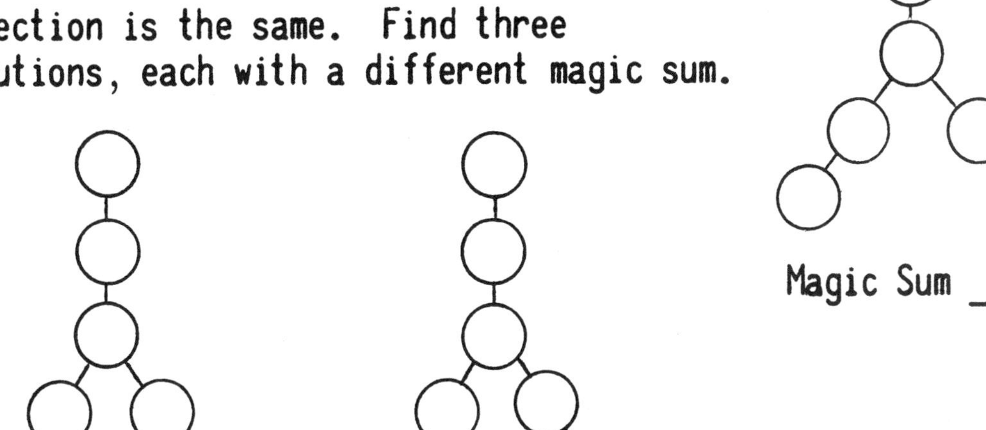

Magic Sum _____

Magic Sum _____ Magic Sum _____

2. What do you notice about the middle numbers of the three solutions? ______________________________

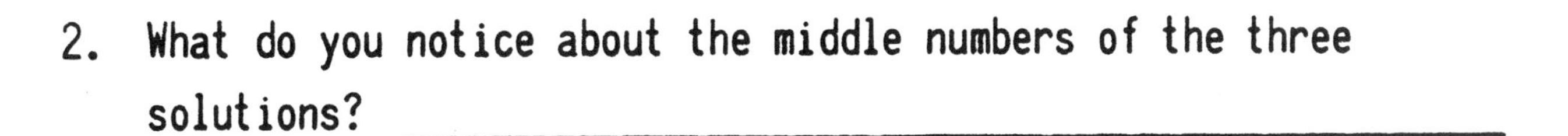

3. Use the digits 1, 2, 3, 4, 5, 6, 7, 8, 9, 10, 11. Place them in the boxes so the sum in each of the five directions is the same. Find three solutions.

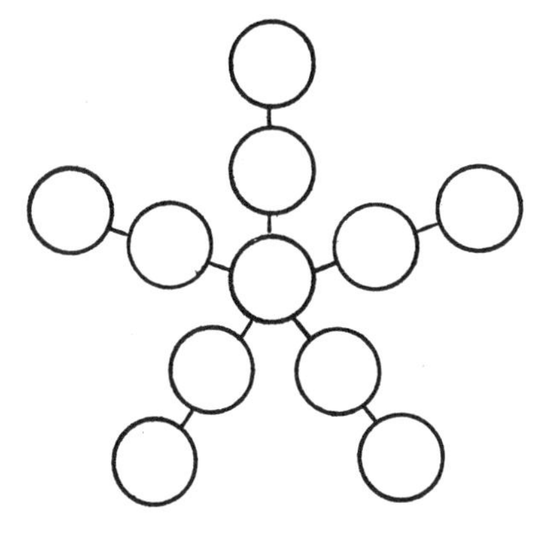

Magic Sum _____

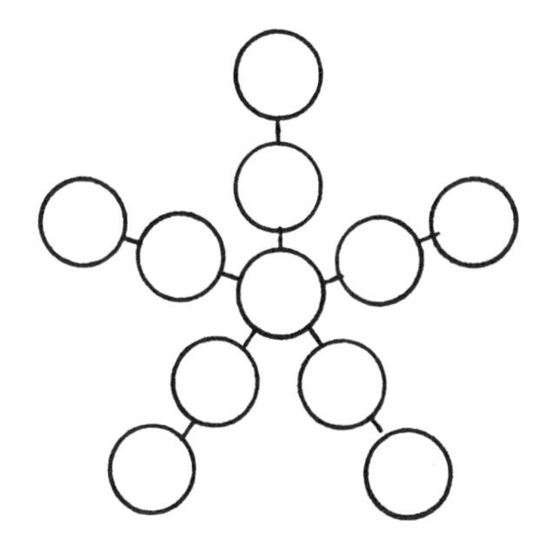

Magic Sum _____

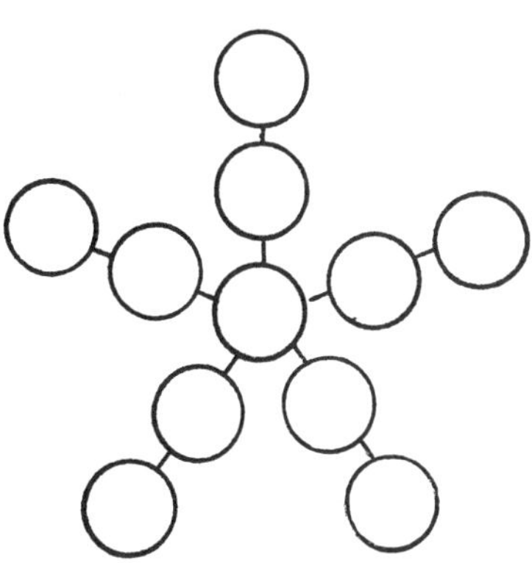

Magic Sum _____

Magic Shapes-2

Problem-solving skills pupils might use:

- Guess and check.
- Apply what you learned from "Magic Shapes 1."
- Look for patterns.
- Study the solution process.

Comments and suggestions:

- Review "One Plan for Using Challenges" (page 366).
- Pupils will likely start working the puzzles by guess and check. Some pupils might suggest trying the strategies used in "Magic Shapes-1" (page 373). If not, you might suggest it.

Answers:

1.

Magic Sum	Middle Number	The Three Branches
10	1	1,2,7 1,3,6 1,4,5
12	4	4,7,1 4,6,2 4,3,5
14	7	7,6,1 7,3,4 7,2,5

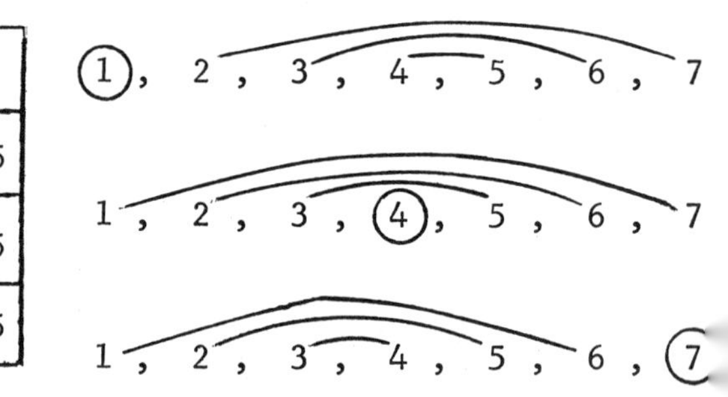

The circled number is the middle number for the puzzle.

2. The middle numbers can be the center digit. The first and last digits can be the middle number also. By this time, pupils should recognize that in each puzzle the pairs of digits in each branch must have the same sum and that these digits must be selected systematically from the given series of digits.

3.

Magic Sum	Middle Number	The Five Branches
14	1	1,2,11 1,3,10 1,4,9 1,5,8 1,6,7
18	6	6,1,11 6,2,10 6,3,9 6,4,8 6,5,7
22	11	11,1,10 11,2,9 11,3,8 11,4,7 11,5,6

Extension:

Suggest that pupils invent a puzzle like these but with 6 branches. Try not to use consecutive numbers.

JEWEL THIEF GAME

Play this game with a partner.

Place 15 jewels (markers) in the box above.

Take turns.

When it is your turn, you may remove 1, 2, or 3 jewels from the box.

Winner is the player to remove the last jewel from the box.

Play a number of games.

Take turns going first.

Find a way to win each time you go first.

Jewel Thief Game

Problem-solving skills pupils might use:

- Guess and check.
- Systematically record solution attempts.
- Study the rules (data) for clues.
- Explain the winning strategy (solution).

Comments and suggestions:

- The challenge could be introduced by giving a duplicate of the page to partners and let them figure out how to play the game by reading the rules themselves. An alternative would be for you to play the game with a volunteer in front of the class on the overhead with markers being used as substitutes for jewels.
- After pupils play several games, you might suggest they work together to seek an "always win" strategy for the person who plays first.
- Suggest that each player record the number of jewels left after his/her turn. This record might give clues for an "always win" strategy for the first player. You may also ask them to find out when it is possible for the second player to win.

Answers:

Winning strategy for the game: You will win if the number of jewels in the box after your turn is divisible by 4.

The first player wins if 3 jewels are taken. The number left is 12. From then on: If the opponent takes 1, take 3. Or if the opponent takes 3, take 1. Or if the opponent takes 2, take 2, always leaving a multiple of 4.

If the first player takes 1 or 2 jewels, the second player takes enough to leave 12. From then on the second player is in control of the game.

Extension:

Play the game with 32 jewels. What is the best strategy for the first player? the second player? Which player has the advantage?

SPELLING FOR DOLLARS - A

1. Suppose letters were money.

A = $1	F = $6	K = $11	P = $16	U = $21
B = $2	G = $7	L = $12	Q = $17	V = $22
C = $3	H = $8	M = $13	R = $18	W = $23
D = $4	I = $9	N = $14	S = $19	X = $24
E = $5	J = $10	O = $15	T = $20	Y = $25
				Z = $26

Use the chart. Find out how much your name is worth.

(Name) ______________________ (Value) __________

2. Find words to complete the chart below. Tell the value of each word.

Number of letters	Words of very little value	Words of much value
2	be ($7) ad ($5)	ox ($39)
3		
4		
5		
6		
7		

Spelling For Dollars-A

Problem-solving skills pupils might use:

. Guess and check.

. Look for a pattern.

Materials needed:

. None

Comments and suggestions:

. Discuss problem 1 with the class. Pupils are usually intereste in finding out who has the "most expensive" name.

. Complete problem 2 over a period of time. Discuss and compare "final" answers.

. Post the results on the chalkboard or on a bulletin board. Lea these results up for awhile. Pupils may find new words to ad to the lists.

Answers:

1. Answers will vary.

2. Answers will vary but here are some for pupils to beat!

Number of letters	Words of little value	Words of much value
2	be ($7)	ox ($39)
3	cab ($6)	wow ($61)
4	babe ($10)	Zulu ($80)
5	cache ($20)	yummy ($97)
6	babble ($24)	tryout ($119)
7	bedding ($45)	turnout ($129)

Extension:

. Find the value of your teacher's name.

. Find other words worth as much as your name.

SPELLING FOR DOLLARS - B

1. Suppose letters were money.

A = \$1	F = \$ 6	K = \$11	P = \$16	U = \$21
B = \$2	G = \$ 7	L = \$12	Q = \$17	V = \$22
C = \$3	H = \$ 8	M = \$13	R = \$18	W = \$23
D = \$4	I = \$ 9	N = \$14	S = \$19	X = \$24
E = \$5	J = \$10	O = \$15	T = \$20	Y = \$25
				Z = \$26

Use the chart. Find out how much "teacher" is worth: $ ______

2. Find a word worth the same as

a. eat ____________________

b. star ____________________

c. team ____________________

d. seat ____________________

3. Find a word worth

a. $1 more than got ______________

b. $3 more than math ______________

c. $11 more than bad ______________

d. $16 more than bad ______________

e. $3 more than home ______________

4. Find as many words as you can worth between $40 and $60.

Spelling For Dollars-B

Problem-solving skills pupils might use:

. Guess and check.

. Look for a pattern.

. Use an organized list.

Materials needed:

. None

Comments and suggestions:

. Pupils who have done "Spelling For Dollars-A" should be able to get started on this activity with a minimum of teacher direction.

. Pupils may find that an easy way to solve the problems in part 2 is to "rearrange" the letters. ("Tea" has the same value as "eat," for example.)

. An easy way to solve the problems in part 3 is to change one letter in the listed word. (Hot, for example, is worth $1 more than got.)

Answers:

1. $60

2. Answers will vary. Here are some the pupils are likely to find if they notice that the letters of each word can be rearranged to spel a new word (see Comments and suggestions above).

   a. tea or ate
   b. rats or tars
   c. meat or mate
   d. teas or eats

3. Answers will vary. Here are some possibilities:

   a. hot b. path c. mad d. bat e. hope

4. Answers will vary.

Extension: None necessary. (Have pupils continue to pursue problem 4.)

A MAGICAL HEXAGON

Use the numbers 1-19 only once. Place them in the hexagons so that the sum of any straight line of hexagons is 38. Lines can have five, four, or three small hexagons.

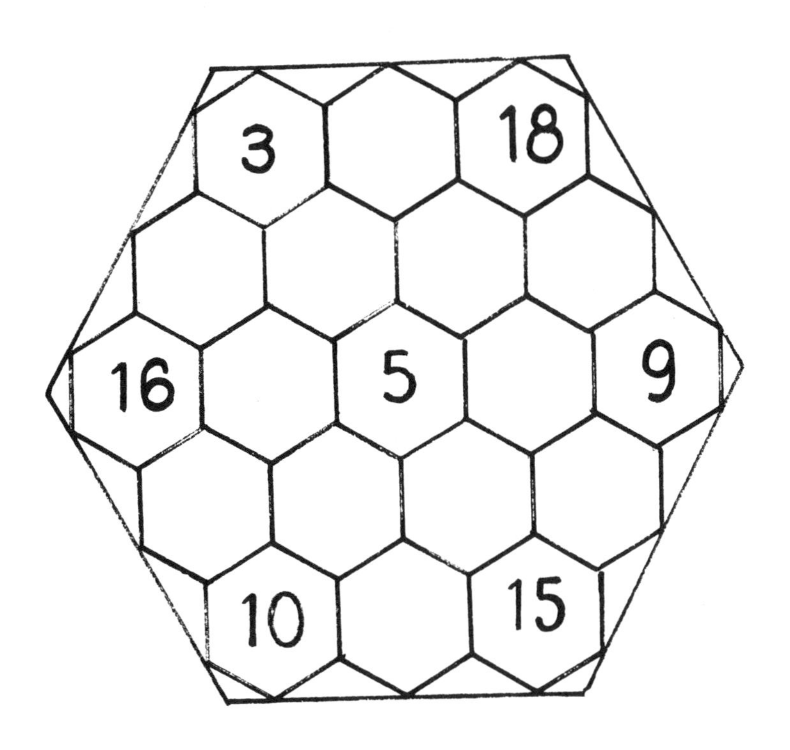

1   2   ~~3~~   4   ~~5~~   6   7   8   ~~9~~   ~~10~~

11   12   13   14   ~~15~~   ~~16~~   17   ~~18~~   19

A Magical Hexagon

Problem-solving skills pupils might use:

- Guess and check.
- Break a problem into manageable parts.
- Eliminate possibilities.

Comments and suggestions:

- Review "One Plan for Using Challenges", page 366.
- Some pupils will break the problem into parts, finding the numbers in the outer ring of hexagons first using addition and subtraction. After the outer ring is solved, six numbers remain. Pupils might follow these steps:
    a. Find the sum of the given numbers already in a 5-hexagon row.
    b. Find two numbers to complete the sum of 38.
    c. Place the numbers and repeat for the other rows.
    d. If one or more sum doesn't work, refine the choice of the numbers in part (b).
- Other pupils may do nothing more than guess and check at the placement of numbers. Markers with the numbers 1-19 may be used with guessing and checking to try possibilities. This procedure avoids a lot of erasing of wrong guesses.

Answer:

The solution to the puzzle is:

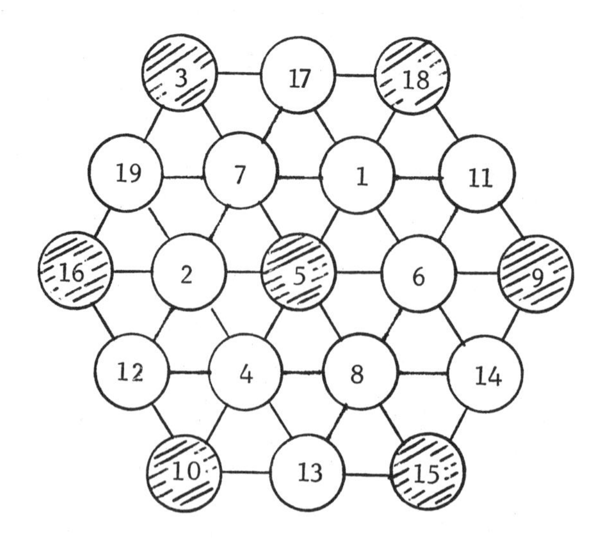

NUMBER RIDDLES

1. Judy Jay made up some number riddles. Solve each.

   a. I am thinking of a number.

      . It is odd.
      . It is between 1 and 100.
      . It is higher than 20.
      . It is smaller than the answer to 6 times 6.
      . It is a multiple of 5.
      . The sum of its digits is 7.

      What is the number? ____________

   b. I am thinking of a new number.

      . It is a multiple of 3.
      . It is not even.
      . It is greater than 20.
      . It is lower than the answer to 7 x 6.
      . The sum of its digits is even.
      . The two digits in the number are the same.

      What is the number? ____________

   c. I am thinking of another number.

      . It is greater than the answer to 5 x 10.
      . It is smaller than 100.
      . It is even.
      . It is not 70 or less.
      . It is not a multiple of 4.
      . It is not a multiple of 3.
      . It is less than 80.

      What is the number? ____________

2. Make up your own set of clues for a number less than 100.

3. Make up a set of clues for a number between 1 and 200.
   Use at least 6 clues.

Number Riddles

Problem-solving skills pupils might use:

- Satisfy one condition at a time.
- Recognize restrictions and eliminate possibilities.
- Eliminate extraneous (unneeded) information.
- Invent problems that satisfy certain conditions.

Comments and suggestions.

- The riddles can be solved even though pupils do not know certain terms. Let pupils know this when the challenge is distributed.
- When each riddle is discussed you might ask these questions:
  - Which information would be considered first in puzzle 1-a? 1-b? 1-c?
  - Is all the information needed? Which bits of information can be eliminated?
- Have pupils in small groups challenge others with the puzzles they have invented.
- This activity can be used to review and clarify the terms— even, odd, multiple, and digit sums.

Answers:

1. a. 25 b. 33 c. 74

2. Answers will vary.

3. Answers will vary.

Extension:

Make up a set of clues for a fractional number.

Make up a set of clues for a mixed number.

ROUND ABOUT PUZZLES

(6)	19	(13)
8		14
(2)	3	(1)

Addition was used to obtain the "inside" numbers (19, 8, 3, 14).

Can you see how?

1. Find the "inside" numbers for this one.

(43)	(9)
(16)	(27)

Now, see if you can find some "outside" numbers. They may be more difficult.

2.

( )	11	( )
14		15
( )	18	( )

3.

( )	17	( )
13		28
( )	24	( )

4.

( )	14	( )
17		13
( )	16	( )

5. Find 3 solutions for this one.

( )	21	( )
19		24
( )	22	( )

( )	21	( )
19		24
( )	22	( )

( )	21	( )
19		24
( )	22	( )

6. Are there other solutions for Exercises 1, 2, 3, and 4?

7. Find a solution for this one. ⟶

( )	10	( )
12		15
( )	16	( )

8. Make a change in Exercise 7 so it is more like Exercise 2. Write your new puzzle on the back of this sheet.

Round About Puzzles

Problem-solving skills pupils might use:

- Make conjectures based upon observed patterns.
- Search for and be aware of other solutions.
- Recognize when a solution is not possible.
- Revise the conditions so a solution is possible.

Comments and suggestions:

- Have pupils check their answers for Ex. 2-4 with classmates. They will be surprised their answers do not agree.
- Encourage pupils individually or with a partner to find out how Ex. 7 is different from the others on the page. Why does there seem to be no solution for Ex. 7 and so many for the others?

Answers:

1. "Inside" numbers are 52, 36, 43, and 59.

2-5. Answers will vary. Possible activity: Have all the different solutions for Ex. 5 placed on the chalkboard.

6. Yes.

7. No solution. Pairs of opposite numbers must have the same sum.

$$10 + 16 \neq 12 + 15$$

8. Two possibilities:

a.

11
12 15
16

b.

10
12 14
16

Note: Curious pupils may want an explanation.

Here is one that might be satisfactory: See 8-a ⟶

The sum of the numbers in the top circles is 11;

the sum of the numbers in the bottom circles is 16;

the grand total then for the numbers in all the circles is 27.

Also — the sum of the numbers in the left circles is 12; the right circles is 15; the grand total again is 27.

The idea behind the puzzle is that numbers when added in different orders must always have the same sum. When this does not happen, something is wrong!

Extension:

Another "Round About Puzzle."

Work it and make another one like it.

Use different numbers.

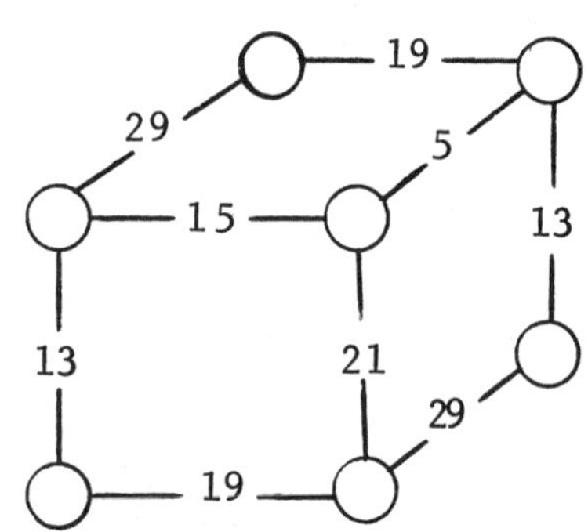

FAIR AND SQUARE

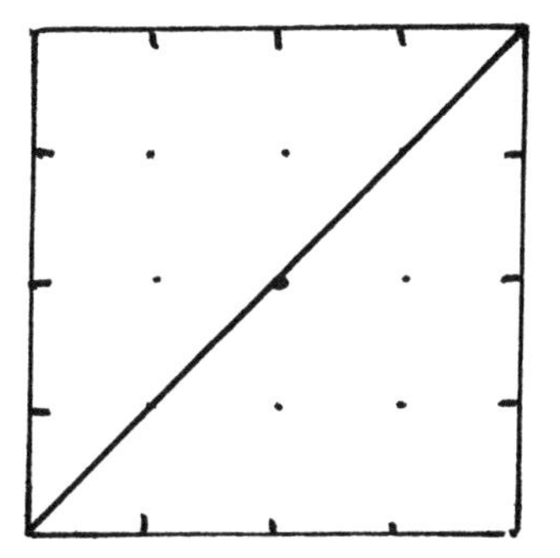

a. The line divides this square into ____ equal parts.

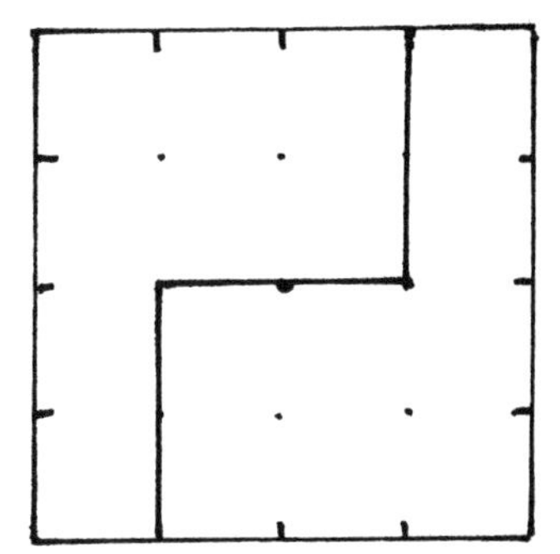

b. This square is divided into 2 equal parts a different way.

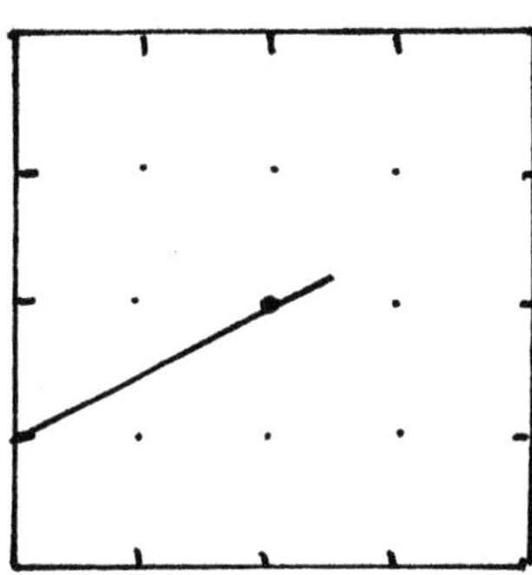

c. Finish dividing this square into 2 equal parts.

Find other ways to divide the squares below into 2 equal parts. Record each way.

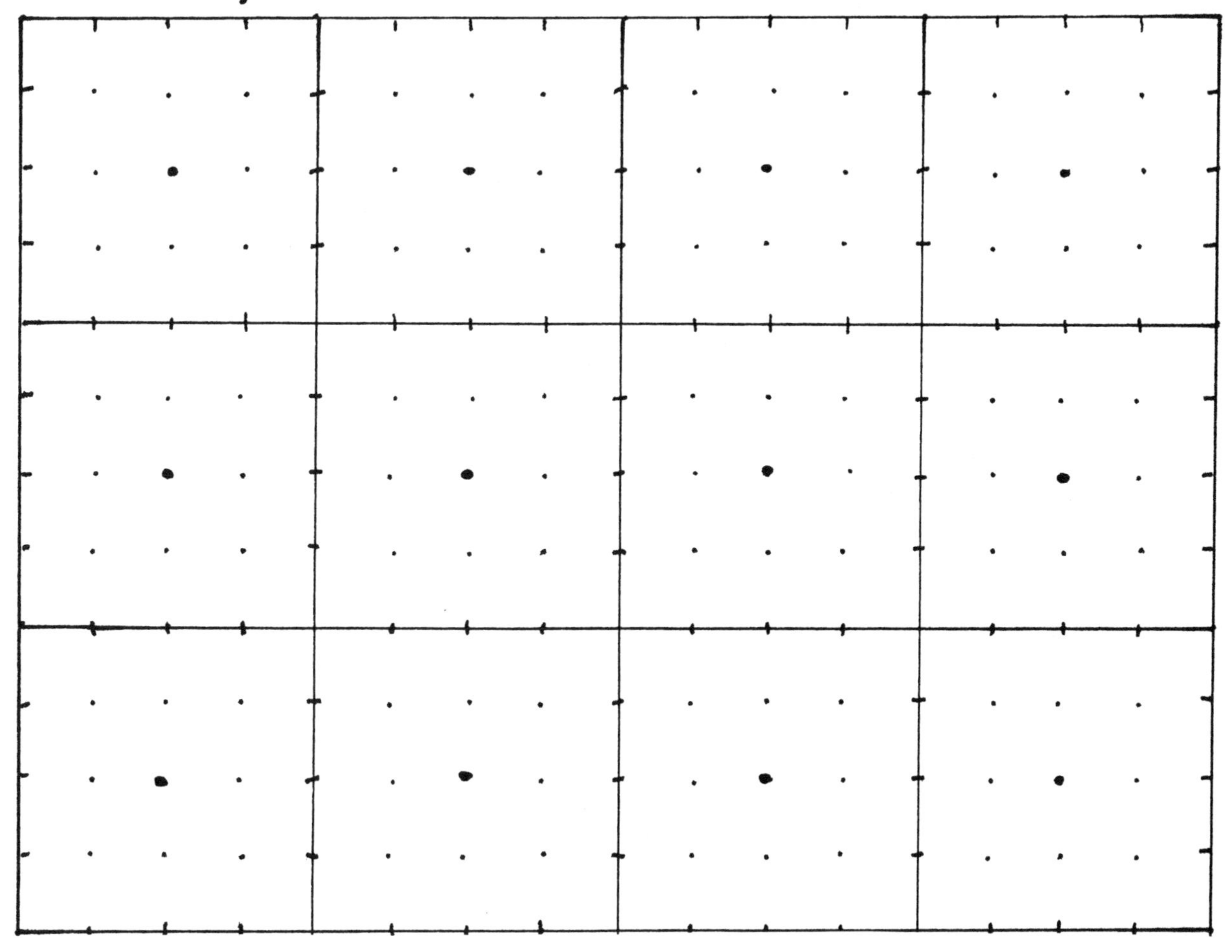

Ask for more special paper. Find still other ways to divide the squares into 2 equal parts.

Fair And Square

Problem-solving skills pupils _might_ use:

. Make a drawing.

. Look for a pattern.

. Find other solutions.

Materials needed:

. One copy of page 389 for each pupil, plus about 2 copies per pupi of page 391.

Comments and suggestions:

. Complete part 1 together. Discuss how the "tiny marks" in each square help solve the problems. Ask pupils how they could "prove" that each square in part 1 is actually divided into two equal part.

. For part 2, have pupils work on their own for awhile before having them work with a partner.

. _Note_: Most pupils will have their squares divided into parts that are the same size and shape (congruent). However, the pieces may be the same size without having the same shape, e.g. When the pieces are congruent, the dividing line always passes through the center point of the square. Try to get pupils to discover this.

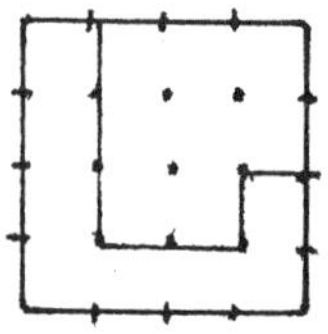

Answers:

1. a. 2   c.

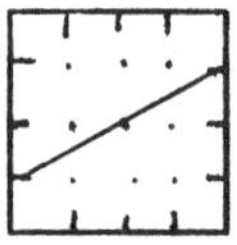

2. and 3. Answers will vary.

Extension:

. Use an additional copy of page 391. Find as many ways as you can to divide the square into _four_ equal parts.

Fair And Square (cont.)

CONSECUTIVE NUMBERS

1. Cut apart the numbers in the boxes at the bottom of the page. Place them in counting order: 0, 1, _, _, _, _, 6, _, _, _.

   We say these are <u>consecutive</u> <u>numbers</u>.

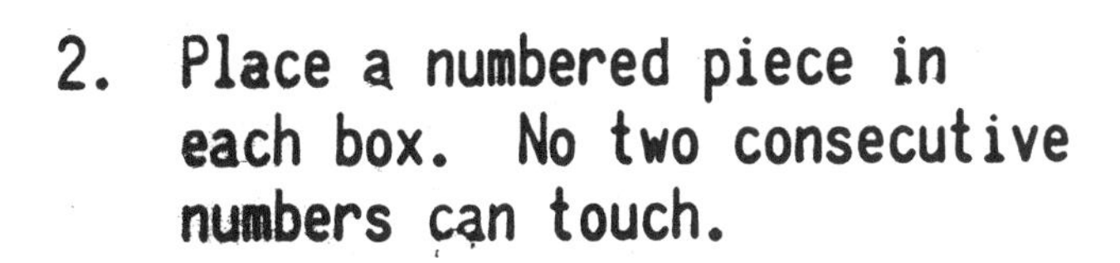

2. Place a numbered piece in each box. No two consecutive numbers can touch.

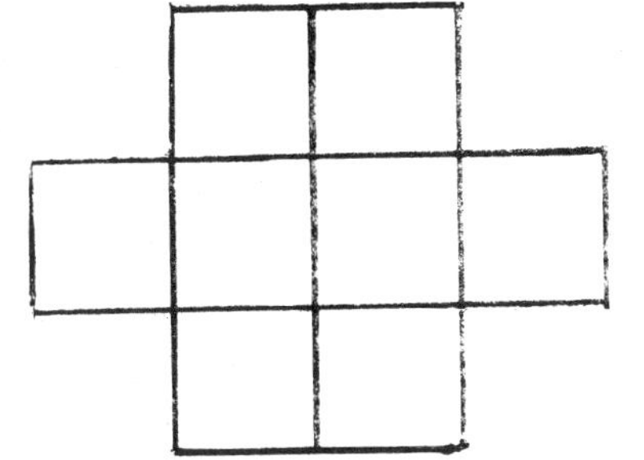

3. Place 0 to 9 so that no two consecutive numbers touch.

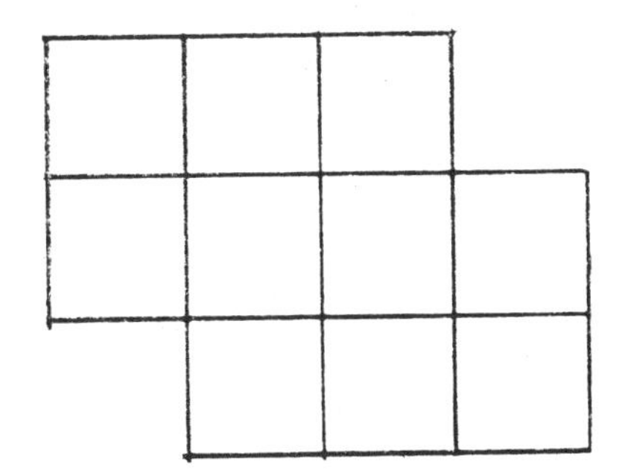

4. Place 1 to 9 so that no two consecutive numbers touch.

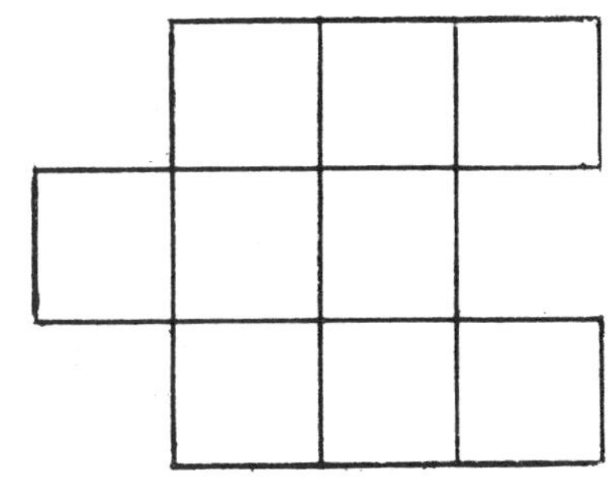

5. Place 1 to 8 so that no two consecutive numbers touch.

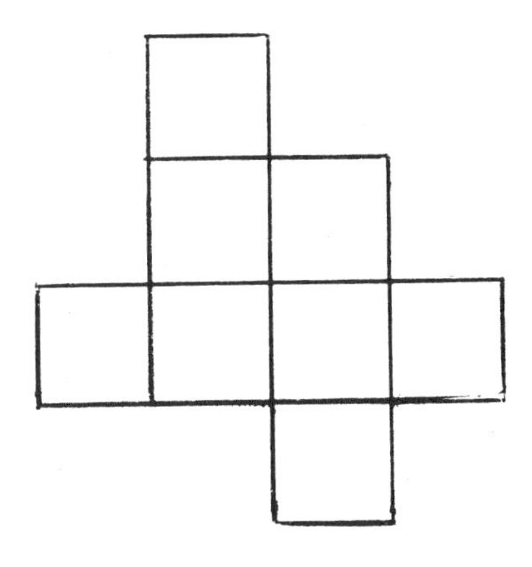

0	4	2	6	9	5	7	1	8	3

Consecutive Numbers

Problem-solving skills pupils might use:

- Guess and check.
- Search for number and geometric patterns (properties).
- Search for and be aware of different solutions.
- Double-check solutions by referring back to given conditons.

Comments and suggestions:

- Hand out the challenge and allow class time for pupils to work the first exercise. If necessary, discuss the concept, consecutive numbers
- Suggest that the use of the numbered pieces may be more convenient than writing in the numbers and then doing a lot of erasing.
- In the culminating work, discuss this key strategy: Place the first and last number side by side in the two squares which are most completely surrounded by other squares.
- Pupils should see other pupils' solutions. Also, emphasize the importance of double-checking one's work.

Answers: (One possible answer is given for each puzzle.)

2.

	4	6	
7	1	8	2
	3	5	

3.

7	3	5	
1	9	0	8
	4	6	2

4.

	3	6	2
8	1	9	
	5	7	4

5.

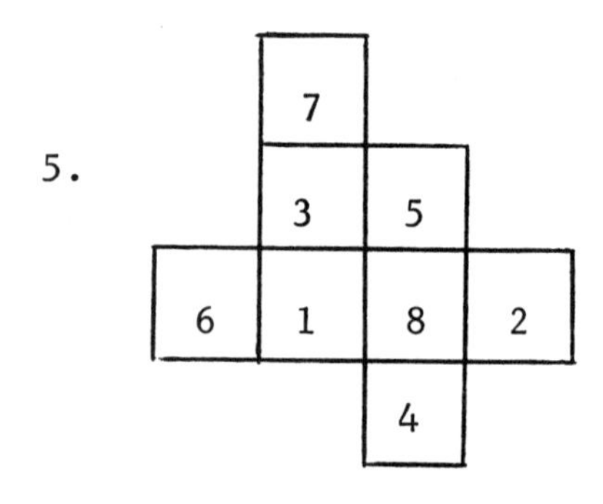

Extension:

See how many different solutions you can get for Ex.5.
We know there is a second solution. Can you find a third?

THE GAME OF 25

1 2 3 4

1. Play this game with a partner (or play one side of the room against the other).

   Player 1 . Touch one of the numbers above (1, 2, 3, or 4).
   . Say that number aloud.

   Player 2 . Touch any of the four numbers above.
   . Say the number and add it to the previous number.

   Continue to take turns touching a number and adding it to the previous total.

   First player to go over 25 loses.

2. Play a number of games.

   Take turns going first.

   Find a way to win if you are the player starting the game.

3. Find a winning strategy if

   - going over 35 loses the game.

4. This time find a winning strategy using the numbers 1, 2, 3, 4, 5, and 6. Going over 50 loses the game.

The Game Of 25

Problem-solving skills pupils _might_ use:

. Guess and check.

. Systematically record solution attempts.

. Study the rules (data) for clues.

. Explain the winning strategy (solution).

Comments and suggestions:

. At first pupils will tend to touch the numbers at random. Encourage them to devise some way to record the sum each side (or player) calls out, along with who won. This data may help find winning strategies.

. After a game or two, pupils may notice that this game is similar to the "Jewel Thief Game" on page 377. A discussion of the likenesses and differences between these games may also suggest winning strategies.

Answers:

Winning strategy for the game:

1. The player who correctly calls out a sum divisible by five can continue to do so and thus win the game. Therefore, the second player has the advantage. For example, the first player calls out 3; second player touches 2 and calls out _5_; first player touches 2--calls out 7; second player touches 3--calls out _10_; first player touches 1--calls out 11; second touches 4--calls out _15_; etc.

2. First player is at a disadvantage but can win if the second player calls out a sum that is _not_ a multiple of 5.

3. The same winning strategy applies--second player has the advantage.

4. The player who first correctly calls out one of these sums--1, 8, 15, 22, 29, 36, 43, 50--can continue to do so and therefore win the game. The first player has the advantage and can always win.

A LOGICAL CHOICE

1. Kelly, Kim, and Kirby each have one favorite sport. The sports are tennis, baseball, and soccer.

   Use the clues below to find each person's favorite sport.

   a. Kelly does not like baseball or soccer.

   b. Kim does not like baseball.

2. Dick, Ed, and Fred play on a basketball team. Their positions are forward, center, and guard.

   a. Dick and the guard bought a present for Fred.

   b. Dick is not the forward.

   Who plays each position?

3. In a certain bank the jobs of cashier, manager, and teller are held by Brown, Jones, and Smith, but not necessarily in that order.

   a. The teller, who was an only child, earns the least.

   b. Smith, who married Brown's sister, earns more than the manager.

   Who has which job?

A Logical Choice

Problem-solving skills pupils <u>might</u> use:

- Break a problem into manageable parts.
- Make and use a table.
- Eliminate possibilities using contradictions.
- Guess and check.

Comments and suggestions:

- Problem-solvers frequently use tables to solve logic problems. However, making tables seems to be a skill elementary pupils are slow to acquire. The first and second logic problems can be solved rather easily by careful reading, guessing, checking, and eliminating possibilities. The third problem may be difficult enough to convince pupils that there must be a better way. If so, introduce them to a strategy involving the use of tables. (See the answers.)

Answers:

1. Kelly must be the tennis player since he does not like baseball or soccer.
   Kim then must be the soccer player since he does not like baseball.
   Kirby must be the baseball player - the only position left.
2. Dick is center since he is not the forward and he along with the guard gave Fred a present.
   Then Fred must be the forward since he received a present from the guard.
   Ed must be the guard - the only position left.
3. Brown is manager; Jones, the teller; Smith, the cashier.

	Cashier	Manager	Teller
Brown		f) yes	b) no
Jones			e) yes
Smith	d) yes	a) no	c) no

a) Smith makes more money than the manager.

b) Brown has a sister; teller does not.

c) Smith does not make the least.

d) One <u>yes</u> is needed in the row.

e) One <u>yes</u> is needed in the column.

f) The only position left.

Extension:

- Encourage pupils to use a table to solve this problem.

  A hampster, a dog, a goat, and a horse are named Arthur, Bossy, Cutey Pie and Diggy. Cutey Pie and the hampster live on the same farm. Arthur and the horse are good friends. Arthur, Bossy, and the goat are the largest of the four animals. What is each animal's name?

  Answer: Diggy, the hampster; Art, the dog; Cutey Pie, the goat; Bossy, the horse.

SUM PROBLEM

1. Cut out the numbers 1 to 9 from the bottom of the page.

   Place them in the spaces. Make a correct addition problem.

   Record your finding.

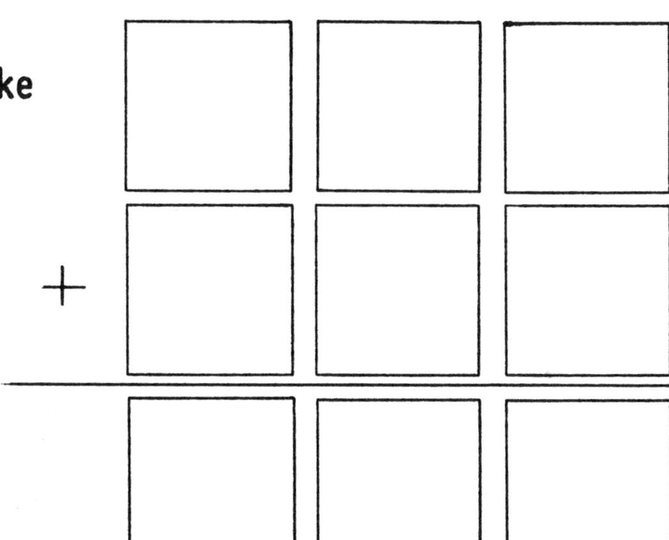

2. Find at least 8 different solutions. Record each below.

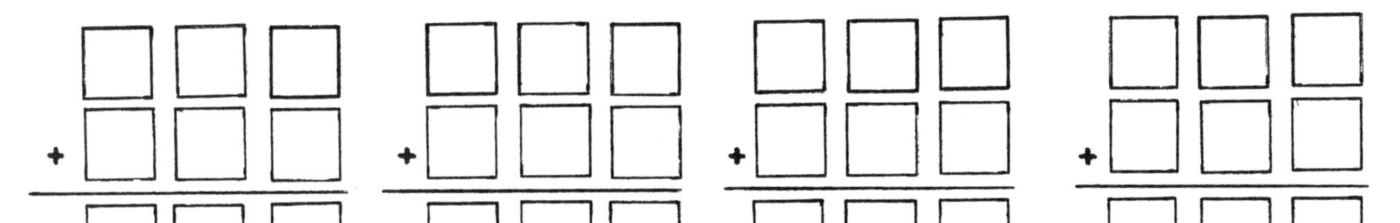

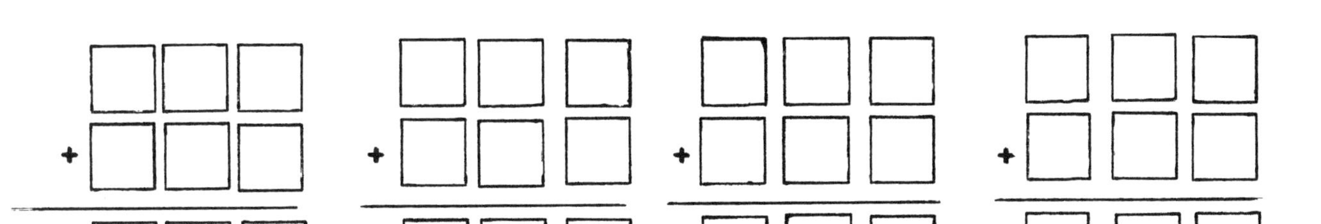

1	2	3	4	5	6	7	8	9

Sum Problem

Problem-solving skills pupils might use:

- . Guess and check.
- . Look for a pattern.
- . Use properties of numbers.

Materials needed:

- . Scissors for each pupil

Comments and suggestions:

- . Introduce part 1 to the class. Have them individually search for a solution.
- . After several pupils have found a solution, ask for one pupil to share an answer. Discuss with that pupil and the class how the solution was reached. Encourage pupils to find still other solutions on their own. Later have them share their solutions with a partner.
- . All of the solutions have at least one "carry" step. Some pupils may be concerned that there is no number chip to use for the "carry number." This may need to be discussed.

Answers:

1. and 2. Answers will vary. All those below are correct.

$$\begin{array}{r} 218 \\ +\ 439 \\ \hline 657 \end{array} \quad \begin{array}{r} 238 \\ +\ 419 \\ \hline 657 \end{array} \quad \begin{array}{r} 239 \\ +\ 418 \\ \hline 657 \end{array} \quad \begin{array}{r} 219 \\ +\ 438 \\ \hline 657 \end{array} \quad \begin{array}{r} 182 \\ +\ 394 \\ \hline 576 \end{array} \quad \begin{array}{r} 184 \\ +\ 392 \\ \hline 576 \end{array}$$

$$\begin{array}{r} 194 \\ +\ 382 \\ \hline 576 \end{array} \quad \begin{array}{r} 192 \\ +\ 384 \\ \hline 576 \end{array} \quad \begin{array}{r} 564 \\ +\ 327 \\ \hline 891 \end{array} \quad \begin{array}{r} 527 \\ +\ 364 \\ \hline 891 \end{array} \quad \begin{array}{r} 524 \\ +\ 367 \\ \hline 891 \end{array} \quad \begin{array}{r} 567 \\ +\ 324 \\ \hline 891 \end{array}$$

$$\begin{array}{r} 237 \\ +\ 654 \\ \hline 891 \end{array} \quad \begin{array}{r} 257 \\ +\ 634 \\ \hline 891 \end{array} \quad \begin{array}{r} 254 \\ +\ 637 \\ \hline 891 \end{array} \quad \begin{array}{r} 234 \\ +\ 657 \\ \hline 891 \end{array} \quad \begin{array}{r} 645 \\ +\ 273 \\ \hline 918 \end{array} \quad \begin{array}{r} 675 \\ +\ 243 \\ \hline 918 \end{array}$$

$$\begin{array}{r} 643 \\ +\ 275 \\ \hline 918 \end{array} \quad \begin{array}{r} 673 \\ +\ 245 \\ \hline 918 \end{array} \quad \begin{array}{r} 542 \\ +\ 376 \\ \hline 918 \end{array} \quad \begin{array}{r} 546 \\ +\ 372 \\ \hline 918 \end{array} \quad \begin{array}{r} 572 \\ +\ 346 \\ \hline 918 \end{array} \quad \begin{array}{r} 576 \\ +\ 342 \\ \hline 918 \end{array}$$

Extensions:

- . Pupils who complete the activity should be encouraged to find still other solutions and record them on the back of the page.

OR

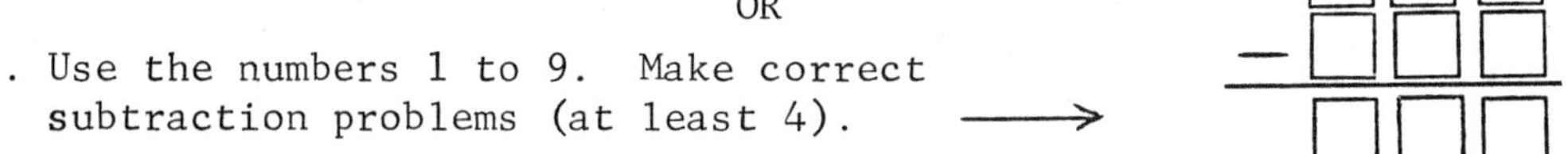

- . Use the numbers 1 to 9. Make correct subtraction problems (at least 4). ⟶

Answer: Rewrite any of the solutions for parts 1 and 2 as subtraction problems.

For example $\begin{array}{r} 567 \\ +\ 324 \\ \hline 891 \end{array}$ could be written as $\begin{array}{r} 891 \\ -\ 324 \\ \hline 567 \end{array}$ or as $\begin{array}{r} 891 \\ -\ 567 \\ \hline 324 \end{array}$. Usually several pupils will use such procedures. It illustrates the relationship between addition and subtraction and is worth discussing with the whole class.

TOTALS OF 10

Cut out the numbers from the bottom of the page.

Place them in the spaces of the puzzle.

Make the sum of the numbers in each row, column, and diagonal 10.

1	1	2	2	3	3	4	4
1	1	2	2	3	3	4	4

Totals Of 10

Problem-solving skills pupils might use:

. Guess and check.

. Look for a pattern.

Materials needed:

. Scissors for each pupil

Comments and suggestions:

. Present the activity as suggested in One Plan For Using The Challenge on page 366.

. If cues are needed for certain pupils, point out that the sum of 1, 2, 3, and 4 is 10--the sum required for each row, column, and diagonal. Another cue--start with the diagonals and then rearrange the numbers for the rows and columns.

Answers:

. Answers will vary. One solution is:

1	3	4	2
4	2	1	3
2	4	3	1
3	1	2	4

Extension:

1. Make a 5 by 5 square. Use 5 sets of the numbers 1 to 5. Solve the same problem. Make the sum 15.

One answer:

2	1	4	3	5
3	5	1	4	2
5	4	3	2	1
4	2	5	1	3
1	3	2	5	4

2. Make a 3 by 3 square. Use 3 sets of numbers, 1 to 3. Try to solve the same problem. Make the sum 6.

   Answer: No solution is possible. Have pupils explain why.

MISSING DIGIT MULTIPLICATION

1. Use the digits 0 to 9, <u>each one time</u>.
   Place them in the spaces below.
   Make each multiplication problem correct.

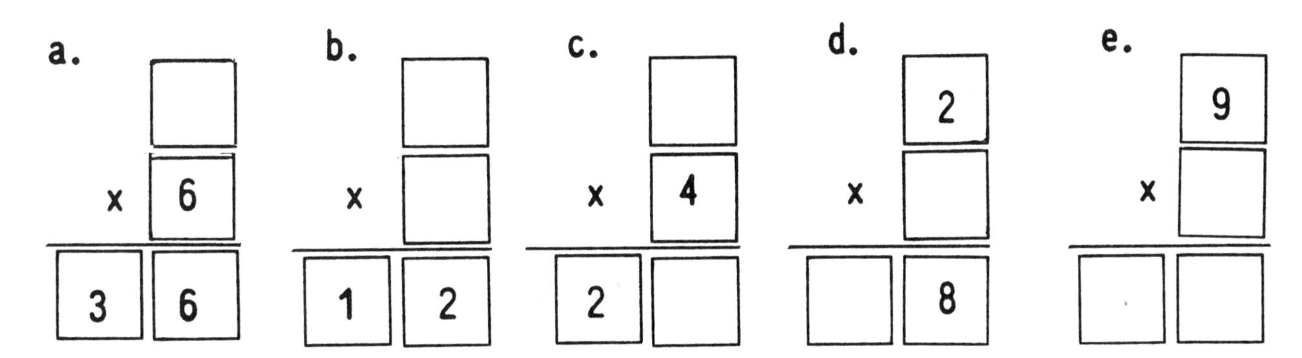

2. Again use the digits 0 to 9, once each.
   Make these problems correct.

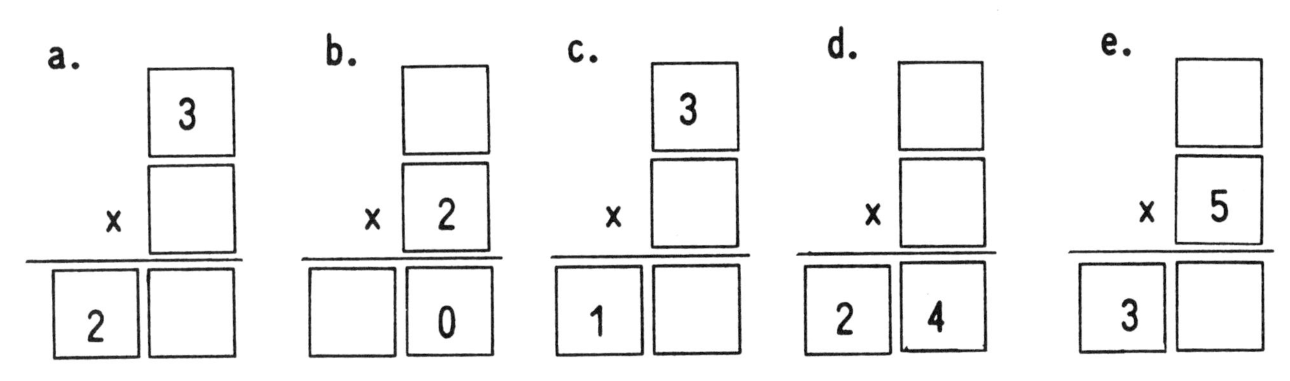

3. Now solve these:

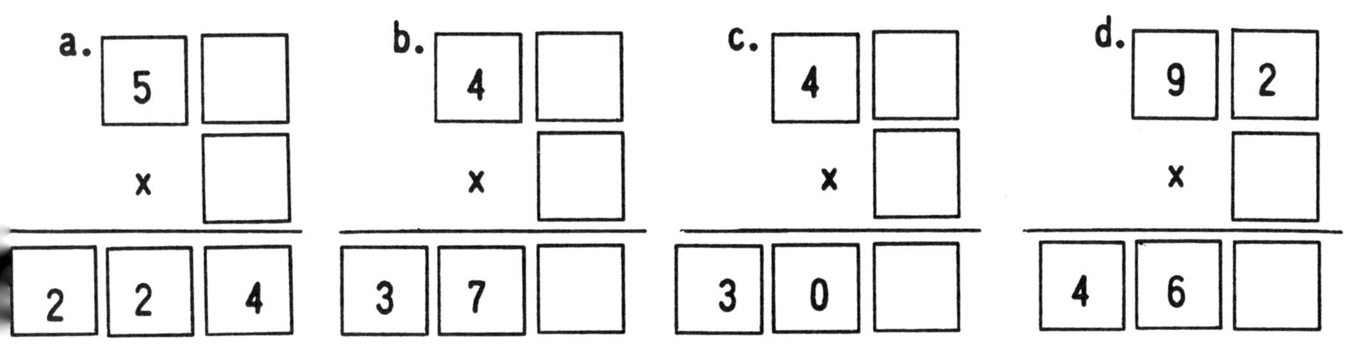

4. Study the four problems in No. 3. Make up four problems like them.

Missing Digit Multiplication

Problem-solving skills pupils <u>might</u> use:

. Guess and check.
. Work backwards.
. Observe likenesses and differences.
. Make reasonable estimates.

Materials needed:

. None required (Some pupils may wish to use small markers labeled 0-9

Comments and suggestions:

. This activity requires a knowledge of basic multiplication facts and of the algorithm for multiplying a 2-digit number by a one-digit number.

. Give the activity to pupils and let them determine what is required on their own. The real challenge is part 4. Have pupils give their invented problems for other class members to work.

Answers:

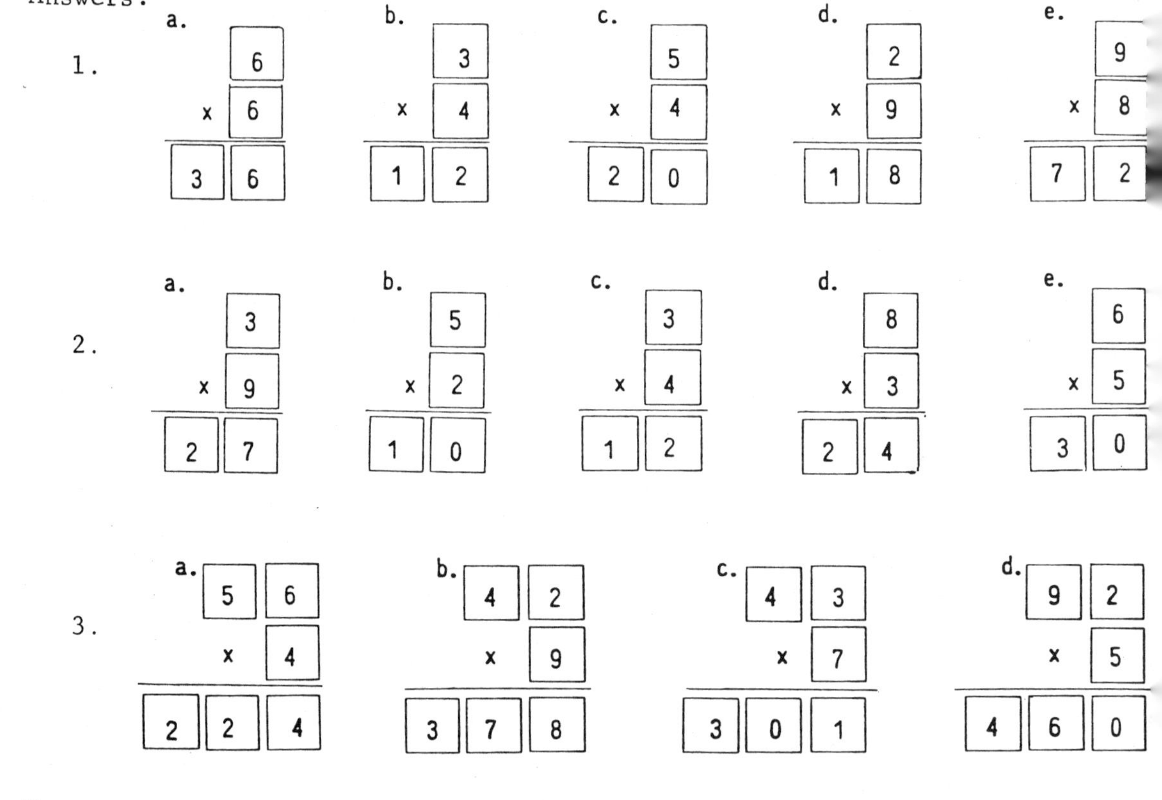

Extension:

. Have pupils make up a set of "missing digit" multiplication problems similar to those in part 3 of the activity.

STICK-UP STICKS

Front	Back
1	10
100	1,000
10,000	100,000
1	10
100	1,000
10,000	100,000
1	10
100	1,000
10,000	100,000

1. Mark nine tongue depressors as shown in the table to the right.

2. Drop all nine sticks on the table. Record the nine numbers that land face up.

   _________ _________ _________

   _________ _________ _________

   _________ _________ _________

   Tell the sum of the nine numbers.

3. Use sticks to show these sums. Cross out any that are not possible.

   a. 212,103 b. 230,021 c. 121,212

   d. 212,230 e. 303,030 f. 212,130

4. Which of these is not possible?

   a. 301,221 b. 221,302

   Why? ______________________________

5. Which of these is not possible?

   a. 240,120 b. 212,121

   Why? ______________________________

Stick-Up Sticks

Problem-solving skills pupils might use:

- Recognize limits and eliminate possibilities.
- Make decisions based upon data.
- Make explanations based upon data.

Materials needed:

- Nine tongue depressors or popsicle sticks for each pair of pupils OR reproduce the pattern for tongue depressors on page 407 on construction paper. Have pupils cut these apart and label the

Comments and suggestions:

- Pupils will need to add six-digit numbers with no carrying.
- This activity can be used with the entire class grouped in teams of two or three pupils. Pupils can share their results as they narrow in on the impossible ones.
- Most pupils will say a sum is not possible if they can't find it after trying. The real reason is more difficult to see and is given in the note at the bottom of this page.
- If this is done as a class activity, the extension could then become the challenge for individuals.

Answers:

4. Crossed out sums: b. (230,021) d. (212,230)

5. Sum not possible: b. (221,302)

6. Sum not possible: a. (240,120)

Note: A sum is not possible if the sum of the digits is not 9 (there is a 1 on each of the 9 sticks). The sum is also not possible if the sums of pairs of digits in order from left to right is not 3 as in 240,120.

Extension: Use just the top 3 sticks. List all possible sums.
Answers: 11; 1001; 100,001; 110; 1100; 100,100; 10,010; 11,000; 110,000

PATTERNS FOR TONGUE DEPRESSORS

Run on construction paper or cover stock.

CROSSING THE RIVER

1. A father and his two daughters need to cross a river. They have a small rowboat that holds only 200 pounds. Father weighs 200 pounds. Each of the daughters weighs 100 pounds.

   How can the father and both daughters all get across the river?

2. A farmer has a fox, a goose, and some corn. They come to a river that they need to cross. They see a small boat that will hold just the farmer and one other thing.

   The fox will eat the goose if left alone and the goose will eat the corn if left alone.

   How can the farmer get all three things across the river?

EXTENSION

Make up your own "crossing the river" problem.

Crossing The River

Problem-solving skills pupils *might* use:

- Break a problem into manageable parts.
- Make and use a drawing or model.
- Record solution possibilities.
- Make explanations.

Comments and suggestions:

- Some pupils will be able to sense the solution for the first problem a explain verbally; others will be able to sense it but not be able to e plain it. If the latter occurs, you may suggest that a drawing would help in making the explanation.
- After a day or two on the challenge page, you may choose to simulate t solution for Problem 1 by using tiles or slips of paper marked "father "daughter 1," and "daughter 2," and then move them back and forth acros an imaginary river. Also, use a scheme to record the boat trips made. The simulation might be suggestive to pupils as to how they might try to solve the second problem.

Answers:

1. Two daughters cross, leaving daughter 1 on the other side. Daughter returns and the father crosses the river alone. Daughter 1 returns to bring back daughter 2.

	River	
F, d_1, d_2		
F	— d_1 d_2 →	
F	← d_2 —	d_1
d_2	— F →	d_1
d_2	← d_1 —	F
	— d_1 d_2 →	F
		F, d_1, d_2

2. Farmer - Fa; Fox - Fo; Goose - G; Corn - C

		River	
(1)	Fa,Fo,G,C		
(2)	Fo,C	—Fa, G→	
(3)	Fo,C	← Fa —	G
(4)	Fo	—Fa, C→	G
(5)	Fo	←Fa, G—	C
(6)	G	—Fa,Fo→	C
(7)	G	←Fa—	Fo, C
(8)		—Fa, G→	Fo, C
(9)			Fa, Fo, G, C

<u>Extension</u>: Have pupils make up their own "Crossing The River" problem.